D1305028

Ronald Hsia

STEEL IN CHINA

ITS OUTPUT BEHAVIOR
PRODUCTIVITY & GROWTH PATTERN

# STEEL IN CHINA

## ITS OUTPUT BEHAVIOR
## PRODUCTIVITY & GROWTH PATTERN

RONALD HSIA, Ph. D.

Professor of Economics
University of Hong Kong

BAND 29

der Schriften des Instituts für Asienkunde in Hamburg

OTTO HARRASSOWITZ · WIESBADEN

This book was printed with financial support from the Rudolf Siederleben'sche
Otto Wolff-Stiftung.

© Otto Harrassowitz, Wiesbaden 1971
Alle Rechte vorbehalten
Photomechanische und photographische Wiedergaben
nur mit ausdrücklicher Genehmigung des Verlages
Gesamtherstellung: MZ-Verlagsdruckerei GmbH, Memmingen
Printed in Germany

Dem Institut für Asienkunde ist die Aufgabe gestellt, die gegenwartsbezogene Asienforschung zu
fördern. Es ist dabei bemüht, in seinen Publikationen *verschiedene Meinungen zu Worte kommen zu
lassen, die jedoch grundsätzlich die Auffassung des jeweiligen Autors und nicht unbedingt des Instituts
für Asienkunde* darstellen.

ISBN 3 447 01317 6

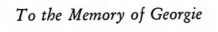

*To the Memory of Georgie*

# PREFACE

I finished the first draft of this book in 1963 before joining the London School of Economics on a visiting appointment. Upon return to Hong Kong, various pressing demands and subsequent ill health prevented me from revising the draft until last summer. In combing through available mainland publications since mid-1963, however, I found little quantitative data on the ensuing development of the Chinese steel industry. Whatever usable information I was able to find has been incorporated.

In writing this volume, I have benefited from the advice of Professors Choh-Ming Li and John K. Fairbank, and from the help of Messrs. Heishiro Ogawa, Horace Eng, K. Y. Yui, David Wong, H. C. Tien and K. C. Chen. I am particularly indebted to Messrs. W. F. Choa and C. L. Wu for their able assistance, and to Professors M. Gardner Clark, Walter Galenson, W. F. Maunder and Edward Ames for reading the manuscript and for their invaluable suggestions.

I wish also to acknowledge my indebtedness to The Asia Foundation, East Asian Research Center of Harvard University and Social Science Research Council Committee on the Economy of China for their support. To Dr. B. Grossmann and Institut für Asienkunde, I am grateful for publication arrangements.

I alone am responsible for the statements, interpretations and possible errors contained in this volume.

Hong Kong, March 1970.                                              Ronald Hsia

# CONTENTS

# INTRODUCTION

One way of studying the industrial development of an economy is to approach the industrial sector as a whole in broad terms. This approach gives a general, overall picture of a country's industrial development seen mainly through essential aggregates. The fact that most of these aggregates can only be expressed in value terms poses special problems in studying a command economy where prices do not reflect genuine scarcity relationships. Furthermore, the overall approach tends to overlook some of the basic factual information on individual industries. This failing points to the relative advantage of examining and analyzing the growth of key industries on the basis of detailed and specific information pertaining to individual industries. This latter approach supplements the study of the industrial sector as a whole in broad terms and helps to check generalizations reached by the overall approach.

The present study of China's steel industry was undertaken because of its conspicuous role in the forced industrialization scheme of the communist regime. This role was made clear from the very beginning; during 1950–1952 the newly formed government allocated nearly 12 per cent of total industrial investment for rehabilitating the steel industry. This share was raised to 14 per cent in the First Five-Year Plan (1953–1957). With the launching of the Leap Forward movement in 1958, steel was given even a higher priority, with other industries unequivocally subordinate to its requirements. The relative importance of the steel industry was maintained in the period of industrial consolidation consequent upon the failure of the Great Leap and the withdrawal of Soviet aid. It was further enhanced during the recent defense campaign.

The iron and steel industry, according to the Chinese State Planning Commission, includes mining and ore dressing, coke manufacturing, iron smelting, steel refining, rolling and casting. Although this definition governs the broad limits of the present study, attention is directed chiefly to smelting, refining and rolling.

This study begins by examining the pre-communist development of China's modern iron and steel industry including wartime changes and Soviet removals of equipment and installations. Such a brief survey is necessary as a point of departure. It also serves as a frame of reference for analyzing the task of rehabilitation, as well as the growth of the industry under communist planning. Part II appraises output restoration to the prewar peak level and examines the nature of capital construction as reflected both in the major rehabilitation projects and in the construction of the key bases. Special attention is given to the type of equipment installed, the expansion of productive capacity and the role of Soviet aid.

The output behavior of the steel industry as a whole and its major products constitutes the subject of Part III. In addition, the relationship between investment and output and the rising importance of steel in the economy are considered. Part IV investigates the productivity of labor and capital equipment. Labor productivity is examined in both value and physical terms. Productivity of different types of furnaces is analyzed in terms of inputs, production techniques and quality levels.

In Part V, the growth pattern of the steel industry is traced through institutional, structural and locational changes. Institutionally, it looks into variations in the relative position of the five sectors within the industry. Structurally, it probes into scale, cost and technology. Locationally, it examines changes by bench-mark years in the distribution of the steel industry among the seven economic regions. Part VI scans developments in the 1960's and summarizes the major observations made in this study.

The present study relies heavily on data released from official Chinese sources. The accuracy of such data cannot be ascertained with precision. They are frequently incomplete, ambiguous, and in some cases even inconsistent. Thus amid the apparent abundance of information, notably for 1958, there is a genuine scarcity of *usable* quantitative data. On the other hand, there is no evidence to show that Chinese statistics are the result of deliberate manipulations. Official statistics on output restoration have been found to be consistent with data on productive capacity and productivity coefficients from different sources. Despite the data limitations, therefore, useful work can be done with them as attempted in this study.

# PART I
# THE COMMUNIST HERITAGE

*Chapter 1*

# PREWAR PRODUCTION

Although the purpose of the present study is to examine and analyze the growth of China's steel industry under the communist regime, its pre-communist development provided the base on which the communists had to build. This chapter is concerned with the output and capacity of the industry prior to the outbreak of Sino-Japanese hostilities in 1937. While output is traced to 1900, only the 1936 capacity is given. The latter marks a point of departure in subsequent discussions of wartime expansion.

Iron production by modern western methods in China began in the 1890's in the Wuhan area of the Central region (see the map at the beginning of the book)[1]. Subsequently, modern iron-smelting and steel-refining facilities were also established in the Northeast region to exploit its rich resources. Developments in both regions[2], as reflected in output behavior, benefited from the boom associated with the First World War. During the war, Anshan in the Northeast became prominent as an iron producer, and the iron-smelting capacity of the Wuhan area was more than doubled. The latter was again substantially expanded in the postwar boom period (1915–1922).

*Prewar Output*

Annual production figures of pig iron[3] from 1900 to 1936 are presented in Table 1.1, which also shows the proportion of iron produced by modern furnace from 1912 onwards. The predominance of native iron in the overall iron output structure was evident in 1912, in which year iron produced by modern furnace amounted to less than 5 per cent (see Column 2 of Table 1.1). From that year on, however, the relative importance of iron output from modern furnaces was increasing, although the rising trend was not uninterrupted. By 1936, its proportion came to almost 83 per cent of the aggregate iron output. This rise reflected an absolute gain of iron production by modern methods rather than any substantial decrease in native iron output. The latter in 1936 amounted to 140,300 tons, as compared with 170,000 tons produced in 1912. Iron production by modern

---

1 Native iron is known to have been produced in China since the Shang-yin period (1766–1122 B.C.). For a brief account of the early developments of China's modern iron and steel industry, see Appendix 1-A at the end of the chapter.
2 The Northeast region and Manchuria are used interchangeably in this study.
3 Annual output data prior to 1900 are unobtainable for the country as a whole. In this study, ton refers to *metric* ton unless otherwise specified.

methods, on the other hand, increased from 7,989 tons in 1912 to 669,696 tons in 1936[4].

*Table 1.1. Output of Pig Iron in China, 1900—1936 (in tons)*

| Year | Output | Proportion of Output by Modern Furnace (per cent) |
|------|--------|--------------------------------------------------|
| 1900 | 25,980 | — |
| 1901 | 28,805 | — |
| 1902 | 15,800 | — |
| 1903 | 38,875 | — |
| 1904 | 38,771 | — |
| 1905 | 32,314 | — |
| 1906 | 50,622 | — |
| 1907 | 62,148 | — |
| 1908 | 66,410 | — |
| 1909 | 74,405 | — |
| 1910 | 119,396 | — |
| 1911 | 83,337 | — |
| 1912 | 177,989 | 4.5 |
| 1913 | 267,513 | 36.5 |
| 1914 | 300,000 | 43.3 |
| 1915 | 336,649 | 49.3 |
| 1916 | 369,815 | 53.9 |
| 1917 | 358,315 | 52.4 |
| 1918 | 328,798 | 48.1 |
| 1919 | 407,743 | 58.1 |
| 1920 | 429,548 | 60.3 |
| 1921 | 399,413 | 57.3 |
| 1922 | 401,844 | 57.5 |
| 1923 | 341,487 | 50.0 |
| 1924 | 360,804 | 52.7 |
| 1925 | 363,836 | 53.1 |
| 1926 | 407,222 | 56.1 |
| 1927 | 436,815 | 59.1 |
| 1928 | 476,989 | 62.5 |
| 1929 | 436,043 | 69.0 |
| 1930 | 498,306 | 75.5 |
| 1931 | 470,879 | 73.2 |
| 1932 | 548,391 | 75.4 |
| 1933 | 609,272 | 77.2 |
| 1934 | 655,727 | 79.4 |
| 1935 | 787,061 | 82.2 |
| 1936 | 809,996 | 82.7 |

Source: Yen Chung-ping *et al, Chung-kuo chin-tai ching-chi-shih t'ung-chi tzu-liao hsüan-chi* (Selected statistical data on the modern economic history of China), Peking: The Science Publishing House, 1955, pp. 102—103 and 141.

4 Yen Chung-ping *et al, Chung-kuo chin-tai ching-chi-shih t'ung-chi tzu-liao hsüan-chi* (Selected statistical data on the modern economic history of China), Peking: The Science Publishing House, 1955, pp. 102—103. Hereafter this source will be abbreviated as *TCTL*.

This increase resulted from the rise of modern iron-smelting plants. Prior to 1914, the Hanyehping Coal and Iron Corporation in the Central region was the only iron producer by modern methods with an annual output of less than 130,000 tons. In 1915, Penki in the Northeast region joined in with an annual output of 35,000 tons, and in 1919 Anshan also in the Northeast turned out 31,000 tons of iron. During the period of postwar boom (1915–1922), another producer, the Yangtze Iron Works, was established in Hankow in Central China to take advantage of the rising prices stimulated by the war.

When the wartime and postwar boom ended, the output of Hanyehping dropped sharply from 148,424 tons in 1922 to 73,018 tons in 1923 and to 26,977

*Table 1.2. Ingot Steel Output and Imports of Iron and Steel Products, 1907–1936 (in tons)*

| Year | Output | Imports |
|------|--------|---------|
| 1907 | 8,538 | 154,537 |
| 1908 | 22,626 | 142,665 |
| 1909 | 37,000 | 256,173 |
| 1910 | 50,113 | 259,064 |
| 1911 | 38,640 | 219,092 |
| 1912 | 2,521 | 151,276 |
| 1913 | 42,637 | 244,739 |
| 1914 | 55,850 | 230,551 |
| 1915 | 48,850 | 125,658 |
| 1916 | 45,043 | 145,847 |
| 1917 | 42,651 | 123,268 |
| 1918 | 56,996 | 149,117 |
| 1919 | 34,851 | 325,158 |
| 1920 | 68,260 | 366,622 |
| 1921 | 76,800 | 272,782 |
| 1922 | 30,000 | 364,875 |
| 1923 | 30,000 | 309,817 |
| 1924 | 30,000 | 493,624 |
| 1925 | 30,000 | 405,266 |
| 1926 | 30,000 | 433,582 |
| 1927 | 30,000 | 389,061 |
| 1928 | 30,000 | 624,898 |
| 1929 | 20,000 | 634,192 |
| 1930 | 15,000 | 527,428 |
| 1931 | 15,000 | 557,628 |
| 1932 | 20,000 | 431,000 |
| 1933 | 30,000 | 528,567 |
| 1934 | 50,000 | 622,408 |
| 1935 | 256,565 | 632,670 |
| 1936 | 414,315 | 649,219 |

Source: Yen Chung-ping *et al, Chung-kuo chin-tai ching-chi-shih t'ung-chi tzu-liao hsüan-chi* (Selected statistical data on the modern economic history of China), Peking: The Science Publishing House, 1955, pp. 141–142.

tons in 1924[5]. The dwindling output and declining iron prices worsened the financial situation of the firm, which had long been heavily burdened with foreign debts. Its iron production came to a standstill in 1926.

The ending of the boom, however, did not severely affect the country's overall iron production, which after a 15 per cent drop in 1923 began to rise in the following year. This upward movement lasted through 1936 with only slight dips in 1929 and 1931. The steady increase in the national iron output should be credited chiefly to the continual expansion of Anshan and Penki. Their combined output increased from 100,424 tons in 1923 to 648,097 in 1936[6].

The prewar production of ingot steel presented a different picture. Its annual output figures are given in Table 1.2, along with data on imports of iron and steel products. These two time series reflected the influence of imports on domestic production. This influence is more vividly revealed when the two time series are plotted on a graph. Indeed, the return of foreign competition after World War I[7] coupled with the fall in steel prices led to the cessation of steel production in Hanyehping.

Another significant point regarding prewar steel production was the under-capacity utilization among firms in operation. Take Hanyehping for example. The annual production level of 56,996 tons marked its highest output but utilized only 60 per cent of its capacity[8]. Such under-capacity production resulted in an exceedingly high iron-steel output ratio of 4.6 for the period from 1912 to 1936 even with the output of native iron excluded. The inclusion of the latter raises the ratio to 7.3. As will be shown later, this "pyramiding" structure was also discernible in terms of capacity, and remained a major characteristic of the Chinese steel industry up to the communist era.

### Prewar Capacity

The rated daily capacity of blast furnaces constructed through 1936 amounted to 3,930 tons. A breakdown of this total by individual furnace is given in Table 1.3 together with the location and date of construction. As the table shows, data on rated daily capacity in tonnage are available for all nineteen furnaces known to be in existence in prewar China, whereas data on furnace volume are obtainable only for four in Liaoning and two in Shansi. Thus for these six blast furnaces,

---

5 H.G.W. Woodhead (Editor), *The China Year Book, 1926*, Chicago: University of Chicago Press, 1928, p. 116.
6 *Ibid.; Sources of Iron Ore in East Asia*, Report No. 154, prepared by Economic and Scientific Section, General Headquarters, Supreme Commander for the Allied Powers, Tokyo, 1950, pp. 147 and 156.
7 Imports of iron and steel products increased from 149,117 tons in 1918 to 325,158 tons in 1919. See Table 1.2.
8 *Chung-kuo ching-chi nien-chien* (Economic year book of China), compiled by the Ministry of Industry, Shanghai: The Commercial Press, 1934, Vol. II, pp. K315—316.

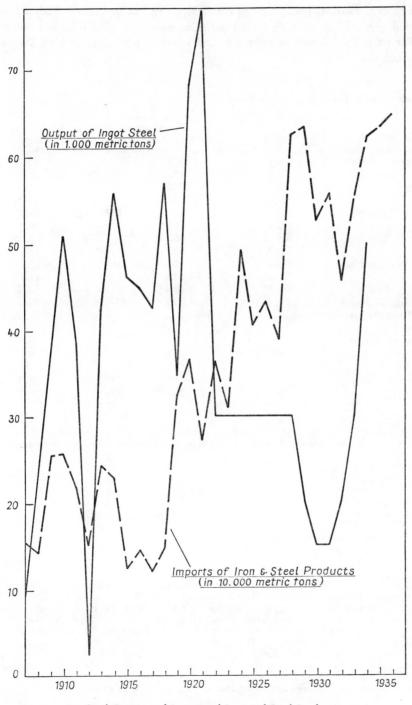

Steel Output and Imports of Iron and Steel Products

the ratio of rated daily capacity to furnace volume can be derived. Such a ratio should approximate the daily output per cubic meter of available furnace volume under normal conditions of operation and serves as a measure of blast furnace productivity.

*Table 1.3. Blast Furnaces in Prewar China*

| Location | Designation | Capacity Tons[a]/Day | M³ | Date of Construction[b] |
|---|---|---|---|---|
| Hanyang, Hupeh | No. 1 | 100[c] | | 1890 |
| | No. 2 | 100[c] | | 1890 |
| | No. 3 | 250 | | 1915[d] |
| | No. 4 | 250 | | 1915[d] |
| Penki, Liaoning | No. 1 | 200 | 332 | 1911[e] |
| | No. 2 | 200 | 336 | 1911[f] |
| Tayeh, Hupeh | No. 1 | 450 | | 1919[g] |
| | No. 2 | 450 | | 1919[g] |
| Anshan, Liaoning | No. 1 | 400 | 585 | 1917[h] |
| | No. 2 | 400 | 602 | 1917[i] |
| | No. 3 | 550[j] | | 1930 |
| Shenchiaki, Hupeh | [k] | 100 | | 1920 |
| Shihchingshan, Hopeh | [k] | 250 | | 1922 |
| Yangchuan, Shansi | [k] | 20 | | [m] |
| Tsiaotso, Honan | [k] | 25 | | 1924 |
| Pootung, Shanghai | [k] | 33 | | [m] |
| | [k] | 12 | | [m] |
| Taiyuan, Shansi | [k] | 40 | 146 | 1934 |
| | [k] | 100 | 291 | 1934 |

a. Rated capacity.
b. Unless specified otherwise, the year indicates the beginning of construction.
c. When first built, the rated daily capacity was 75 tons; it was subsequently enlarged to 100 tons.
d. Date of completion.
e. Completed 1915.
f. Completed 1917.
g. Completed 1922.
h. Completed 1919.
i. Completed 1920.
j. The initial rated capacity was 500 tons.
k. No designation.
m. Unknown.

Sources: *Chung-kuo ching-chi nien-chien* (Economic year book of China), compiled by the Ministry of Industry, Shanghai: The Commercial Press, 1934, Vol. II, pp. K315–321; Yang Ta-chin, *Hsien-tai chung-kuo shih-yeh chih* (Annals of the industries of modern China), Changsha: The Commercial Press, 1938, pp. 372–373; Chao Yi-wen, *Hsin chung-kuo ti kung-yeh* (The industry of new China), Peking: Statistics Publishing House, 1957, p. 38; D.K. Lieu, *Industrial Development in Communist China*, New York, 1955, pp. 21 and 25; Industrial Statistics Section, State Bureau of Statistics, *Wo-kuo kang--t'ieh, tien-li, mei-t'an, chi-hsieh, tang-chih, tsao-chih kung-yeh ti chin-hsi* (The past and present of China's iron and steel, electric power, coal, machine-making, textile and paper industries), Peking: Statistics Publishing House, 1958, p. 3; and other sources.

The coefficient of utilization of useful furnace capacity is computed to be 0.621 and 0.595 ton for furnace Nos. 1—2 at Penki, 0.684 and 0.664 ton for furnace Nos. 1—2 at Anshan, 0.274 and 0.345 ton for the two furnaces at Taiyuan. The wide discrepancy between the ratios for the furnaces in the Northeast and those for the furnaces in Shansi appears to be puzzling. Such a discrepancy finds support in the representative or average utilization coefficient of 0.520 ton for 1936 disclosed by the Industrial Statistics Section of the State Bureau of Statistics[9]. That the value of the 1936 "average" coefficient comes closer to the values of the ratios

Table 1.4. Steel Furnaces in Prewar China

| Location | Number | Type | Rated Capacity of Each (tons per heat) | Date Starting Operation |
|---|---|---|---|---|
| Hanyang, Hupeh | 1 | Bessemer | 30 | 1893 |
| | 6 | Martin | 30 | 1907 |
| Pootung, Shanghai | 1 | Open hearth | 12 | 1924 |
| | 1 | Open hearth | 35 | 1924 |
| Taiyuan, Shansi | 1 | Open hearth | 30 | 1934 |
| Kaochangmiao, Shanghai | 2 | Martin | 15 | Before 1933 |
| Hanyang, Hupeh | 1 | | 15 | Before 1933 |
| Chungking, Szechwan | 1 | Electric | 10 | Before 1933 |
| Anshan, Liaoning | 4 | Open hearth, tilting | 100 | 1935 |
| | 3 | Mixing furnace | (300) | 1935 |
| | 2 | Open hearth, tilting | 150 | 1935 |

Sources: *Chung-kuo ching-chi nien-chien* (Economic year book of China), compiled by the Ministry of Industry, Shanghai: The Commercial Press, 1934, Vol. I, p. J241, Vol. II, pp. K315—316; *Hsien-tai chung-kuo shih-yeh chih* (Annals of the industries of modern China), Changsha: The Commercial Press, 1938, p. 373; *Sources of Iron Ore in East Asia*, Report No. 154, prepared by Economic and Scientific Section, General Headquarters, Supreme Commander for the Allied Powers, Tokyo, 1952, p. 146; Industrial Statistics Section, State Bureau of Statistics, *Wo-kuo kang-t'ieh, tien-li, mei-t'an, chi-hsieh, fang-chih, tsao-chih kung-yeh ti chin-hsi* (The past and present of China's iron and steel, electric power, coal, machine-making, textile and paper industries), Peking: Statistics Publishing House, 1958, pp. 2—3; Edwin W. Pauley, *Report on Japanese Assets in Manchuria to the President of the United States*, Washington, D. C., July 1946, *passim*; and other sources.

for the Northeastern group can be explained by the fact that out of a total daily capacity of 2,000 odd tons in China Proper[10], only that of some 120 tons was in operation in 1936[11].

China's prewar steel capacity was about half her iron capacity. Twenty-three

9 Industrial Statistics Section, State Bureau of Statistics, *Wo-kuo kang-t'ieh, tien-li, mei-t'an, chi-hsieh, fang-chih, tsao-chih kung-yeh ti chin-hsi* (The past and present of China's iron and steel, electric power, coal, machine-making, textile and paper industries), Peking: Statistics Publishing House, 1958, p. 10. Hereafter the source will be referred to as *KTMCFT*.
10 China Proper is a geographical term used in the pre-communist period to refer to the part of China excluding Manchuria, Mongolia, Sinkiang, Tibet, Tsinghai, and Ningsia.
11 D.K. Lieu, *Industrial Development in Communist China*, New York, 1955, p. 21.

steel furnaces are known to have been installed in the country before 1937. Their location, description, capacity and date of operation are given in Table 1.4.

One characteristic of China's iron and steel industry in the prewar period was the "pyramiding" capacity structure. The capacity at an earlier stage of the integrated productive process was considerably larger than that at the ensuing stage of the process. Part of the "pyramiding" structure is revealed in the data presented in Tables 1.3 and 1.4, according to which the pig iron capacity amounted to 3,930 tons while the steel ingot capacity 1,042 tons. On the assumption of two heats in 24 hours for open hearths on the average, the iron-steel capacity ratio would come to 1.9. Likewise the ingot-rolling capacity ratio was about 3[12].

Such a capacity structure reflected primarily the underdevelopment of the Chinese economy. Its technological backwardness and other attributes of underdevelopment prevented it from developing steel finishing capacity in keeping with smelting capacity and the latter with ore dressing and mining capacities. The working of these forces was complicated by the predominance of foreign interests in China's iron and steel industry. These foreign interests geared the development of iron and steel in China to the needs of the steel industries in their own countries. Consequently, China remained in 1936 an exporter of iron ore and pig iron and an importer of iron and steel products[13].

12 Chao Yi-wen, *Hsin chung-kuo ti kung-yeh* (The industry of new China), Peking: Statistics Publishing House, 1957, p. 15.
13 In 1936, China exported 1,301,038 tons of iron ore, and imported 649,219 tons of iron and steel shapes and products. *TCTL*.

## APPENDIX 1 – A

# EARLY DEVELOPMENTS OF CHINA'S MODERN IRON AND STEEL INDUSTRY

The history of China's *modern* iron and steel industry can be traced to 1890[1] when the Hanyang Iron and Steel Works was established in Hupeh under the sponsorship of the noted Chinese official Chang Chih-tung[2]. The construction of the plants was essentially completed in 1893, but production was held up for lack of coke supply. For two years the mining staff was unable to cope successfully with the problem of flooding coal mines at Wangshanshih near Tayeh. Consequently the management decided to ship coke from Maanshan. The coke being produced by indigenous methods, however, proved not up to the quality requirements of modern blast furnaces. Subsequently coke was imported from Germany. An experiment conducted on a mixture of imported German coke with Maanshan coke was unsuccessful.

The difficulty in securing proper coke supply was reflected in the output picture. The entire iron output of Hanyang amounted merely to 5,660 tons from 1893 through 1895[3]. The problem of coke supply remained unsolved until the Pingsiang Coal Mines began operation in 1897, although the solution was not entirely satisfactory both in terms of the quality of the Pingsiang coke and in terms of the high transport cost necessitated by long-distance hauls[4].

Steel production in Hanyang in the initial period was not without problems either. They stemmed from the incompatibility of the pig iron produced there with the type of equipment installed for converting iron to steel. Of the two converters the Hanyang Iron and Steel Works initially imported from Britain, one was of the acid type incapable of removing the excessive phosphorous

---

1 Pan Wei, Governor of Kweichow, established in 1886 the Chingku Iron Works in Kweichow. It was suspended in 1893 due to insufficiency of capital funds and the difficulty of obtaining coal supply. No production from this plant has been reported. See Research Section of the Department of Economics and Political Science, University of Hupeh, *Chung-kuo chin-tai kuo-min ching-chi-shih chiang-i* (Lectures on the modern economic history of China), Peking: Higher Education Publishing House, 1958, p. 218. Hereafter the source will be referred to as *CCKCC*.

2 The repeated defeats of China by Western Powers prompted the more enlightened officials of the Ch'ing government to turn their attention to the development of coal and steel in order that China might have its own munitions industry. Among the first to subscribe to this idea was Li Hung-chang, a noted Chinese diplomat of the latter part of the nineteenth century. In several of his edicts to the emperor, he emphasized the importance of developing steel and coal in connection with ship-building, machine-making and the manufacture of armaments. *Li-wen-chung-kung ch'üan chi* (The complete work of Li Hung-chang), Vol. 24, *passim*.

3 *KTMCFT*, p. 2.

4 D.K. Lieu, *op. cit.*, p. 18.

content in its pig iron. Consequently, only sub-standard steel was produced. In fact, production of steel up to standard specifications did not begin until 1907 when 8,538 tons were turned out[5].

These production problems reflected the technical level of the engineering staff. It is known that forty foreign engineers were employed on its staff[6]. The entire engineering staff may well have been larger than this number. Assuming that this number constituted the entire engineering staff, its ratio to the labor force came to 1 : 75[7]. This ratio was nearly twice as high as during the early communist period[8]. The belated solution of production problems at Hanyang and the consequent waste reflected not only the technical incompetency of the engineers but also inefficiency on the part of the management.

The Hanyang Iron and Steel Works was originally established as a government enterprise. Between 1890 and 1895, the government invested a total of 5,829,629 taels[9]. This amount of investment can be related to the initial equipment which included two blast furnaces with a rated daily capacity of 100 tons each[10], and two Bessemer converters; and to the output of 5,660 tons of iron and a negligible amount of usable steel. The high capital-output ratio served as a clear indication of the inefficient management and the need for reorganization. This need coincided with the financial difficulty of the Ch'ing government arising from the Sino-Japanese war. Consequently in June 1895, the government issued a directive to the effect that the Hanyang Iron and Steel Works was to be reorganized into a government-private joint enterprise by taking in private capital and allowing a businessman to take charge of its operation. Thus Sheng Hsuan-huai, a prominent entrepreneur, took over the management of the Hanyang Works.

With the inflow of private capital and managerial skills, the enterprise expanded. In 1908 the Hanyang Iron and Steel Works, the Tayeh Ore Dressing Plants, and the Pingsiang Coal Mines were amalgamated. The integrated enterprise was known as the Hanyehping Coal and Iron Corporation. By 1915, its annual output capacity of steel reached 90,000 tons, and that for iron, 210,000 tons[11]. Responsible for the added capacity were two newly-constructed blast furnaces with a rated daily capacity of 250 tons each, and six new acid open-hearth furnaces. The expansion included, in addition, the installation of new rolling equipment[12]. Further expansion took place in 1919 when construction

---

5 *TCTL*, p. 141.
6 *CCKCC*, p. 219.
7 The size of its initial labor force is known to be 3,000. It grew to over 6,000 in the 1900's. *Ibid.*; Huang Tso-hsün, *Chung-kuo k'uang-ch'an* (China's mineral products), Shanghai: The Commercial Press, 1926, p. 54.
8 At the beginning of 1950, the ratio of the technical staff to the labor force was 1 : 140. *New China News Agency (NCNA)*, Peking, January 2, 1950.
9 *CCKCC*, p. 219.
10 *KTMCFT*, p. 2.
11 *Ibid.*
12 A good part of the early expansion was financed by a loan of 1.2 million yen from Japan with Hanyehping's output of ore and pig iron as security. Huang Tso-hsün, *op. cit.*, pp. 45—46.

began in Tayeh on two blast furnaces, with a rated daily capacity of 450 tons each.

By this time, iron production was also developed by the Japanese at Penki and Anshan in Manchuria. Other locations in which iron production was developed subsequently up to the outbreak of Sino-Japanese hostilities in 1937 included Shenchiaki in Hupeh, Shihchingshan in Hopeh, Yangchuan and Taiyuan in Shansi, and Tsiaotso in Honan.

## Chapter 2

# WARTIME EXPANSION

### Expansion in Manchuria

The importance of Manchuria in China's iron and steel industry can be judged by its share in the national output total. In 1937 when the Sino-Japanese hostilities broke out, this share amounted to 97.6 per cent for pig iron produced by modern furnace, and 92.8 per cent for ingot steel.

Development of the steel industry in Manchuria was greatly stepped up following the outbreak of the Sino-Japanese war. As the backbone of the war economy, the industry was given top priority by the Japanese authorities. The most important iron and steel bases were located in Liaoning, centering on Anshan, Penki and Tungpientao. The last district was considered to have great potential, but was not developed until after 1938.

Table 2.1 shows the growth pattern of iron and steel production in Manchuria during the war period. The outbreak of hostilities affected output favorably. Both iron and steel output showed a substantial increase in 1937. The increase continued through 1943; thereafter it declined drastically owing chiefly to shortages of coal, manganese ore, iron ore, skilled labor, spare parts, repair material and electric power supply, and subsequently to air raids by the United States[1]. Inasmuch as 50 per cent of Manchuria's pig iron output was exported to Japan[2], the shortage of shipping facilities in the last phase of the Pacific War was particularly relevant to the falling off of iron production in Manchuria. The decline in steel output was, however, more drastic; it was 46 per cent in 1944 and 68 per cent in 1945.

The production increase up to 1944 resulted preponderantly from the addition of smelting equipment. During 1937–1943, eight blast furnaces were blown in, six in Anshan and two in Penki. The rated daily capacity of the newly added blast furnaces totalled 5,340 tons. The particulars of these furnaces are given in Table 2.2. In the same period, eight open hearths and four mixers were added to Anshan. Table 2.3 presents their particulars. The addition of equipment enlarged Manchuria's iron smelting capacity by 205 per cent (see Tables 1.3 and 2.2), while the increase in pig iron output during the war, as shown in Table 2.1, did not exceed

1 *Iron and Steel Metallurgy of the Japanese Empire*, Report No. 50, prepared by Natural Resources Section, General Headquarters, Supreme Commander for the Allied Powers, Tokyo, 1946, pp. 35—36.
2 Yu-kwei Cheng, *Foreign Trade and Industrial Development of China: An Historical and Integrated Analysis through 1948*, Washington, D.C., 1956, p. 191.

*Table 2.1. Production of Iron and Steel in Manchuria, 1936—1945 (in tons)*

| Year | Pig Iron | Ingot Steel |
|------|----------|-------------|
| 1936 | 648,096 | 364,315 |
| 1937 | 811,066 | 516,349 |
| 1938 | 854,954 | 585,094 |
| 1939 | 1,025,297 | 529,606 |
| 1940 | 1,074,311 | 532,295 |
| 1941 | 1,417,327 | 561,372 |
| 1942 | 1,340,808 | 731,163 |
| 1943 | 1,584,880 | 871,987 |
| 1944 | 1,246,085 | 473,731 |
| 1945 | a | 150,000[b] |

a. Unknown.
b. Estimated.

Sources: *Sources of Iron Ore in East Asia,* Report No. 154, prepared by Economic and Scientific Section, General Headquarters, Supreme Commander for the Allied Powers, Tokyo, 1952, pp. 147, 156; Edwin W. Pauley, *Report on Japanese Assets in Manchuria to the President of the United States,* Washington, D.C., July 1946, p. 92; Industrial Statistics Section, State Bureau of Statistics, *Wo-kuo kang-t'ieh, tien-li, mei-t'an, chi-hsieh, fang-chih, tsao-chih kung-yeh ti chin-hsi* (The past and present of China's iron and steel, electric power, coal, machine-making, textile and paper industries), Peking: Statistics Publishing House, 1958, pp. 4—5.

*Table 2.2. Blast Furnaces Erected in Manchuria during the War*

| Location | Designation | Capacity Tons[a]/Day | M³ | Date Starting Operation |
|----------|-------------|------------------------|-----|--------------------------|
| Anshan, Liaoning | No. 4 | 600 | 930 | 1937 |
| | No. 5 | 700 | 936 | 1938 |
| | No. 6 | 700 | 936[b] | 1938 |
| | No. 7 | 700 | 936[b] | 1938 |
| | No. 8 | 700 | 936[b] | 1938 |
| | No. 9 | 700 | 936 | 1943 |
| Penki, Liaoning | No. 3 | 600 | 758 | 1941 |
| | No. 4 | 600 | 758 | 1942 |
| Tungpientao, Liaoning | c | 20 x 2 | d | 1945 |

a. Rated capacity.
b. Estimated.
c. No designation.
d. Unknown.

Sources: *Sources of Iron Ore in East Asia,* Report No. 154, prepared by Economic and Scientific Section, General Headquarters, Supreme Commander for the Allied Powers, pp. 146 and 157; D.K. Lieu, *Industrial Development in Communist China,* New York, 1955, p. 25; and *Chukyo tekkogyo chosa hokokusho — Kigyohen* (Survey report of the steel industry of communist China — enterprise edition), prepared by the Cabinet Research Chamber of the Japanese Government, Tokyo, 1955, pp. 40 and 210; and other sources.

145 per cent. There was thus a greater degree of under-utilization of available capacity during the war than before the war. Even at the peak output level of 1943, the rate of capacity utilization was about 62.8 per cent[3].

Although under-capacity operation also applied to steel making, its extent was reduced in wartime. The enlargement of steel capacity during the war came to 1,290 tons/heat, or 84 per cent over the prewar capacity (see Tables 1.4 and 2.3). The increase in ingot steel output in the war period was considerably more, amounting to as much as 139 per cent (see Table 2.1). In spite of the greater increase in production, only 61.7 per cent of the available capacity was utilized in 1943[4].

During the war, Manchuria also developed its rolling capacity, which totalled 962,400 tons toward the end of the war. Over 95 per cent of this amount was located in Anshan, while the remainder was distributed in Fushun, Penki, Dairen and Shenyang. Anshan (with twelve mills) was equipped to produce blooms, billets, rails, bars, rods, plates, sheets, pipes and wires. The 1943 output data of some of these rolled products are given in Table 2.4 along with their capacities. It is immediately clear that under-capacity operation was also true of steel rolling. The degree of capacity utilization varied from 28.1 per cent for plate steel to 55.6 per cent for sheet steel. For all the rolled products for which data are obtainable, it appears that the unused capacity was relatively larger than for ingot steel.

Under-capacity operation is wasteful. It can be attributed to many factors, among which were shortages of skilled labour, material inputs, and spare parts; the necessity of adjusting to the need of the Japanese steel industry; and the cautious attitude of the Japanese metallurgical engineers in observing a wide

*Table 2.3. Steel Furnaces Erected in Manchuria during the War*

| Location | Number | Type | Rated Capacity of Each (tons per heat) | Date Starting Operation |
|---|---|---|---|---|
| Anshan, Liaoning | 2 | Open hearth | 150 | 1937 |
|  | 6 | Open hearth | 150 | 1942 |
|  | 4 | Mixing furnace | (300) | 1942 |
| Shenyang, Liaoning | 3 | Open hearth | 30 | 1937 |

Sources: *Sources of Iron Ore in East Asia*, Report No. 154, prepared by Economic and Scientific Section, General Headquarters, Supreme Commander for the Allied Powers, Tokyo, 1952, p. 146; and *Chukyo tekkogyo chosa hokokusho-Kigyohen* (Survey report of the steel industry of communist China — enterprise edition), prepared by the Cabinet Research Chamber of the Japanese Government, Tokyo, 1955, pp. 249 and 252.

3 The rated annual capacity of the blast furnaces existing in 1943 was 2,524,000 tons, and the annual output 1,584,880 tons.
4 In 1943, the rated annual capacity of the existing steel furnaces came to 1,413,000 tons and the output 871,987 tons.

*Table 2.4. Annual Output and Capacity of Rolled Products at Anshan, 1943*
   *(in thousand tons)*

| Item | Output | Rated Capacity | Rate of Capacity Utilization (per cent) |
|---|---|---|---|
| | (1) | (2) | $(3) = \dfrac{(1)}{(2)} \times 100$ |
| Rail and large bars | 131 | 250 | 52.4 |
| Small bars | 74 | 170 | 43.5 |
| Plate | 59 | 210 | 28.1 |
| Rod | 64 | 120 | 53.3 |
| Sheet | 35 | 63 | 55.6 |

Sources: *Iron and Steel Metallurgy of the Japanese Empire*, Report No. 50, prepared by Natural Resources Section, General Headquarters, Supreme Commander for the Allied Powers, Tokyo, 1946, pp. 39—41; and *Chukyo tekkogyo chosa hokokusho-Kigyohen* (Survey report of the steel industry of communist China — enterprise edition), prepared by the Cabinet Research Chamber of the Japanese Government, Tokyo, 1955, Supplementary Volume, p. 8.

safety margin from the rated capacity in order to prolong the useful life of the equipment. This attitude is in striking contrast to the subsequent communist practice regarding the rate of equipment utilization.

## Developments in China Proper

The removal of equipment to the interior in anticipation of Japanese occupation was a notable wartime development of China's steel industry. Most of the equipment of the Hanyang plant which could be moved was shipped to Szechwan at the outbreak of the Sino-Japanese hostilities. This included parts of two 250-ton blast furnaces and four 30-ton open-hearth furnaces. The 100-ton blast furnace of the Liuhokow plant in Hupeh was moved in its entirety to Chungking to form the nucleus of the Tatukow plant[5]. Some metallurgical equipment was also shipped inland from the coast as a matter of war economic policy.

This policy plus the availability of coal and iron ore deposits in Szechwan and the active promotion of the National Resources Commission (NRC) made Chungking an iron and steel center in unoccupied China. Its coal supply came from the Kialing River coal field with a reserve of 491 million tons and the Nanchwan coal field with a reserve of 40 million tons. Its iron ore supply

5 Yen Szu-kuo, "Kang-t'ieh kung-yeh" (Iron and steel industry), *Chung-kuo kung-yeh* (The Chinese industry), Taipei: Chinese Cultural Publication Committee, 1954, Vol. II, pp. 11—16; and *Chukyo tekkogyo chosa hokokusho — Kigyohen* (Survey report of the steel industry of communist China — enterprise edition), prepared by the Cabinet Research Chamber of the Japanese Government, Tokyo, 1955, p. 705. Hereafter the latter source will be referred to as *CTCHK*.

came from Chukiang with a reserve of 14.8 million tons[6]. The importance of Chungking as an iron and steel center can be gauged by its share in the overall installed capacity. During the war there were, in unoccupied China, eleven blast furnaces with a total rated daily capacity of 365 tons, and twenty steel furnaces with a total capacity of 64 tons/heat. Chungking's share in the overall iron and steel capacities came to 75.3 per cent and 66.4 per cent respectively. The remaining capacity was distributed in the following localities: Anning in Yunnan, Weiyuan, Chikiang and Pisan in Szechwan, Yungsin in Kiangsi and Chienkiang in Kwangsi[7].

During the war, NRC played an important role in promoting the development of the steel industry in unoccupied China. Not only did it go into joint

Table 2.5. *Production of Iron and Steel in Unoccupied China by Ownership, 1938—1944 (in tons)*

| Year | Pig Iron | | Ingot Steel | |
|------|-----------------|--------------------------|-----------------|--------------------------|
|      | Output Quantity | Share of NRC (per cent) | Output Quantity | Share of NRC (per cent) |
|      | (1) | (2) | (3) | (4) |
| 1938 | 52,900 | a | 900 | a |
| 1939 | 62,730 | a | 1,200 | a |
| 1940 | 55,200 | 4.5 | 1,500 | a |
| 1941 | 63,637 | 7.0 | 2,011 | 5.8 |
| 1942 | 96,000 | 14.0 | 3,300 | 45.6 |
| 1943 | 77,000 | 27.1 | 7,480 | 62.1 |
| 1944 | 40,134 | 31.2 | 13,361 | 56.9 |

a. Unknown.

Sources: Yen Chung-ping *et al, Chung-kuo chin-tai ching-chi-shih t'ung-chi tzu-liao hsüan-chi* (Selected statistical data on the modern economic history of China), Peking: The Science Publishing House, 1955, pp. 100 and 157; Yu-kwei Cheng, *Foreign Trade and Industrial Development of China: An Historical and Integrated Analysis through 1948*, Washington, D.C., 1956, p. 264; and Kia-ngau Chang, *The Inflationary Spiral: The Experience in China, 1939—1950*, Cambridge: The Technology Press of Massachusetts Institute of Technology, 1958, p. 381.

operations with private producers, but it also operated mines and smelting plants. The extent of control exercised by NRC over the production of iron and steel is shown in Table 2.5, which also gives the overall output figures.

From the data presented in Table 2.5, some observations can be made. First, on the whole the control of NRC over the production of iron and steel was increasing during the war years for which data are obtainable. Second, while steel output increased steadily throughout the period 1938—1944, the output of pig iron began to decline after 1942. The initial decline in 1943 was entirely in the

6 *Ching-chi tung-yüan* (Economic mobilization), Chungking, Vol. I, No. 1 (June 15, 1938), pp. 14—22.
7 *Chung-kuo kung-yeh, op. cit.*, Vol. I, pp. 16—23.

private sector of the steel industry. In fact, the output of enterprises under NRC increased from 13,468 tons in 1942 to 20,853 tons in 1943[8]. The downturn in iron production coincided with the output behavior of the capital goods industry as a whole, attributable to the fact that beginning in 1942, fewer new factories were established and only maintenance and replacement of the existing equipment were needed. Third, in spite of the spectacular rate of increase in steel production, it amounted in 1944 to only a fraction of the prewar output in China Proper. Some of the smelting equipment moved to Szechwan was never put into operation.

In the territories occupied by Japan, the dismantling and removal of plant equipment to the interior prior to occupation confronted the Japanese with an arduous task of rehabilitation. In the case of Tayeh, for instance, the rehabilitation was initially confined to iron ore production. In other cases, rehabilitation was accompanied by expansion. Japan invested a total of 3,550 million yen (equivalent of US$834 million) in implementing the plan for raising North China's annual iron output to one million tons[9]. Toward this goal, the North China Iron Corporation was formed in 1942 with the Shihchingshan Iron Works as the main smelting center. The latter's iron smelting capacity was to be substantially expanded by importation of large blast furnaces from Japan. But as an interim measure, eleven small furnaces were built and blown in during the latter part of 1943. In the meantime, one 380-ton furnace arrived from Japan and was blown in toward the end of the year. It was designated as No. 2 blast furnace of Shihchingshan. In 1944, a 600-ton furnace was shipped in from Japan to be designated as No. 3 blast furnace. But before its construction was completed, the war ended. The Shihchingshan expansion plan also included taking over the two 450-ton furnaces of Tayeh. In fact, they were already being shipped to North China, when the war ended. In the midst of confusion caused by the cessation of hostilities, their whereabouts became unknown.

In addition, the Japanese occupation authorities set up a number of iron and steel plants in China Proper including Tangshan, Tientsin, Tsingtao and Woosung. The rated daily blast furnace capacity of the new plants totalled 1,580 tons and the steel furnace capacity of the new plants 70.5 tons/heat[10]. Clearly the emphasis was on iron production.

To ensure an adequate ore supply for the new blast furnaces and for furnaces in Anshan and Penki, the Japanese directed their attention to the development of iron ore production. This led to the expansion and modernization of the Lungyen mines in Hopeh, for which a total of 180 million yen (equivalent of US$42.3 million) had been invested[11]. As a result, the mining operation at Pengchiapao, Lungyen, was completely mechanized and became the most modern iron mine in

8 *TCTL*, p. 157.
9 *CTCHK*, p. 313. The equivalent in US dollars is computed on the basis of 1 yen to US$ 0.234925.
10 *Chung-kuo kung-yeh, op. cit.*, Vol. I, pp. 28—32.
11 *CTCHK*, p. 269.

the Far East. The intensive search for rich iron ore deposits under the Japanese occupation authorities resulted in the discovery of, among others, the Tientu mines and the Shihlu mines on Hainan Island. The former being better situated, half of its reserve of 5 million tons had been extracted and shipped out during the Japanese occupation. The Shihlu mines, though less accessible, had an estimated reserve of over 100 million tons. During the Japanese occupation, a considerable amount of work had been done on mining installations, harbour construction and railway building. The Japanese plan for exploiting these mines envisaged an annual output of 3 million tons[12].

12 *Chung-kuo kung-yeh, op. cit.,* Vol. I, p. 30.

*Chapter 3*

# SOVIET REMOVALS

*Postwar Output Behavior*

With the Japanese surrender in August 1945, production of iron and steel in occupied China (including Manchuria) was at a standstill while production in the unoccupied areas was also adversely affected by the uncertainty following the abrupt ending of the war. Although the nationalist government took over most of the iron and steel plants in occupied China Proper in the last quarter of 1945, the takeover of plants in Manchuria was delayed first by interim occupation by Soviet troops and subsequently by the struggle with communist forces for control of the iron and steel centers. These events, particularly the former, inflicted serious damage to the production capacity of the steel industry and made the task of rehabilitation extremely difficult for the nationalist government. The task was further complicated by the deterioration of general economic conditions in the country.

Consequently the 1946 output for the country as a whole amounted merely to 81,000 tons of iron and 15,700 tons of steel[1]. The pre-1945 peak annual output was 1,801,000 tons for pig iron and 922,738 tons for ingot steel[2]. Thus the 1946 output amounted to 4.5 per cent of the peak iron production and 1.7 per cent of the peak steel production.

Considerable progress was made in the restoration of steel production in 1947. The 1947 ingot steel output was raised to 63,000 tons, or 6.8 per cent of the pre-1945 peak. The restoration of iron production was at a much lower rate. Its 1947 output rose merley to 85,000 tons, or 4.7 per cent of the past peak. For the slower recovery of iron production, an explanation may be found in the extent of the damage caused by Soviet removals and military hostilities between nationalist and communist troops, not only to the iron smelting capacity but also to mining installations, ore-dressing plants and coke manufacturing plants.

*Soviet Occupation and Equipment Removal*

On V-J Day when the Japanese surrender was announced, Soviet troops were close to the iron and steel centers in Manchuria. Thus they were the first to occupy

1 Kia-ngau Chang, *The Inflationary Spiral: The Experience in China, 1939—1950,* Cambridge: The Technology Press of Massachusetts Institute of Technology, 1958, p. 381.
2 *KTMCFT,* p. 19.

the important plants and declared them as "plants under the control of the Soviet Army." The occupation of each plant was followed immediately by the demand on the management for a detailed inventory of all installations and equipment. In the case of Anshan, this demand was made under the pretence that it was needed for the future formation of a "Sino-Soviet Joint Steel Corporation." However, within two weeks of the occupation, they began to remove some of the installations on the basis of the inventory requested.

The initial Soviet policy regarding removals was to exclude equipment installed prior to the outbreak of Sino-Japanese hostilities in July 1937. However, this policy was not rigidly implemented. Despite the fact that the heavy rolling mill and the sheet mill at Anshan were in operation before July 1937, the equipment of both mills was removed by Soviet troops. On the other hand, the equipment of Anshan's No. 1 steel plant, which was completed after the outbreak of Sino-Japanese hostilities, was left behind.

The removal of equipment and installations constituted a tremendous task. In Anshan, for instance, the amount of equipment removed totalled 64,756 tons. The removals involved 612,426 man-days and 2,896 railway wagon loads. The job actually took 53 days[3]. In Soviet removals of equipment from Penki, a majority of the 40,000 Chinese workers were involved, in addition to the Japanese employees. The urgency of the removal task was reflected in the participation of some 300—400 men from the Soviet occupation forces and in the high wage rates offered. Those engaged in the removals were paid three times as much as under the Japanese management prior to V—J Day. The fact that Soviet soldiers were working together with Chinese and Japanese in the dismantling and removals had the additional effect of raising the efficiency of non-Soviet workers. In spite of all this, it took one month to complete the removal at Penki.

With respect to Soviet removals of plant equipment and installations of the iron and steel centers in Manchuria, the chief concern is the extent of damage to productive capacities in the various sectors of the steel industry caused by such removals. It will serve as a basis for appraising the rehabilitation task of the communist regime. The degree of damage to the steel industry was estimated by a special U.S. mission (headed by Edwin W. Pauley) sent by President Roosevelt to Manchuria in June-July 1946 to investigate the Japanese assets removed by Soviet occupation troops. The estimates are presented in Table 3.1.

Table 3.1 reveals that the extent of capacity loss in Manchuria through Soviet removals was greater in iron-smelting than in steelmaking. This partly explains the slower recovery of iron production in the immediate postwar years. In addition, the complete removal of iron ore concentration facilities is highly relevant, since the bulk of ores in Manchuria is lean in iron content and requires concentration before it can be charged into a blast furnace. Similarly the substantial capacity loss in coke manufacturing further limited the recovery of iron production.

3 *CTCHK*, p. 9.

The extent of damage caused by Soviet removals was also investigated late in 1946 by a Japanese mission headed by Kubo Makoto. The Makoto Mission, composed of twenty-one experts formerly holding key positions in Manchuria, was organized under the auspices of the North-eastern Industrial Association and the Japanese Rehabilitation Liaison Office. Its findings indicate a greater amount of

*Table 3.1 Capacity Loss in Manchuria Caused by Soviet Removals (in tons)*

| Sector | Rated Annual Capacity Prior to Soviet Occupation | Capacity Lost through Removals | |
|---|---|---|---|
| | | Amount | As Percentage of Rated Capacity |
| | (1) | (2) | $(3) = \dfrac{(2)}{(1)} \times 100$ |
| Iron ore mining | 8,645,000a | b | c |
| Iron ore concentration | 2,030,000 | 2,030,000 | 100 |
| Coke manufacturing | 2,800,000 | 2,016,000 | 72 |
| Iron smelting | 2,524,000 | 1,786,000 | 71 |
| Sponge Iron | 112,550 | 110,550 | 98 |
| Ingot steel | 1,330,000 | 750,000 | 56 |
| Blooms, billets, slabs | 1,000,000 | 500,000 | 50 |
| Shapes & plates | 910,000 | 586,200 | 64 |
| Special steels | | | |
| Electric furnace steel | 71,920 | 36,000 | 50 |
| Forging | 6,400 | 6,400 | 100 |
| Rolling | 26,500 | d | 50 |

a. Including 5.5 million tons of inferior ores, i. e., ores containing less than 40 per cent Fe.
b. All iron mines had been stripped of essential machinery.
c. The extent of capacity loss cannot be determined.
d. The exact quantity cannot be determined.

Source: Edwin W. Pauley, *Report on Japanese Assets in Manchuria to the President of the United States,* Washington, D.C., July 1946, pp. 90—95.

damage in value terms caused by Soviet removals than reported by the Pauley Mission. According to the latter, damage to the steel industry amounted to US$131,260,000 in comparison with US$204,052,000 estimated by the Makoto Mission[4]. The different systems of classification and reporting make it impossible to attempt a meaningful comparison of the estimates of damage in physical terms caused by Soviet removals. The summary findings of the Makoto

4 Edwin W. Pauley, *Report on Japanese Assets in Manchuria to the President of the United States,* Washington, July 1946, p. 125. Hereafter this source will be referred to as *Pauley Report; A Report on Russian Destruction of Our Industries in the North-eastern Provinces,* edited by the Chinese Association for the United Nations, Taipei, 1952, p. 12.

Mission regarding capacity losses suffered by the various iron and steel manufacturers are presented in Table 3.2.


### Other Deterrent Factors to Postwar Recovery


The loss of capacity in the steel industry was due preponderantly, but not
entirely, to Soviet removals. Though localized, the military hostilities between
nationalist and communist troops following the Japanese surrender caused considerable damage to iron ore mines and smelting facilities. Anshan, for example,


Table 3.2. Capacity Loss of Individual Firms due to Soviet Removals

| Firm | Loss as a Percent of Pre-V-J Day Capacity |
| --- | --- |
| Anshan and Penki | 100 (pig iron) |
|  | 62 (steel) |
|  | 86 (mining) |
|  | 79 (chemical processing) |
| Sumitomo Metal Industry | 75 |
| Steel Tube Mfg. Works | 100 |
| Nippon Steel Tubing Factory | 33 |
| Anshan Steel Products | 38 |
| Kubota Cast Iron Tube Manufacturer | 100 |
| Manchu Steel | 40 |
| Manchu Galvanizer | 55 |
| Anshan High Quality Steel | 49 |
| Penki Special Steel | 100 |
| Overall | 82 |

Source: *A Report on Russian Destruction of Our Industries in the North-eastern
Provinces,* edited by the Chinese Association for the United Nations, Taipei, 1952, p. 13.


was under the control of communist forces in February 1946, right after the
departure of Soviet troops. In the ensuing months, it changed hands at least
three times between communist and nationalist troops. When the latter finally
gained complete control of it in May 1946, it was found that blast furnaces
Nos. 1, 2, 4 and the remains of No. 9 had been severely damaged. The destruction
in terms of annual capacity loss amounted to 342,000 tons, or 14 per cent of the
pre-1945 overall blast furnace capacity of Manchuria[5]. The situation in Penki was
worse in that for two and a half years (from the departure of Soviet occupation
troops in the spring of 1946 up to its takeover by communist forces in November 1948) Penki was the focal point in the nationalist-communist armed
conflict. The remains of its installations spared by Soviet removals were thus
destroyed. Similarly, the Lungyen Iron Mines and the Tangshan Steel Plant in


5 *Pauley Report,* p. 92.

North China, and the Tayeh Iron Mines in Central China suffered serious damage during the civil strife in the immediate postwar years.

Aside from the damage directly caused by military hostilities, the confusion arising from warfare was seized upon by local elements as a golden opportunity for looting parts, materials and even equipment. For instance, the hammer in the Fushun Steel Mill which had escaped Soviet removal was removed by the natives[6]. Although the exact amount of damage due to looting cannot be ascertained, it undoubtedly made the task of rehabilitation more difficult.

6 *CTCHK*, p. 291.

# PART II
# OUTPUT RESTORATION AND CAPITAL CONSTRUCTION

*Chapter 4*

# OUTPUT RESTORATION

Output restoration was achieved under the communist regime by (1) capacity rehabilitation, (2) a higher rate of equipment utilization, and (3) increasing the productivity of capital equipment. While the extent of capacity restoration is discussed in the text along with capacity utilization and equipment productivity, individual rehabilitation projects are examined in the appendix to this chapter.

Since the communist economic planners defined rehabilitation in terms of production rather than capacity, the completion of rehabilitation in 1952 merely meant that output was restored to the pre-communist peak level. It did not imply that the pre-1945 capacity was restored. Thus it is important to determine whether it was feasible to restore the output level without re-establishing the prewar peak capacity. Such an enquiry constitutes the purpose of this chapter.

In order to answer the question whether the communist claim of output recovery to the prewar peak level was within the realm of possibility, it is necessary to know first how the highest pre-communist output was determined and what constituted the capacity basis of this output. Then the possible 1952 output level for each of the major sectors of the steel industry can be worked out on the basis of the extent of capacity rehabilitation, the rate of equipment utilization and the productivity of capital equipment. This procedure, in addition, will serve as a check on the consistency of communist statistics.

*Recovery of Production*

To examine output restoration, it is necessary to determine the time period in which the highest pre-communist output occurred. Insofar as pig iron and ingot steel are concerned, the earlier communist practice of calculating the highest previous peak production on the basis of the 1936 output quantity for China Proper and the 1943 quantity for the Northeast was replaced by the practice of identifying the highest output for the entire country in a single calendar year, 1943[1]. Such a shift is justified, since both pig iron and ingot steel output of China Proper in 1943 exceeded the 1936 level (see Table 4.1).

The period of the peak output of finished steel (virtually all rolled products), on the other hand, has not been officially specified. Because of the lack of sufficient data on the operating capacity of China Proper in 1943, the highest pre-

1 *KTMCFT*, pp. 4 and 11.

communist output of finished steel is taken as a combination of the 1936 output quantity for China Proper and the 1943 output quantity for the Northeast.

Data on the annual output of the major sectors of the steel industry during the rehabilitation period are presented in Table 4.2, which also shows the extent of recovery from the pre-communist peak level. Although the 1949 outputs of pig iron and ingot steel appear very low in comparison with their pre-1945 peaks, these nevertheless represent a considerable improvement over 1947. Pig iron production in 1947 amounted to 4.7 per cent of the pre-1945 peak and ingot steel production 6.8 per cent[2]. The corresponding percentage figures for 1949 were 14.0 and 17.2 respectively (see Column 3 of Table 4.2).

The highest rate of recovery was in finished steel; its 1951 output already surpassed the pre-communist peak level. The rate of recovery in ingot steel came next. Its pre-communist peak output was almost restored in 1951, and was surpassed in 1952 by a margin of over 46 per cent. The restoration of pig iron production lagged far behind, although by 1952 its output was also above the previous peak. The relative rates of recovery in pig iron and ingot steel production during 1949—1952 conformed to the pattern of the immediate postwar years. This pattern was attributable to the greater degree of damage suffered in iron smelting, ore-dressing and coke-making facilities[3].

*Operating Capacity of Pre-Communist Peak Output*

To determine the extent of capacity restoration, it is necessary to know not only the operating capacity at the end of the rehabilitation period but also that on which the pre-communist peak output was based. Accordingly the operating capacity of the country in 1943 needs to be estimated for both pig iron and ingot steel. For finished steel, it is necessary to derive the operating capacity of the Northeast in 1943 and of China Proper in 1936.

*Table 4.1. Production of Pig Iron and Ingot Steel in China, 1936 and 1943 (in tons)*

| Product | Year | National Total | Manchuria | China Proper |
|---------|------|----------------|-----------|--------------|
|         |      | (1)            | (2)       | (3) = (1) — (2) |
| Pig iron | 1936 | 809,996 | 648,096 | 161,900 |
|          | 1943 | 1,801,000 | 1,584,880 | 216,120 |
| Ingot steel | 1936 | 414,315 | 364,315 | 50,000 |
|             | 1943 | 922,738 | 871,987 | 50,751 |

Sources: Industrial Statistics Section, State Bureau of Statistics, *Wo-kuo kang-t'ieh, tien-li, mei-t'an, chi-hsieh, fang-chih, tsao-chih kung-yeh ti chin-hsi* (The past and present of China's iron and steel, electric power, coal, machine-making, textile and paper industries), Peking: Statistics Publishing House, 1958, pp. 4 and 5; and Tables 1.1, 1.2 and 2.1.

2 See Chapter 3.
3 See Table 3.1.

Table 4.2. *Restoration of Major Products, 1949–1952 (in tons)*

| Product | 1943 Pre-Communist Peak Output | 1949 Quantity | 1949 Extent of Recovery (per cent of peak output) | 1950 Quantity | 1950 Extent of Recovery (per cent of peak output) | 1951 Quantity | 1951 Extent of Recovery (per cent of peak output) | 1952 Quantity | 1952 Extent of Recovery (per cent of peak output) |
|---|---|---|---|---|---|---|---|---|---|
| | (1) | (2) | $(3) = \frac{(2)}{(1)} \times 100$ | (4) | $(5) = \frac{(4)}{(1)} \times 100$ | (6) | $(7) = \frac{(6)}{(1)} \times 100$ | (8) | $(9) = \frac{(8)}{(1)} \times 100$ |
| Pig iron[a] | 1,801,000 | 251,991 | 14.0 | 977,794 | 54.3 | 1,447,940 | 80.4 | 1,928,585 | 107.1 |
| Ingot steel | 922,738 | 158,378 | 17.2 | 605,796 | 65.7 | 895,982 | 97.1 | 1,348,509 | 146.1 |
| Finished Steel | 686,000[b] | 141,104 | 20.6 | 463,921 | 67.6 | 807,798 | 117.8 | 1,311,897 | 191.2 |

a. Including pig iron produced by indigenous methods.
b. Year not specified.

Source: Industrial Statistics Section, State Bureau of Statistics, *Wo-kuo kang-t'ieh, tien-li, mei-t'an, chi-hsieh, fang-chih, tsao-chih kung-yeh ti chin-hsi* (The past and present of China's iron and steel, electric power, coal, machine-making, textile and paper industries), Peking: Statistics Publishing House, 1958, pp. 4 and 11.

*Iron smelting capacity in 1943* — Whereas the rated daily capacity of the blast furnaces of the Northeast in operation during 1943 amounted to 7,050 tons[4], that in China Proper is unknown. Since the rated daily blast furnace capacity of China Proper in operation during 1936 amounted to 120 tons[5], one can adjust capacity changes according to output variation on the assumption of an unchanged capacity-output relationship in China Proper between 1936 and 1943. Such an adjustment yields 160 tons as the rated daily blast furnace capacity of China Proper in operation during 1943[6]. Thus the operating capacity corresponding to the precommunist peak output came to 7,210 tons per day.

*Steel refining capacity in 1943* — Because of data limitations, this discussion is confined to the operating capacity of open hearths. The latter in Manchuria can be derived from Tables 1.4 and 2.3 to be 1,990 tons in 1943. The open-hearth capacity in operation in China Proper during 1943, however, has to be estimated.

Of the twelve open hearths in existence in prewar China Proper (with a total capacity of 302 tons/heat[7]), nine were not in operation in 1936. These include the seven furnaces (six 30-ton and one 15-ton) of the Hanyehping Coal and Iron Corporation in Hanyang and the two furnaces (one 35-ton and one 12-ton) of the Hohsing Iron and Steel Works in Pootung[8]. Thus the operating open-hearth capacity of China Proper amounted to 60 tons/heat in 1936[9]. The 1943 capacity can be estimated by assuming an unchanged capacity-output relationship and output structure for China Proper between 1936 and 1943. Since ingot steel output of China Proper is known to have been 50,000 tons in 1936 and 50,751 tons in 1943 (see Table 4.1), the 1943 operating open-hearth capacity is estimated to be 61 tons/heat. The overall open-hearth capacity in operation during 1943, therefore, amounted to 2,051 tons/heat.

*Rolling capacity in 1936 China Proper and 1943 Northeast* — The rolling capacity of China Proper in operation during 1936 was about 150,000 tons, with two-thirds in Shanghai and the remainder in Taiyuan. The operating capacity in Manchuria during 1943, as pointed out in Chapter 2, amounted to 962,400 tons. Thus the overall operating capacity corresponding to the pre-communist peak production came to 1,112,400 tons.

### Extent of Capacity Restoration

Before examining the extent of capacity restoration, it is necessary to look into the operating capacity of the major sectors of the steel industry in 1952. This will also provide a basis for evaluating output restoration.

4 Derived from data given in Tables 1.3 and 2.2.
5 See Chapter 1.
6 Derived from data given in Table 4.1.
7 See Table 1.4.
8 *Chung-kuo kung-yeh*, p. 13.
9 This operating capacity checks with output statistics. Table 4.1 gives 50,000 tons as the ingot steel output of China Proper in 1936.

*Iron smelting capacity in 1952* — According to the State Bureau of Statistics, there were, under the jurisdiction of the Iron and Steel Bureau of the Central Ministry of Heavy Industry and of provincial and municipal governments, thirty-

*Table 4.3. Major Blast Furnaces in Operation, 1952*

| Location | Designation | Rehabilitated Capacity | | Completion Date of Rehabilitation |
|---|---|---|---|---|
| | | Tons[a]/day | m³ | |
| Penki, Liaoning | No. 1 | 200 | 332 | July 1949 |
| | No. 2 | 200 | 336 | July 1949 |
| Anshan, Liaoning | No. 1 | 400 | 585 | September 1949 |
| | No. 2 | 400 | 602 | June 1949 |
| | No. 4 | 600 | 786 | January 1950 |
| Shihchingshan, Hopeh | No. 1 | 250 | 406 | June 1949 |
| | No. 2 | 380 | 512 | April 1951 |
| Taiyuan, Shansi | No. 1 | 80[b] | 146 | Spring 1950 |
| | No. 2 | 150[c] | 291 | Autumn 1949 |
| Yangchuan, Shansi | No. 1 | 10[d] | 45 | July 1949 |
| | e | 25 | 64 | Early 1949 |
| | e | 25[f] | 64 | Early 1949 |
| Pootung, Shanghai | e | 33 | 64 | Spring 1951 |
| Woosung, Shanghai | e | 30 | 64[h] | Summer 1952[g] |
| Pootung, Shanghai | e | 20 | 45[h] | 1950 |
| Tatukou, Chungking | e | 100 | 132[h] | i |
| Hsuanhwa, Inner Mongolia | e | 25 | 64 | 1951 |
| | e | 25 | 64 | 1951 |
| | e | 25 | 64 | 1951 |
| | e | 25 | 64 | Summer 1952 |
| | e | 25 | 64 | Summer 1952 |
| Tayeh, Hupeh | e | 30[j] | 64 | i |
| Kunming, Yunnan | e | 30 | 64[h] | 1951[k] |
| Urumchi, Sinkiang | e | 30 | 64[h] | 1951[k] |
| | | 3,118 | 4,986 | |

a. Rated capacity.
b. It was expanded to 80 tons in 1946 from the prewar capacity of 40 tons.
c. The pre-communist capacity was 120 tons.
d. The pre-communist capacity was 20 tons.
e. No designation.
f. Erected after the war and before the communist takeover.
g. Removed from Pootung.
h. Estimated.
i. In operative order at the time of the communist takeover.
j. Erected in 1946.
k. New construction.

Sources: *Chukyo tekkogyo chosa hokokusho-Kigyohen* (Survey report of the steel industry of communist China — enterprise edition), prepared by the Cabinet Research Chamber of the Japanese Government, Tokyo, 1955, *passim;* and Industrial Statistics Section, State Bureau of Statistics, *Wo-kuo kang-t'ieh, tien-li, mei-t'an chi-hsieh, fang-chih tsao-chih kung-yeh ti chin-hsi* (The past and present of China's iron and steel, electric power, coal, machine-making, textile and paper industries), Peking: Statistics Publishing House, 1958, pp. 16–17.

four blast furnaces in operation during 1952[10]. Of this number, twenty-four larger ones can be identified. Pertinent data concerning these furnaces are given in Table 4.3. Their combined capacity in terms of useful furnace volume constituted 96.3 per cent of the 1952 national total[11]. The remaining furnaces unidentifiable are very small, with an average capacity of 21.4 cubic meters.

From the data presented in Table 4.3, the combined rated daily capacity of these furnaces is calculated to be 3,118 tons. This figure can be adjusted to include the capacity of the unidentifiable small furnaces on the assumption that the ratio of rated tonnage capacity to useful furnace volume is 1 to 1.5[12]. Thus adjusted, the overall rated daily capacity of all the blast furnaces in operation during 1952 comes to 3,247 tons, or 45.0 per cent of the operating capacity of 7,210 tons per day corresponding to the pre-communist peak output in 1943.

*Open-hearth capacity in 1952* — There were in operation during 1952 twenty-six open hearths[13]. The particulars of these furnaces are given in Table 4.4. As can be seen from the table, the total rehabilitated capacity by 1952 amounted to 1,575 tons/heat. Since the 1943 open-hearth capacity has been estimated to be 2,051 tons/heat, the extent of rehabilitated open-hearth capacity thus comes to 76.8 per cent.

*Rolling capacity in 1952* — The overall rolling capacity in operation in 1953 has been estimated to be 1,590,500 tons[14]. From this, the capacity added in 1953 can be deducted to arrive at the 1952 operating capacity. With such an adjustment, the latter comes to 1,200,500 tons[15]. Since the operating capacity corresponding to the pre-communist peak output has been estimated to be 1,112,400 tons, the extent of rehabilitated capacity is thus 107.9 per cent.

10 *KTMCFT*, p. 16.
11 The overall blast furnace capacity of the country in 1952 was officially reported to be 5,179 cubic meters. *Ibid.* The combined capacity of the twenty-four identifiable furnaces, as shown in Table 4.3, comes to 4,986 cubic meters.
12 Alternatively, it may be assumed that the same ratio of useful volume to rated tonnage capacity applies to both groups of furnaces, identifiable and unidentifiable. Thus adjusted, the overall rated daily capacity of all the blast furnaces in operation during 1952 comes to 3,239 tons. This figure differs only slightly from that of 3,247 based on the ratio of 1 to 1.5 (i.e., the ratio of rated tonnage capacity to useful furnace volume).
13 In addition, eleven Bessemer converters and forty electric furnaces were in operation during 1952.
14 F. Okazaki, *Chugoku no tekkogyo to kikaikogyo no gijutsu suijun* (Technical level of the steel and machinery industry in China), Tokyo, 1962, p. 135.
15. Particulars of the mills rehabilitated in 1953 are as follows:

| Location | Type of Mill | Capacity (tons) |
|---|---|---|
| Anshan | Large bar mill | 300,000 |
| Anshan | Seamless tube mill | 60,000 |
| Shenyang | Small bar mill | 30,000 |
| | | 390,000 |

Source: F. Okazaki, *op. cit.*, pp. 103, 105 and 107. Deducting 390,000 tons from the 1953 total of 1,590,500 tons gives 1,200,500 tons as the overall capacity of the rolling mills in operation in 1952.

## Possible 1952 Output Level

The rehabilitated capacity by 1952, as noted above, came to 45.0 per cent for iron, 76.8 per cent for steel and 107.9 per cent for rolled products. The restoration of output by 1952, on the other hand, has been reported respectively at 107.1,

*Table 4.4. Open Hearths in Operation, 1952*

| Location | Designation | Rehabilitated Capacity | | Completion Date of Rehabilitation |
|---|---|---|---|---|
| | | Tons[a]/heat | m² | |
| Anshan (No. 1 Plant) | No. 1 | 100 | 50 | August 1949 |
| | No. 2 | 100 | 50 | April 1949 |
| | No. 3 | 100 | 50 | June 1949 |
| | No. 4 | 100 | 50 | End of 1949 |
| | No. 5 | 150 | 50 | May 1950 |
| | No. 6 | 150 | 50 | May 1950 |
| | No. 7 | 180 | 60 | November 1952 |
| | No. 8 | 180 | 60 | August 1952 |
| Anshan | c | 15 | 15[f] | End of 1949 |
| (Chiu Shen Plant) | c | 15 | 15[f] | End of 1949 |
| Tientsin | c | 40[b] | 24 | 1949/50 |
| | c | 40[b] | 24 | 1949/50 |
| Taiyuan | No. 1 | 50 | 26 | July 1949 |
| | No. 2 | 50 | 26 | July 1949 |
| | No. 3 | 50 | 26 | September 1952[d] |
| Shanghai (No. 1 Plant) | c | 20 | 15[f] | First half 1951 |
| | c | 20 | 15[f] | First half 1951 |
| Shanghai (No. 2 Plant) | c | 20 | 15[f] | First half 1951 |
| | c | 20 | 15[f] | First half 1951 |
| Shanghai (No. 3 Plant) | c | 40[e] | 24 | First half 1951 |
| | c | 40[e] | 24 | First half 1951 |
| Tayeh | c | 15 | 15[f] | First half 1951[d] |
| Chunking (Southeast No. 101 Plant) | c | 20 | 15[f] | End of 1950 |
| | c | 20 | 15[f] | End of 1950 |
| Chunking (Southwest No. 104 Plant) | c | 20 | 15[f] | 1949 |
| | c | 20 | 15[f] | 1949 |
| | | 1,575 | 726.1 | |

a. Rated capacity.
b. They were expanded to 40 tons from the pre-communist capacity of 30 tons each; one of these was constructed in 1946.
c. No designation.
d. New construction.
e. Expanded from the pre-communist capacity of 10 tons each.
f. Maximum capacity.

Sources: *Chukyo tekkogyo chosa hokokusho—Kigyohen* (Survey report of the steel industry of communist China — enterprise edition), prepared by the Cabinet Research Chamber of the Japanese Government. Tokyo, 1955, *passim*; and Industrial Statistics Section, State Bureau of Statistics, *Wo-kuo kang-t'ieh, tien-li, mei-t'an, chi-hsieh, fang-chih, tsao-chih kung-yeh ti chin-hsi* (The past and present of China's iron and steel, electric power, coal, machine-making, textile and paper industries). Peking: Statistics Publishing House, 1958, p. 17.

146.1 and 191.2 per cent of the pre-communist peak production. To determine whether such official claims on output restoration were feasible, it is necessary to look into the rate of capacity utilization and the productivity of capital equipment.

*Possible pig iron output* — In the pre-communist period, China's blast furnace capacity was far from being fully utilized. The capacity available in 1936 China Proper is estimated to have been 40,200 tons per year, but its output amounted to 21,650 tons[16]. Thus only 54 per cent of the available capacity was utilized. By virtue of the previous assumption of an unchanged capacity-output relationship in China Proper between 1936 and 1943, the rate of capacity utilization in 1943 China Proper should be the same. In 1943 Manchuria, the rate of capacity utilization was 62.8 per cent[17]. To restore the pre-communist peak production, therefore, would have required the rehabilitation of not more than 63 per cent of the pre-communist capacity. According to the finding above, however, the blast furnace capacity rehabilitation amounted in 1952 only to 45.0 per cent of the pre-communist capacity. Consequently the recovery of production cannot be explained solely on the ground of the rate of capacity utilization.

An additional explanation may be sought in the effectiveness of equipment utilization measured by a coefficient. The 1952 average coefficient for all furnaces in China is known to be 1.024 ton per cubic meter of useful furnace volume[18]. The total useful volume of the major blast furnaces in operation in the latter part of 1952, as shown in Table 4.3, came to 4,986 cubic meters. This figure should be adjusted to make proper allowance for the three furnaces whose rehabilitation was completed in the summer of 1952[19]. On the assumption that all three were blown in on July 1, 1952, only half the volume of their useful capacity should be included in the total volume in operation throughout the year. Thus adjusted, the total useful volume of the major furnaces in operation throughout 1952 becomes 4,890 cubic meters. In addition to the major blast furnaces, there were in operation during 1952 ten smaller ones with a total useful capacity of 193 cubic meters. Adding this to the adjusted total of the major ones yields an overall useful volume of 5,083 cubic meters for the thirty-four blast furnaces under the jurisdiction of the central, provincial and municipal governments, which were in operation throughout 1952.

Multiplying the 1952 average utilization coefficient (1.024 ton/m³/day) by the aggregate useful furnace volume in operation throughout the year (5,083 m³) gives 5,205 tons as the output from the thirty-four blast furnaces in 24 hours. The actual time for a furnace to be operating under blast normally does not equal the calendar time. Assuming the absence of any major repair for the furnaces in 1952,

16 D.K. Lieu, *op. cit.*, p. 8.
17 See Chapter 2.
18 *KTMCFT*, p. 10.
19 All three are of 64 cubic meter capacity. Two were located in Hsuanhwa and one was removed from Pootung to Woosung.

no furnace would be shut down completely during the year[20]. Inasmuch as the blast furnace coefficient bears reference to nominal time, including the hot down time when the blast was shut off for minor repairs[21], there is no need to be concerned with the time required for hot repairs. Thus multiplying the daily output of the operating blast furnaces (5,205 tons) by the normal 360 days gives an annual output of 1,873,800 tons.

This amount falls short of the official 1952 output figure of 1,928,585 tons by 54,785 tons. As indicated in Table 4.2, the official pig iron production statistics include the output by indigenous methods. Although the quantity of the latter has not been specified in the official statistics, it is known that iron production by handicraft workshops amounted to 50,130 tons in that year[22]. Assuming that handicraft output represented production by indigenous methods, the official 1952 iron output figure is thus reasonably consistent with available capacity and productivity claims. This output level could be attained through a relatively high rate of utilization of the existing capacity and an increased productivity of the capital equipment, even though only 45.0 per cent of the pre-communist capacity was recovered by the end of the rehabilitation period.

*Possible open-hearth steel output* — According to the State Bureau of Statistics, China's ingot steel output in 1952 was 46.1 per cent over the pre-communist peak output and amounted to 1,348,509 tons[23]. Of this amount, 69.7 per cent or 939,911 tons came from open-hearth furnaces[24]. As pointed out above, 76.8 per cent of the pre-1945 operating open-hearth capacity was rehabilitated by 1952. The recovered pre-1945 capacity was larger than the extent of capacity utilization in the pre-communist period. In Manchuria where over 95 per cent of the pre-1945 steel making capacity was found, the rate of capacity utilization at the height of productive activity during 1943 was only 61.7 per cent[25]. Simple arithmetic will show that a near full utilization of the rehabilitated capacity should place the reported 1952 output from open-hearth furnaces within the realm of possibility.

Alternatively, by examining the effectiveness in the utilization of open hearths, the same conclusion can be reached. The 1952 average coefficient for the nation's open hearths came to 4.782 tons/$m^2$/day[26]. The total floor area of all the open-hearth furnaces of the country in operation toward the end of 1952, as given in Table 4.4, came to 726.1 square meters. This total should, however, be adjusted to make proper allowance for furnaces which were in operation only during part of 1952. As the table shows, rehabilitation of Nos. 8 and 7 open hearths of

20 Such an assumption is not unrealistic since all the furnaces had been rehabilitated since 1949 (see Table 4.3) and since a blast-furnace campaign (the operating time between major repairs) normally lasts more than four years.
21 Such as repairs to fittings, loading apparatus, or hearth.
22 *KTMCFT*, p. 30.
23 See Table 4.2.
24 See Table 6.4.
25 See Chapter 2.
26 *KTMCFT*, p. 10.

No. 1 steel plant at Anshan was not completed until August and November respectively; that of No. 3 open hearth at Taiyuan, not until September. Assuming that all three started in the middle of the month, only about one quarter of their combined area of furnace floor was used in 1952. Therefore, 109.5 square meters should be deducted from the national total. The overall floor area of open-hearth furnaces in operation throughout 1952 thus amounts to 616.6 square meters. Multiplying this by the 1952 average open-hearth coefficient of 4.782 tons/m²/day gives 2,949 tons as the daily output of all the open hearths in operation in 1952.

To arrive at the nominal operating time of an open-hearth furnace in a calendar year, it is necessary to exclude the cold down time between major repairs from the calendar time[27]. The length of cold down time during the year can be estimated on the basis of the amount of time necessary for each cold repair and the frequency of major repairs. While each cold repair in early 1953 required 6 days[28], the annual frequency of repairs depends on the length of a campaign and the time required for each heat. The latter is known to be 9 hours for a 100-ton open hearth[29]. A campaign in 1953 lasted more than 120 heats[30]. Since the length of a campaign in 1952 is merely known to be somewhat shorter than in 1953, it may be assumed to be exactly 120 heats. Thus each campaign in 1952 should have lasted 45 days, at the end of which period a 6-day repair job became necessary. Dividing the normal working year of 360 days by the 51-day cyle gives 7.059 as the frequency of cold repairs in 1952. Since each cold repair took 6 days, the cold down time during 1952 amounted to approximately 42 days.

Deducting the cold down time from the working year gives the nominal time of 318 days for the nation's twenty-six open-hearth furnaces operating in 1952. Multiplying the daily output of these furnaces (2,949 tons) by the nominal time (318 days) gives 937,782 tons as the 1952 ingot steel output from open hearths. The estimated amount thus comes remarkably close to the reported 1952 output quantity of 939,911 tons.

*Possible output of rolled products* — As pointed out above, by 1952 the pre-communist rolling capacity was exceeded by 7.9 per cent. Since for most rolled products the pre-communist rate of capacity utilization was below 60 per cent[31], the rehabilitated capacity was substantially more than sufficient to recover the previous peak production. However, the estimated 1952 rolling capacity of 1,200,500 tons falls short of the latest official output figure by 111,397 tons or 8.5 per cent. Aside from possible improvements in the coefficient of rolling

---

27 The time required for hot repairs (which are a necessary process in each heat cycle) has already been accounted for in the open-hearth coefficient. An increase in the coefficient may reflect, among other factors, the shortening of hot down time, i.e., an improved speed of hot repairs.
28 *CTCHK*, p. 65.
29 *Ibid.*
30 *Chung-kung-yeh t'ung-hsin* (Heavy industry bulletin), published thrice a month, Peking, No. 29, 1954, p. 32.
31 See Table 2.4.

equipment utilization, this discrepancy can be attributed to (1) the common practice of starting production in partially constructed mills, (2) a possible inclusion in official production statistics of the output of rolled steel from establishments in the defense industry, and (3) a state of confusion regarding finished steel statistics, to be discussed at some length in Chapter 6.

## Concluding Remarks

Output restoration for the major products of the steel industry attained by the end of the rehabilitation period does not imply that the pre-communist productive capacity was reinstated. Except for rolling, capacity rehabilitation in 1952 amounted to a fraction of the pre-communist peak level. It was 45.0 per cent for blast furnace capacity and 76.8 per cent for open hearth capacity. The restoration of output, on the other hand, was reported to be 107.1 per cent for pig iron and 146.1 per cent for ingot steel. Nevertheless, official claims about their capacity, productivity and output are found to be mutually consistent. Finished steel, though, cannot be treated with the same degree of certainty because of data inconsistency. However, the narrow margin between its latest official output figure and the estimated operating capacity may suggest that the former does not necessarily fall outside the realm of possibility.

On the whole, it appears that the restoration of output in excess of the pre-communist peak level was accomplished by a higher rate of equipment utilization as well as the enhanced productivity of capital equipment. The latter factor, in particular, serves as an effective lever between capacity and output. The 1952 national average blast furnace utilization coefficient, for instance, was raised to 1.024 from the pre-communist figure of 0.890[32]. This signifies that technological advance, the force behind the higher productivity of capital equipment, tends to render elastic the economic limits set by a given level of technology.

32 *Kang-t'ieh* (iron and steel), Peking, semi-monthly, No. 18, 1959, p. 796.

# MAJOR REHABILITATION PROJECTS

The primary purpose in examining the major projects is to determine the extent of rehabilitated capacity from 1949–1952 to furnish a basis for an evaluation of output restoration. Thus any capacity expansion arising from reconstruction undertaken in this period must be included. In addition, the important rehabilitation projects completed at the major iron and steel centers after 1952 will be noted.

## *Anshan*

Although Anshan was taken over by the communists in February 1948, its rehabilitation work did not begin until the end of the year. This belated start was due to the practical impossibility for the Department of Industry of the Northeast Administrative Council to give any supervision. The latter was forthcoming only when the seat of the regional government was moved from Harbin to Shenyang in November 1948. At that time, the Anshan Iron and Steel Corporation (Anshan Steel) was formed to take in the various iron mining, smelting, steel refining, and rolling units in the area. Anshan Steel was under the direct supervision of the Department of Heavy Industry of the Northeast People's Government.

Rehabilitation work at Anshan was classified into two categories: (1) the restoration of those installations and equipment which were less seriously damaged, and (2) the reconstruction of those installations and equipment which were seriously damaged by Soviet removals. Projects within the first category were started in December 1948. By the end of 1950, practically all the iron smelting, steel refining and rolling equipment which had not been affected by Soviet removals was rehabilitated, and production was resumed in the following year. Projects in the second category did not get started until 1952.

*Rehabilitation of blast furnace capacity* — At the end of the war, there were altogether nine blast furnaces at Anshan with a total daily rated capacity of 5,450 tons[1]. Six of them (Nos. 3, 5, 6, 7, 8 and 9) with a total daily capacity of 4,050 tons were disabled by Soviet removals of the essential installations and equipment[2], and required reconstruction. The remaining three furnaces which had been damaged by communist troops in the civil conflict were rehabilitated

1 See Tables 1.3 and 2.2 in Chapters 1 and 2 respectively.
2 Removals consisted of the hoisting equipment, turbo-blowers, hot stove burners, pig iron casting machines and pig ladles. *Pauley Report,* p. 110.

during 1949—1950. No. 2 blast furnace was blown in in June 1949; No. 1 in September 1949; and No. 4 in February 1950. By this time, the restored blast furnace capacity at Anshan amounted to 1,400 tons per day. This remained the daily rated iron smelting capacity of Anshan at the end of 1952.

Reconstruction of No. 8 blast furnace began in August 1952[3] and production was resumed in March 1953. Of the essential installations necessary for this reconstruction job, some (e. g. the hoisting machine and the testing rod) were supplied by Soviet Russia, others were obtained by dismantling No. 9 blast furnace, and the remainder came from domestic manufacturers. With the completion of reconstruction, the entire process (from the transport of sintered ores to weighing, hooking and hoisting, and to the shutting of the tap hole and the slag notch) became automatized. In fact, the reconstructed No. 8 blast furnace was the first fully automatic furnace in Anshan. Automation appeared to be the model for the subsequent reconstruction of blast furnaces there. By August 1957, reconstruction of the remaining five blast furnaces was completed. Particulars regarding their reconstruction together with that of No. 8 are given in Table 4-A.1.

*Table 4—A.1. Reconstruction of Blast Furnaces at Anshan*

| Designation | Completion Date | Rehabilitated Capacity | |
|---|---|---|---|
| | | Tons[a]/day | m³ |
| No. 8 | March 1953 | 700 | 911 |
| No. 7 | December 1953 | 700 | 916 |
| No. 6 | September 1954 | 700 | 916 |
| No. 5 | July 1955 | 700 | 917 |
| No. 9 | July 1956 | 700[b] | 944 |
| No. 3 | August 1957 | 500[b] | 917 |

a. Rated capacity.
b. The capacity of the pre-communist period.

Sources: Industrial Statistics Section, State Bureau of Statistics, *Wo-kuo kang-t'ieh, tien-li, mei-t'an, chi-hsieh, fang-chih, tsao-chih kung-yeh ti chin-hsi* (The past and present of China's iron and steel, electric power, coal, machine-making, textile and paper industries), Peking: Statistics Publishing House, 1958, pp. 16—17; *Chukyo tekkogyo chosa hokokusho — Kigyohen* (Survey report of the steel industry of communist China — enterprise edition), prepared by the Cabinet Research Chamber of the Japanese Government, Tokyo, 1955, p. 40; *Ibid.*, Supplementary Volume, p. 3; *An-shan jih-pao*, Anshan, November 17, 1957; *Jen-min jih-pao*, July 21, 1956; *Kung-jen jih-pao*, July 22, 1957; *Kuang-ming jih-pao*, August 11, 1957; and other sources.

*Rehabilitation of open-hearth capacity* — When the war ended, Anshan had two open-hearth plants with a total rated annual capacity of 1.33 million tons.

---

3 The reconstruction of this furnace entailed the installation of 2,000 odd machine parts, 980 tons of machinery, 11,000 meters of pipes and cables, 16 motors and 5 blasting machines.

Soviet removals stripped No. 2 plant of all its equipment[4]. Thus 750,000 tons of ingot steel capacity was destroyed. According to the Pauley Mission, the remaining ingot steel capacity at Anshan after Soviet removals amounted to half a million tons. Under the nationalist control, only No. 1 open-hearth furnace of No. 1 plant was in operation for a very limited period, viz., August–October 1946. Owing to the lack of maintenance for an extended period and lootings during the civil conflict, all the equipment in No. 1 plant needed rehabilitation upon the communist takeover in February 1948. From then till the end of 1952, rehabilitation projects were confined to equipment in No. 1 plant. Its Nos. 2 and 3 open-hearth furnaces were rehabilitated in April and June 1949. By May 1950, all six (two 150-ton and four 100-ton) open-hearth furnaces and the three 300-ton tilting active mixers were restored and resumed production.

In 1952, the Anshan authorities decided to convert the three active mixers into 180-ton open hearths. By the end of the year the conversion job was completed on two of the three. They became Nos. 7 and 8 open-hearth furnaces of No. 1 plant. At that time the annual ingot steel capacity of Anshan amounted to 696,000 tons[5]. The conversion of the third mixer was not completed until February 1953, by which time a new open hearth (No. 9) was added to No. 1 plant.

Reconstruction of No. 2 steel plant was started in the latter part of 1954. Its completion in December 1956 boosted Anshan's ingot capacity by 1.6 million tons per year[6]. The latter is compared with the pre-communist rated annual capacity of 750,000 tons, which was totally destroyed by Soviet removals.

*Rehabilitation of rolling capacity* — Before August 1945, the aggregate rolling capacity at Anshan was 916,000 tons per year[7]. Capacity loss due to Soviet removals of rolling mills and assorted equipment amounted to 586,200 tons. Nearly all the mechanical and electrical equipment from No. 2 blooming mill and its attendant billet mill, small bar mill, plate mill and sheet mill was removed. No. 1 blooming mill and No. 1 small bar mill were spared by the Soviets, but were damaged during the civil conflict mainly through looting of parts and equipment. Between June 1946 and February 1948, the nationalists tried to make use of the remaining facilities and turned out a total of 1,500 tons of rolled products; the period of operation was not more than six months[8]. Rehabilitation under the communists began in December 1948. By the end of 1952, the following mills resumed production:

---

4 Removals consisted of two 600-ton hot metal mixers, the tilting mechanisms of four 300-ton active mixers and six 150-ton open-hearth furnaces, four open-hearth charging machines, seven large ladle cranes, seven cranes on the charging side of the open hearths, four or five cranes over the soaking pits, two ingot tilters and a line roll ingot conveyor. *Pauley Report*, p. 115.
5 The annual productive capacity of the two converted open-hearth furnaces is known to be 96,000 tons each. *CTCHK*, p. 57. That of the original six furnaces is calculated on the basis of two heats per day and 360 days per year.
6 *China News Service* (hereafter *CNS*), September 9, 1957.
7 *CTCHK*, Supplementary Volume, p. 8.
8 *CTCHK*, p. 66.

| Project | Date of Completion | Capacity Rehabilitated by the end of 1952 (in tons per annum) |
|---------|-------------------|-------------------------------------------------------------|
| Roll foundry | March 1949 | 1,200 |
| No. 1 sheet mill | July 1948 | 15,000 |
| No. 1 small bar mill | May 1949 | 120,000 |
| Medium bar mill | June 1949 | 160,000 |
| No. 1 blooming mill | July 1949 | (650,000) |
| Welded steel pipe mill | July 1949 | 30,000 |
| No. 2 small bar mill | December 1950 | 35,000 |
| Plate mill | Latter part of 1949 | 100,000 |
| Large bar mill | December 1952 | 300,000 |

Rolling capacity rehabilitated by the end of 1952 amounted to 761,200 tons or 83.0 per cent of the 1945 capacity. It should be noted that in some cases capacity expansion took place in the rehabilitation process.

## Penki

The Manchuria Iron Manufacturing Company was brought under communist control in November 1948, with its name changed to the Penki Coal and Iron Company. Its management was under the supervision of the Department of Heavy Industry of the Northeast People's Government.

Rehabilitation work at Penki began early in 1949 with the help of the retained Japanese technical personnel. Before the end of the year, production was resumed on two 200-ton blast furnaces (Nos. 1 and 2) in the old plant which was not touched by the Soviet removal. The latter affected the Kungyuan plant. The briquetting and sintering facilities at Kungyuan were seriously damaged through removals[9]. Although the stocks of Nos. 3 and 4 blast furnaces (600 tons each) at Kungyuan did not appear to be in bad shape, practically all their installations and corollary equipment had been removed by the Soviets[10]. As they were not rehabilitated by the end of 1952, the pig iron capacity at Penki amounted then to merely one quarter of the 1945 capacity. Penki's special steel and rolling capacities, on the other hand, were fully restored in 1952.

## Shihchingshan

It has been pointed out that the Shihchingshan Iron Works became in 1942 the main smelting centre of the North China Iron Corporation[11]. Its annual smelting

9 From the briquetting plant, twenty presses were removed; from the sintering plant, twelve AIB sintering pans and corollary equipment including electric motors taken away. *Pauley Report*, p. 106.
10 The removal consisted of the hoisting equipment, turbo-blower, hot stove valves, mud gun and washer. *Ibid.*
11 See Chapter 2

capacity was subsequently expanded to 240,000 tons, with the addition of one 380-ton blast furnace and eleven small furnaces[12]. Further expansion was interrupted by the abrupt ending of the war in 1945. After the Japanese surrender, the sudden cessation of operation when there was iron fluid in process in No. 2 furnace caused it to be blocked up. Thus in the immediate postwar years, only the 250-ton No. 1 blast furnace was in operation.

This remained the operating condition at Shihchingshan at the time of the communist takeover in December 1948. Under its new name, the Shihchingshan Iron and Steel Works was first under the supervision of the North China People's Government. When the Central People's Government was inaugurated in October 1949, its supervision was transferred to the Iron and Steel Bureau of the Ministry of Heavy Industry. The change of name upon the communist takeover signified its intention to convert the Shihchingshan plant into an integrated iron and steel complex.

The major rehabilitation project at Shihchingshan under the communists was the 380-ton No. 2 blast furnace which had been shipped there from Japan before the war ended. This project was completed in April 1951. By that time the pre-1946 smelting capacity was on the whole restored. Two 25-ton blast furnaces were added in March 1953.

*Taiyuan*

Soon after their takeover of the Taiyuan Iron and Steel Works in April 1949, the communist authorities planned to develop it into the largest iron and steel center in China Proper. Consequently its rehabilitation consisted mostly of reconstruction coupled with expansion and modernization. Thus the 120-ton No. 2 blast furnace was reconstructed in the fall of 1949 into a 150-ton furnace, and the daily rated capacity of No. 1 furnace was expanded in 1950 from 50 to 80 tons. The capacity expansion of these furnaces was accompanied by the mechanization of their auxiliary equipment. Similarly the two 40-ton open-hearth furnaces were turned into 50-ton ones, with new corollary installations.

The importance attached to the Taiyuan Iron and Steel Works can also be seen from the launching of new construction projects during the rehabilitation period and the transfer of equipment from steel mills in other localities. Construction of a new coke oven battery (No. 2) with a capacity of 400 tons per day was started in April 1950 and completed in October of the same year. A new 50-ton open-hearth furnace together with auxiliary equipment was completed in September 1952. Included among the equipment transferred to Taiyuan were two 3-ton electric arc furnaces from Shenyang, two 8-ton electric arc furnaces from Tangshan, and two sets of thin plate rolling equipment from Shanghai.

The designation of the Taiyuan Iron and Steel Works as a key point of capital construction was followed by the assigning of top priority in the supply of

12 *CTCHK*, Supplementary Volume, p. 2.

construction material, labour and skills. Beginning in 1952, budgetary limits on its major capital construction projects were relaxed[13]. This became feasible with the truce in Korea, which also made possible a substantial increase in investment outlays in the steel industry during 1952 (see Chapter 7).

As a result of reconstruction and new construction projects, the annual pig iron capacity of Taiyuan was expanded from 70,000 tons (prior to 1946) to 165,000 tons by 1953. Concomitantly its annual open-hearth and rolling capacities increased, respectively, from 50,000 and 45,000 tons to 150,000 and 80,000 tons. It did not produce any special steel in the pre-communist period, but by 1953 it acquired almost 14 per cent of the country's electric furnace capacity[14].

## Other Steel Centers

That the preceding examination has been confined to the major steel centers does not imply the absence of rehabilitation and reconstruction or even new construction at other steel centers. In the Hsuanhwa plant of the Lunyen Iron Works, for instance, five 25-ton blast furnaces were rehabilitated and resumed production during 1951–1952, and Nos. 1 and 4 blast furnaces were restored to production in July 1953. Similarly reconstruction on six of the eleven blast furnaces at the Maanshan Iron Works was undertaken in 1952. At the Southwest Iron and Steel Works, early in 1953 two new 120-ton blast furnaces were blown in. A new 15-ton open-hearth furnace was built in the Tayeh Steel Plant in 1951. All these and others were bound to affect the overall capacity of the steel industry.

Equipment transfers such as occurred at the Taiyuan Iron and Steel Works were also effected at other steel centers. Tayeh is a notable example. Toward the end of 1950, the amount of steel smelting and rolling equipment shipped there from Dairen consisted of four electric arc furnaces, one alloy furnace, one medium bar and two small bar rolling equipment. In addition, two Bessemer converters were shipped to the Tayeh Plant from Harbin. The decision on the transfer of such equipment was made from the standpoint of national security during the Korean War. Concomitantly it was consistent with the policy of the communist regime regarding the locational distribution of China's steel industry.

13 For such projects, no control figure in investment expenditure was assigned.
14 *CTCHK*, Supplementary Volume, pp. 4, 6, and 8.

*Chapter 5*

# KEY STEEL BASES

This chapter examines the development of the three key steel bases (Anshan, Wuhan and Paotow) which were planned to constitute the backbone of China's steel industry. The First Five-Year Plan envisaged the reconstruction and expansion of the Anshan Iron and Steel Corporation (Anshan Steel) as the most urgent task. The economic planners in China view Anshan as the core of the Northeast industrial base, and a valuable source of technical support for building new industrial bases. The Plan also specified the construction of two major steel centers in Wuhan and Paotow, around which to form two new industrial bases. In examining the construction or reconstruction of these steel bases, special attention is directed to the type of equipment installed, the expansion of productive capacity, and the role of Soviet aid.

*Anshan Steel*

Of the three key steel bases, Anshan Steel is undoubtedly the most important. Its importance was even more conspicuous in the period of the First Five-Year Plan. It was the single largest supplier of iron and steel for the major construction projects envisaged in the Plan. In 1953, for example, some 900 iron and steel consuming units throughout the country placed orders with Anshan Steel[1]. To shoulder this burden effectively, it was necessary for Anshan Steel to expand its productive capacity as rapidly as feasible. This was reflected in the transfer of the best technicians from various parts of the country and in the large number of Soviet experts[2] stationed at Anshan Steel.

*Blast furnace capacity* — By the end of the First Five-Year Plan in 1957, Anshan had nine blast furnaces in operation (see Table 5.1). Of these, six were fully automatic. As pointed out in Chapter 4, Nos. 1, 2 and 4 furnaces were rehabilitated by the end of 1950. However, major repairs were undertaken on No. 2 furnace in June 1953, and on No. 4 in February 1959. As a result, their capacities were expanded by 11 m$^3$ and 185 m$^3$ respectively[3]. Of the remaining furnaces,

1 *Jen-min jih-pao*, April 19, 1953.
2 There were as many as 2,000 Soviet experts working in Anshan Steel. Cheng Chu-yuan, *Anshan Steel Factory in Communist China*, Hong Kong, 1955, p. 6.
3 F. Okazaki, *Chugoku no tekkogyo to kikaikogyo no gijutsu suijun* (Technical level of the steel and machinery industry in China), Tokyo, 1962, p. 15.

only No. 8 had a major repair in 1957, which took nearly two months (September 18 to November 10) and led to an expansion of capacity by 64 cubic meters[4].

Construction began on June 15, 1958 on a new 1,513 m³ furnace (No. 10). It was completed on November 11, 1958 and went into production on November 19. Its production record in the early months of 1959 shows an output of 56,420 tons in January, 57,092 tons in February and 53,225 tons during March 1—25[5]. The addition of this furnace with such a large capacity represented a great boost to the pig iron output of Anshan. Thus, ten blast furnaces were in operation at Anshan by February 1959, with an aggregate daily output of 16,000 tons[6].

*Table 5.1. Blast Furnace Capacity at Anshan, 1953, 1957 and 1961 (in cubic meters)*

| Designation | 1953[a] | 1957[a] | 1961[b] | Remarks |
|---|---|---|---|---|
| No. 1 | 585 | 585 | 585 | In operation September 1949. |
| No. 2 | 596 | 596 | 596 | In operation June 1949; major repairs June 1953. |
| No. 3 | — | 917 | 917 | Reconstructed July 1957. |
| No. 4 | 917 | 917 | 1,102 | In operation February 1950; major repairs 1959. |
| No. 5 | — | 917 | 917 | Reconstructed July 1955. |
| No. 6 | — | 916 | 916 | Reconstructed September 1954. |
| No. 7 | 916 | 916 | 916 | Rehabilitated December 1953. |
| No. 8 | 911 | 975 | 975 | Rehabilitated March 1953; major repairs November 1957. |
| No. 9 | | 944 | 944 | Reconstructed July 1957. |
| No. 10 | | | 1,513 | Constructed November 1958. |

a. Year end.
b. Not specified.
Source: F. Okazaki, *Chugoku no tekkogyo to kikaikogyo no gijutsu suijun* (Technical level of the steel and machinery industry in China), Tokyo, 1962, p. 15.

*Steel refining capacity* — The rehabilitation during 1949—1953 of No. 1 steel plant involved the restoration of open hearth Nos. 1—6, and the conversion of the three 300-ton tiling mixers into Nos. 7—9 open hearths. While the latter were intended for special refining purposes, a new mixer was added and went into operation in 1955[7].

From the latter part of 1953, Anshan Steel pursued a policy of reconstructing its open hearths to raise their output. Thus, No. 1 furnace of No. 1 steel plant was reconstructed in January 1955 and brought about a 20 per cent increase in output[8]. Similarly the capacities of Nos. 7 and 9 furnaces were doubled through

4 *Anshan jih pao*, November 17, 1957; *NCNA*, Anshan, November 13, 1957.
5 *NCNA*, Anshan, March 26, 1959.
6 Tatsunosuke Takasaki, *Hochuki* (A visit to China), Tokyo, 1960, p. 26.
7 *Kuang-ming jih-pao*, Peking, August 29, 1955.
8 *Ta-kung pao*, Hong Kong, March 21, 1955. The capacity of this furnace was further enlarged in 1956—1957 as shown in Table 5.2.

reconstruction in 1957[9]. The 1959 output was planned at 2 million tons as against 1,026 thousand tons in 1953[10]. The capacities of the furnaces in No. 1 steel plant are presented in Table 5.2.

*Table 5.2. Open-Hearth Capacity at Anshan, 1953 and 1961 (in tons per heat)*

| Steel Plant/Designation | 1953a | 1961b |
|---|---|---|
| *No. 1 Steel Plant*c | | |
| No. 1 | 120 | 225 |
| No. 2 | 120 | 225 |
| No. 3 | 120 | 225 |
| No. 4 | 120 | 225 |
| No. 5 | 180 | 300 |
| No. 6 | 180 | 300 |
| No. 7 | 180 | 360 |
| No. 8 | 180 | 360 |
| No. 9 | 180 | 360 |
| 1 mixer | — | 600d |
| *No. 2 Steel Plant*e | | |
| No. 10 | — | 360 |
| No. 17 | — | 360 |
| Nos. 10—19 average | — | 340 |
| 1 mixer | — | 600d |
| *No. 3 Steel Plant*f | | |
| No. 20 | — | 440 |
| No. 21 | — | 440 |
| No. 22 | — | 440 |
| No. 23 | — | 660 |
| No. 24 | — | 660 |

a. Year end.
b. Not specified.
c. Nos. 1—6 were rehabilitated during June 1949 to 1953; Nos. 7—9 were converted from 300-ton mixers for special refining purposes; Nos. 1—9 were reconstructed from August 1953 to July 1957, but with no further expansion of the resulting capacity up to 1961; the mixer was added in August 1955.
d. Rated capacity.
e. During November 1954 to December 1956, while Nos. 10—15 were rehabilitated, Nos. 16—19 were added; Nos. 10—19 averaged 245 tons per heat during 1957.
f. Nos. 20—21 were built in June 1958; No. 22 in July 1958; No. 23 in October 1958; and No. 24 in December 1958.

Source: F. Okazaki, *Chugoku no tekkogyo to kikaikogyo no gijutsu suijun* (Technical level of the steel and machinery industry in China), Tokyo, 1962, p. 57.

While, as noted previously, open hearth Nos. 10—15 in No. 2 steel plant were rehabilitated between November 1954 and December 1956, four new open hearths (Nos. 16—19) and a new 600-ton mixer were added. These ten 180-ton open

9 F. Okazaki, *op. cit.*, p. 57.
10 *Jen-min jih-pao*, March 28, 1959.

hearths were subsequently reconstructed with their aggregate capacity raised from 2,450 tons to 3,400 tons, as can be seen from Table 5.2. Also, the heat time was reduced through better operation. On September 25, 1958, for instance, the plant as a whole completed 25 charges to yield an output of 7,030 tons[11]. As a result, the combined ingot output of Nos. 1 and 2 steel plants reached 4.5 million tons in 1958[12].

Anshan Steel added a new open-hearth shop in the latter part of 1958, known as No. 3 steel plant (see Table 5.2). It had three 440-ton (Nos. 20—22) and two 660-ton furnaces (Nos. 23—24). No. 22 open hearth was designed to apply the three-ladle tapping technique. The latter represented a Chinese development along the Soviet experience of bifurcating the spout and tapping steel into two ladles. The Chinese innovation was in trifurcating the tapping apparatus[13]. Its purpose was to cope with the limits set by the capacity of the casting cranes, in order to accommodate the "over-charging" method of production. The application of the three-ladle tapping technique was expected to raise the furnace productivity by 35 per cent[14]. In addition, there was an estimated 15—20 per cent saving on investment outlays for plant construction and casting cranes on the basis of per-unit output[15].

Nos. 23 and 24 furnaces were the largest in China and in the world when installed. No. 23 began operation on October 31, 1958. Its normal daily output ranged from 1,300 to 1,500 tons[16]. No. 24 furnace began operation on November 21, 1958. Both furnaces were similar in design[17].

*Rolling capacity* — Early attention and emphasis on rehabilitating rolling mills resulted in a large number of them being in operation by the end of the First Five-Year Plan in 1957. Subsequently, however, production capacities of individual mills were expanded. Having examined the major rehabilitation projects in Chapter 4, a cursory look into changes in rolling capacity through reconstruction and new construction is called for.

The blooming capacity of Anshan Steel was greatly expanded after 1953. The rehabilitated capacity of No. 1 blooming mill, as given in Chapter 4, was 650,000 tons. It was raised to 750,000 tons in 1953[18]. This mill was subsequently recon-

---

11 *NCNA*, Anshan, September 6, 1958.
12 *Ibid.*
13 The Taiyuan Iron and Steel Works in March 1958 succeeded in developing the three-ladle tapping technique. The use of this technique together with measures for enlarging the interior of the furnace made it possible to increase the charging capacity of No. 3 open hearth from the original rated capacity of 49 tons to 130 tons. This resulted in a 47.5 per cent increase in its productivity and 4.5 per cent decrease in per-ton production costs. See Ministry of Metallurgical Industry, *Kuan-yu t'ai-yuan kang-t'ieh ch'ang san-ts'ao-ch'u-kang ti pao-kao* (Report on the three-ladle steel-tapping experiment of the Taiyuan Iron and Steel Works), Peking, March 1958; *Kang-t'ieh*, No. 23, 1959, p. 1126.
14 *NCNA*, Anshan, June 2, 1958.
15 *NCNA*, Peking, August 7, 1958.
16 *NCNA*, Anshan, November 1, 1958.
17 *Ibid.*, November 21, 1958.
18 *CTCHK*, p. 68.

structed with its capacity increased to 2 million tons[19]. As noted previously, No. 2 blooming mill had been completely stripped through Soviet removals. Its reconstruction was planned with the assistance of Soviet specialists, and all its important installations were supplied by the Soviet Union. Construction work was started in October 1954. Upon completion in April 1956, this mill added 3.6 million tons to the annual blooming capacity of Anshan Steel[20].

Rehabilitation of the large bar mill, as pointed out in the Appendix to Chapter 4, was completed in December 1952. For this task, a sizable construction labor force was engaged, amounting to 20,000 workers. In the course of rehabilitation, the removed installations were replaced with Soviet-made equipment. During 1953, reconstruction of the mill continued so that by the end of the year its capacity was expanded from 300,000 tons to a maximum of 500,000 tons[21].

As reconstructed, the mill had four sections: ingot stripper, reheating, rolling and finishing. In the reheating section, two continuous heating furnaces were installed, each with a capacity of over two tons. The continuous heating process has a distinct advantage over the batch-type process in terms of both economy and better product. The latter results from more even and gradual heating process, whereas the economy arises chiefly from the elimination of serious delays in the rolling, hammering and pressing operations.

Between 1953 and 1960, the mill was reconstructed to allow for capacity expansion. By 1960, the mill had a Soviet-made 800 mm 3-stand 3-high bloomer, three shears for heavy cutting, a roller-straightener and two shaping machines. Its major products included billets for seamless tubes, angles, channels and girders. Although its exact capacity in 1960 is not known, its 1959 output amounted to 960,000 tons[22].

When Anshan Steel decided to build a new plate mill as an attendant mill to No. 2 blooming system, the original plate mill was designated as No. 1 mill. Construction of No. 2 plate mill began in June 1956 and was completed in December 1957. All its major installations were of Soviet origin. Its 1961 planned output was given at 300,000 tons[23].

Of the two pre-1945 sheet mills at Anshan, No. 1 was spared in the Soviet removal and restored to operation in July 1948. Early in 1956, a 2-high rougher and a 2-high finisher were installed in this mill to improve its operation. As the major installations of No. 2 sheet mill had been removed by the Russians, this mill had to be reconstructed. Its reconstruction was a major task and constituted one of the 141 Soviet-aid projects. This task lasted from May 1953 to June 1954 and involved a construction labor force of 3,000 workers. As reconstructed, the mill had a rated capacity of 50,000 tons and was equipped with a reheating furnace, a Soviet-made 3-stand N.K.M.Z. type rougher, a 2-stand pull-over type

19 Its 1959 output, for instance, was planned at 2.6 million tons.
20 F. Okazaki, op. cit., p. 103.
21 CTCHK, p. 68.
22 Tatsunosuke Takasaki, op. cit., p. 27.
23 F. Okazaki, op. cit., p. 105.

finisher, and a 3-stand 2-high semi-continuous cold reducing train. In between the rougher and the finisher was installed a speed-reducing gear. Its output includes sheets for the manufacture of tin plate and other products.

Like No. 2 sheet mill, the seamless tube mill was disabled by Soviet removals, and its reconstruction was included among the 141 Soviet-aid projects. This project was started in July 1952 and completed on October 31, 1953. The scale of this reconstruction can be judged by the input of over 1,000 tons of structural metals, some 130,000 m³ of cement, and 43,000 meters of pipes and electric wires. Its major installations included Soviet-made continuous heating furnaces, a piercing machine, a tube-rolling machine, and a diameter-setting machine. Between 1953 and 1959, its actual output capacity was increased from 60,000 to 300,000 tons[24].

Available data indicating the expansion of rolling capacity of Anshan Steel for certain bench-mark years are given in Table 5.3. The increase in blooming capacity is particularly noteworthy. It amounted to more than seven-fold within eight years. Also deserving attention is the four-fold expansion in the capacity of seamless tubes within the same period. Such substantial increases were significant in that the rolling sector constituted a bottleneck in the development of the Chinese steel industry.

*Table 5.3. Expansion of Rolling Facilities at Anshan, 1953, 1957 and 1961*
*(in thousand tons per annum)*

| Name of Plant | 1953a | 1957a | 1961e |
|---|---|---|---|
| No. 1 blooming mill | 750 | n. a. | 2,600f |
| No. 2 blooming mill | — | 3,600c | 3,600c |
| Large bar mill | 500 | n. a. | 960g |
| No. 2 plate mill | — | 300c | 300c |
| No. 2 sheet mill | — | 50d | n. a. |
| Seamless tube mill | 60b | n. a. | 300g |

a. Year end.
b. Rated capacity.
c. Planned output.
d. Rated capacity in 1954.
e. Not specified.
f. Planned output for 1959.
g. Actual output in 1959.
n.a. Not available.

Source: F. Okazaki, *Chugoku no tekkogyo to kikaikogyo no gijutsu suijun* (Technical level of the steel and machinery industry in China), Tokyo, 1962, p. 105.

## Wuhan Steel

The decision to build a large base in the Tayeh-Wuhan region became official on May 15, 1952, when Mao Tse-tung approved the preliminary construction

24 *Ibid*

plan of the Wuhan Iron and Steel Corporation (Wuhan Steel). This new combine was planned to have an annual ingot steel capacity of 3 million tons. Equipped with the latest Soviet technology, Wuhan Steel was designed by the Leningrad Metallurgical Designing Institute in collaboration with some thirty other Soviet designing institutes as a complete integrated system of production encompassing eighteen major plants[25] and thirty-one supplementary and subsidiary workshops.

The building of Wuhan Steel as a major base did not start from scratch. China's first modern iron and steel works (Hanyang) was established in the Wuhan region[26]. Thus in addition to the necessary natural resources, the building of a steel base in Wuhan enjoyed the advantage of the availability (though limited) of skills.

Its ore and other raw materials supplies came from eight ferrous and non-metallic mines. The Tayeh mines[27] turning out ores of more than 50 per cent iron content on the average, constituted the most important source of supply. Another large ore base was in Sinyu, Kiangsi province. The coal supply of Wuhan Steel came from Honan, Shensi and four other provinces. The raw materials needed for its refractory plant were supplied chiefly by the clay pits at Chiaotso, Honan province, although the Wulungchuan mine south of Wuchang also constituted a source of raw material supply[28].

Planning for the construction of Wuhan Steel dates back to March 1952. Beginning early in 1954, Soviet experts participated in site selection. Out of twenty-three possible sites along the Yangtze River in Hupeh province and along the Hankow-Canton Railway north of Changsha, Chingshan was finally chosen as the site for the iron and steel works, extending over an area of 10-odd square kilometers. With the official approval in June 1955 of the first-stage construction projects[29] drawn up by the Soviet Union, the preliminary work[30] was concluded.

To embark on the tremendous task of building a major steel base, nine construction companies were formed with specific responsibilities such as construction management, civil engineering, electrical engineering, transport, machine repairs, and storage. Early in 1956 construction equipment arrived at the building site from all parts of the country[31]. The construction labor force was composed of some thirty thousand workers from various parts of China, a division of troops

25 The major units include mining, ore-dressing, sintering, coke and chemical plant, iron-smelting, open-hearth shops, rolling mills, refractory plant and others.
26 See Appendix 1 — A.
27 In the prospecting of the Tayeh mines, large new deposits were discovered between Shihtzeshan and Chienlinshan.
28 The Wulungchuan mine produces good-quality limestone and dolomite which can be used more advantageously as reducing agents in the blast furnace than as inputs of the refractory plant.
29 The first-stage capital construction in the original plan was scheduled to be completed in 1961, by which time Wuhan Steel was to have an ingot steel capacity of 1.5 million tons. CNS, September 9, 1957.
30 Including prospecting, site selection, assembling of materials and a construction labor force, and drawing up of plans.
31 *Jen-min jih-pao*, February 10, 1956; *Ta-kung pao*, Hong Kong, March 26, 1956.

from the People's Liberation Army, and nine thousand farmers from Hupeh province[32].

From August 1955, capital construction was started on the Tayeh mines, the thermoelectric plant, living quarters for employees, subsidiary workshops for machine repairs, foundry and metal work, and the water supply system. Construction of the major plants, however, did not begin until 1957, although the levelling of the building site had been under way since the spring of 1956.

On April 8, 1957, work began on two projects at Chingshan: the coke and chemical plant, and the refractory plant. The rated capacity of the refractory plant (130,000 tons) was more than sufficient to meet the needs of Wuhan Steel. The coke and chemical plant was a Soviet-aid project. Coke ovens were of the P.B.R. type made in the Soviet Union. The plant's capacity of coke output was rated at 3 million tons. It was designed to have six batteries each with 65 ovens. The coking time of each oven was 15 hours for a load of 16 tons. No. 1 coke oven battery was completed on July 31, 1958 and No. 2 battery in the first half of 1959. By June 1959 the two batteries had put out a total of over 800,000 tons[33]. The construction of No. 3 battery took 35 days and was completed on May 11, 1959. The construction time for this battery was reportedly planned for 90 days. The cutting down in construction time resulted in a 24.6 per cent reduction in costs, or some 600,000 yuan[34]. The costs of building No. 3 battery can thus be established at 1,844 thousand yuan. This battery began production on July 5, 1959. Before 1959 ended, No. 4 coke-oven battery was built and began operation on December 29th.

Before examining the construction of No. 1 blast furnace, two plants for the concentration of iron ores should be mentioned briefly. One is the ore-dressing plant in Tayeh. Designed with Soviet aid, this plant was installed with equipment for both froth flotation and magnetic separation processes. Its construction began on October 16, 1957 and was completed in 1959. Another is the sintering plant in Chingshan. It was also built with Soviet assistance. At this plant where the Dwight Lloyd method was used, the entire production process was mechanized. Its planned capacity was 3 million tons of sinter per year. The first stage of its construction, including the installation of four sintering machines, began on September 20, 1957. It took 170 days to install the first sintering machine and corollary equipment which went into production on August 29, 1959[35].

Construction of No. 1 blast furnace was started on July 1, 1957. Some 5,000 tons of equipment made in both China and the Soviet Union were installed[36]. The construction labor force amounted to some 50,000 workers (including white-

32 *Kung-jen jih-pao* (Workers' daily), Peking, July 27, 1956; *Jen-min jih-pao*, February 28, 1957.
33 *Hung-chi* (Red flag), Semi-monthly, Peking, No. 13, 1959, p. 23.
34 *Jen-min jih-pao*, May 12, 1959. The official exchange rate of 2.355 yuan to one US dollar can be mentioned only as a conceptual aid. Conversion according to this rate, however, is not meaningful.
35 *Yeh-chin pao* (Metallurgy), weekly, Peking, No. 1, 1960, p. 32.
36 *Ibid.*, No. 35, 1957, pp. 18 – 19.

collar workers)[37]. Its useful volume[38] came to 1,386 m³ and rated daily capacity 2,070 tons[39]. This furnace was blown in on September 13, 1958. Its daily output averaged 1,386 tons for the first ten days of operation. In November of the same year, the highest daily output reportedly reached 2,339 tons[40]. This level of output appeared to be unduly high; it could represent an over-estimation.

Construction of No. 2 blast furnace began on February 21, 1959. Although its useful volume was designed to be 50 m³ larger than that of No. 1 furnace[41], its construction time was drastically reduced. While the construction of No. 1 furnace took 14 months and 12 days, that of No. 2 only 4 months and 20 days[42] Thus the latter was blown in on July 9, 1959. This drastic reduction in construction time could be attributed partly to the external economies provided by the construction of No. 1 furnace, and perhaps partly to a different method of measuring the period of construction. No. 3 furnace with a useful volume of 1,513 m³ was completed in September 1961[43]. All furnaces were built with Soviet assistance and designed for automatic operation. Top pressure and blast temperature were under automatic control. Stove changing and skip charging were also automatic.

On July 15, 1959, Wuhan Steel began building a new steel plant at Chingshan with nine open hearths and one mixer. It constituted a major Soviet-aid project. The original plan was to divide this construction project into two stages, the first stage to be completed in 1959 and the second in 1962. Subsequently the construction plan was revised to eliminate the two-stage distinction and move up the completion date to 1960. The plant was designed to be highly mechanized with automatic control over furnace temperature and other conditions of steel-refining.

The 250-ton No. 1 open hearth produced its first heat of steel on September 30, 1959[44]. Improvement in the performance of this furnace was reflected in its productivity. Between September 30 and October 18, 1959, its daily output increased from 162 tons to 600 tons. This increased productivity was attributable partly to the reduction of time required per heat. The latter was halved during

37 *Kung-jen jih-pao*, Peking, September 14, 1958.
38 Measured from centerline of the iron notch to the bottom of the large bell in the open position.
39 *CNS*, Wuhan, November 30, 1958.
40 *Ibid.*
41 *Jen-min jih-pao*, July 15, 1959.
42 *Yeh-chin pao*, No. 1, 1960, p. 30.
43 *Newsdom*, June 15, 1963, p. 19. Since the availability of this added capacity in 1961 is also found in F. Okazaki, *op. cit.*, p. 33, it is indeed puzzling to read the report in *Peking Review*, April 18, 1969, p. 33, that No. 3 blast furnace at Wuhan was completed early in April 1969. One can assume *either* that the earlier report of the completion of this blast furnace in September 1961 was invalid, *or* that the recent report of its completion in April 1969 represented reconstruction (at the end of a campaign) rather than new construction. Pending further evidence, the second assumption is adopted in this study. This assumption is supported by the observation of a Japanese journalist during his visit to China towards the end of 1963 that No. 3 blast furnace at Wuhan was then under repair. (See *Japan Times*, December 8, 1963.) If a new campaign started early in 1964, the furnace should have been due for reconstruction in 1968 or 1969.
44 F. Okazaki, *op. cit.*, p. 32.

the same period — from 14 hours 25 minutes to 7 hours 5 minutes[45]. The performance of No. 1 open hearth thus became normal with its daily output approaching its rated capacity of 200,000 tons per year[46].

The completion of the auxiliary projects in connection with building No. 1 open hearth greatly shortened the construction time of the 500-ton No. 2 open hearth. Construction of the latter began on September 22, 1959 and was completed in exactly one month[47]. The furnace produced its first heat of steel on October 30, 1959. Its annual productive capacity was rated at 300,000 tons. The construction time of the 500-ton No. 3 open hearth was further reduced to 21 days, due chiefly to the use of labor-saving devices. There was, for instance, a 34 per cent decrease in the amount of labor used in laying the bricks of the hearth, by virtue of the use of the conveyor belt for delivering bricks[48]. Although the time required per heat was planned at 12 hours 45 minutes, it was subsequently demonstrated that a minimum of 9 hours 50 minutes was feasible[49]. Nos. 4 and 5 open hearth (both of 500-tons) were known to be in operation in October 1960. Very little information is obtainable on their construction.

The rolling capacity of Wuhan Steel was planned to be 3 million tons. Construction was started on July 28, 1959 on a modern blooming and slabbing mill designed with the assistance of Soviet experts. Its major installations, supplied mostly by the Soviet Union, include a 2-high Y.3T.M. reverse blooming and slabbing train equipped with high lift, a 50-ton K.H.M3 roll table, an estimated 30-ton ingot stripper crane, and two batch-type sidefiring furnaces. This mill went into operation in April 1960 with a rated capacity of 3 million tons per year[50]. The extent of automation was limited judging by the absence of a punch card system and the use of only dial gauges in the operation room.

Construction of a larger bar mill for producing large rails and structural steels began early in 1960. It was designed by Chinese engineers to be a highly automatic mill. In addition, a plate mill was reported to be under construction in 1960, although no particulars concerning this mill were disclosed. Essential data concerning the major construction projects undertaken at Wuhan Steel are summarized in Table 5.4.

### Paotow Steel

Sizable iron ore deposits were discovered in 1950 on the Ulanchapu steppe near Paotow[51]. The reserves at Peiyunopo (130 Km. west of Paotow) were subsequently estimated at 150 million tons. The ores were of good quality with iron

45 *NCNA*, Wuhan, October 8, 21 and 30, 1959.
46 *Ibid.*, December 8 and 17, 1959.
47 *Yeh-chin pao*, No. 1, 1960, p. 32.
48 *Jen-min jih-pao*, December 18, 1959.
49 *Yeh-chin pao*, No. 2, 1960, p. 5.
50 The mill turned out blooms of 200 mm. square, and slabs of 600 mm. x 150 mm. x 2 m.
51 The discovery was made by No. 241 prospecting team of the Ministry of Geology.

*Table 5.4. Major Construction Projects of Wuhan Steel*

| Project | Capacity | Construction/Operation Dates |
|---|---|---|
| Refractory plant (Chingshan) | 130,000 tons/annum | Started on April 8, 1957. |
| Coke and chemical plant (Chingshan) | 3,000,000 tons/annum | Started on April 8, 1957. |
| No. 1 coke oven battery | 500,000 tons/annum | Completed on July 31, 1958. |
| No. 2 coke oven battery | 500,000 tons/annum | Completed in the first half of 1959. |
| No. 3 coke oven battery | 500,000 tons/annum | Completed on May 11, 1959; began operation on July 5, 1959. |
| No. 4 coke oven battery | 500,000 tons/annum | Began operation on December 29, 1959. |
| Ore-dressing plant (Tayeh) | n. a. | Started on October 16, 1957; completed in 1959. |
| Sintering plant (Chingshan) | 3,000,000 tons/annum (planned) | Started on September 20, 1957. |
| First sintering machine | n. a. | |
| Blast furnace (Chingshan) | | |
| No. 1 blast furnace | 1,386 m³ (2,070 tons/day) | Started on July 1, 1957; blown in on September 13, 1958. |
| No. 2 blast furnace | 1,436 m³ (2,500 tons/day) | Started on February 21, 1959; blown in on July 9, 1959. |
| No. 3 blast furnace | 1,513 m³ | Completed in September, 1961. |
| Steel plant (Chingshan) | n. a. | Started on July 15, 1958. |
| No. 1 open hearth | 250 tons/heat (200,000 tons/annum) | Produced its first heat on September 30, 1959. |
| No. 2 open hearth | 500 tons/heat (300,000 tons/annum) | Started on September 22, 1959; produced its first heat on October 30, 1959. |
| No. 3 open hearth | 500 tons/heat | In operation in October 1960. |
| No. 4 open hearth | 500 tons/heat | In operation in October 1960. |
| No. 5 open hearth | 500 tons/heat | Started on July 28, 1959; began operation in April 1960. |
| Blooming and slabbing mill | 3,000,000 tons/annum | |
| Large bar mill | n. a. | Started in early 1960. |
| Plate mill | n. a. | Under construction in 1960. |

n.a. Not available.

Sources: *China News Service*, September 9, 1957; *Hung-chi* (Red flag), Peking, No. 13, 1959, p. 23; *Yeh-chin pao*, (Metallurgy), Peking, No. 1, 1960, p. 32; CNS, Wuhan, November 30, 1958; NCNA, Wuhan, October 8, 21 and 30, 1959; *Jen-min jih-pao*, July 15 and December 18, 1959; and other sources.

content of 50–60 per cent[52]. In the meantime, rich coal deposits were found in Shihkuaikou, Saratsi and Kuyang, all in the vicinity of Paotow, and also from Tatung, Shansi province. The reserves of the Shihkuaikou alone were estimated at 480 million tons[53]. In addition, limestone, dolomite and other refractory raw materials were available in the area. Thus Paotow became an ideal location for a large steel base.

In 1953, the planning authorities decided to establish the Paotow Iron and Steel Corporation (Paotow Steel) comparable in scale and vertical integration to Anshan Steel. As this new steel base in Paotow had to start from scratch, its construction became a difficult task owing to the complete lack of external economies. The relatively small population of Paotow (attributable to the lack of industries) further added to the difficulties. This was in contrast to the building of a steel base in the Wuhan-Tayeh area, which was populous and enjoyed the availability of skills traceable to its long history of steel production.

In the designing and building of Paotow Steel, Soviet aid proved indispensable. Early in 1954, Soviet geologists helped to ascertain ore reserves. Subsequently, a team of over thirty Soviet metallurgical engineers led by the director and the chief engineer of the Leningrad Ferrous Metallurgical Designing Institute participated in site selection and drawing up blueprints for the construction projects. In addition, a greater portion of technical designing was undertaken by the Leningrad Institute and a dozen odd metallurgical designing institutes in USSR. The latest Soviet technology was incorporated in the designing of Paotow Steel. Also significant was the contribution of one or two prominent Soviet metallurgists in solving various production problems at the pilot stage.

Preparatory work for building Paotow Steel extended from the latter part of 1953 to mid-1957. During this period, efforts were stepped up in gathering geological, topographical, hydrographical and meteorogical data, which were necessary for site selection and general layout planning of the steel base. Construction projects launched in this period included coal fields at Shihkuaikou, power plants and industrial establishments, transport facilities needed for providing the infrastructure of a major steel base and living accommodations for the construction force[54]. In addition, construction material, equipment and labor had to be assembled. It was estimated that some 350,000 tons of finished steel and some 400,000 tons of cement would be needed in the construction of Paotow Steel. The equipment to be installed was estimated to weigh more than 200,000 tons[55]. By spring 1955, a labor force of 30 thousand odd persons covering nineteen trades were gathered in Paotow. The construction labor force reached 70,000 in 1959[56].

---

52 *CTCHK*, p. 721.
53 *Chung-kung wen-t'i* (Problems of the Chinese communists), Hong Kong, 1954, Vol. I, p. 95.
54 Two large buildings were reserved for Soviet personnel, capable of accommodating a total of 250 persons.
55 *Kang-t'ieh* (Metallurgy), Semi-monthly, Peking, No. 18, 1959, p. 859.
56 *Ibid.*; *CTCHK*, p. 721.

After four years of preparatory work, the Paotow Metallurgical Construction Company was formed at the beginning of 1957 with its personnel transferred mainly from metallurgical construction companies at Anshan and Penki[57]. On July 25, 1957, construction of Paotow Steel proper was formally launched. The first-stage construction was concentrated on eleven projects of the machine-building and repair plant, which was to manufacture parts for the equipment in the entire process (from the production of refractory material and coke-making to iron-smelting, steel-refining and rolling). These eleven projects included plants or workshops for iron and steel casting, machine repairs, forging and metal structure work.

In 1958 construction work at Paotow steel was intensified in order that No. 1 blast furnace could begin operation by October 1, 1959. To accomplish this task, more investment was made in the capital construction of this steel base in 1958 than during 1953–1957. Furthermore the 1959 capital investment doubled that of 1958.

Construction projects started in 1958 included a refractory plant, a coke and chemical plant, No. 1 blast furnace and a large steel plant. The designed capacity of the refractory plant with five workshops was 150,000 tons, sufficient to meet Paotow Steel's needs for refractory materials[58]. By the end of 1959, the plant was in partial operation.

As in the case of Wuhan Steel, the coking plant at Paotow was designed with Soviet assistance to have six batteries, each with 65 ovens[59]. The rated capacity for coke production has been given as 2.68 million tons for the entire plant. Since only three batteries each with an annual rated capacity of 500,000 tons are known to have been in operation by the beginning of 1960[60] and no information is obtainable on the other three, the overall capacity of the plant is unknown.

In the building of No. 1 blast furnace and ancillary projects, some 26 thousand tons of equipment were needed. About 90 per cent of such equipment was manufactured in China while the rest came from the Soviet Union and other bloc countries. Work on the foundation of No. 1 blast furnace was started on July 14, 1958. The confusion of the Leap Forward caused some delay in its construction, as the needed equipment could not be shipped to the construction site in time. In the third quarter of 1959, however, work was stepped up. The installation of the furnace shell was completed in 26 days and its lining took 28 days[61]. Consequently the furnace was blown in on September 25, 1959, considerably ahead of schedule.

---

57 *Nei-meng-ku jih-pao* (Inner Mongolia daily), Huhehot, January 4, 1957.
58 *NCNA*, Paotow, December 26, 1959 and January 8, 1960.
59 *Ibid.*, December 16, 1958.
60

| Coke oven battery designation | Completion date | Construction time (days) |
| --- | --- | --- |
| No. 1 | December 22, 1958 | — |
| No. 3 | October 12, 1959 | 33 |
| No. 4 | May 22, 1959 | 37 |

61 *Kang-t'ieh*, No. 18, 1959, p. 859.

According to the original schedule, the construction of No. 1 blast furnace was to be completed in 1960 simultaneously with the ore-dressing and sintering plant. Thus the completion of No. 1 blast furnace ahead of schedule posed a production problem for the lack of proper inputs. The experiment with the help of Soviet metallurgists of charging directly into the furnace ores of high iron content without dressing and agglomeration solved the production problem in the interim period.

The useful volume of No. 1 blast furnace came to 1,513 m³, i. e. 77 m³ larger than No. 2 blast furnace of Wuhan Steel. Like the latter, No. 1 blast furnace of Paotow Steel was designed with Soviet assistance to achieve a high degree of automation. Its rated annual capacity is known to be 900,000 tons. However, its daily output averaged only 840 tons during the initial period from September 25 — October 5, 1959. The daily average for the first five days of October was raised to about 1,000 tons with a peak of 1,207 tons[62]. Evidently the furnace was not yet operating with the expected efficiency, its output being substantially below its rated capacity.

Construction of the large steel plant began in July 1958. This plant was designed to be fully automatic and capable of applying the three-ladle tapping technique. Although the concrete foundations for No. 1 open hearth and a mixing furnace were laid in September 1958, their construction was not completed till 1960. No. 1 open hearth went into production on May 1, 1960. Its actual capacity was 660 tons and its daily output estimated to be 1,300—1,500 tons. The mixer was completed in April 1960 with a daily capacity of 1,300 tons. Most of Paotow's ingot steel was shipped to Shanghai, Tientsin and the Northeast[63].

No particulars concerning either Nos. 2 and 3 open hearths or No. 2 blast furnace are obtainable though they were known to be under construction in June 1960.

Construction of the ore-dressing and sintering plant with an annual capacity of one million tons was started in 1959. It was not completed in 1960 as scheduled. Perhaps, the direct use of high-quality ores of Peiyunopo in the blast furnace, as pointed out previously, may have reduced the urgency of having to produce sinter.

The construction plan of Paotow Steel envisaged a system of rolling mills encompassing a blooming mill, a large bar mill, a medium bar mill, a plate mill and a seamless tube mill. Only the plate mill is known to have gone into operation, with its annual capacity estimated at 100,000—150,000 tons. Essential data concerning the major construction projects undertaken at Paotow Steel are summarized in Table 5.5.

62 *NCNA*, Paotow, October 5, 1959.
63 *Jen-min jih-pao*, October 16, 1959; May 3, 1960.

Table 5.5. *Major Construction Projects of Paotow Steel*

| Project | Capacity | Construction/Operation Dates |
|---|---|---|
| Refractory plant (with 5 workshops) | 150,000 tons/annum | Started in 1958; in partial operation by the end of 1959. |
| Coke and chemical plant | 2,680,000 tons/annum | Started in 1958. |
| No. 1 coke oven battery | 500,000 tons/annum | Completed on December 22, 1958. |
| No. 3 coke oven battery | 500,000 tons/annum | Completed on October 12, 1959. |
| No. 4 coke oven battery | 500,000 tons/annum | Completed on May 22, 1959. |
| Ore-dressing and sintering plant | 1,000,000 tons/annum | Started in 1959; not completed in 1960 as scheduled. |
| Blast furnace | | |
| No. 1 blast furnace | 1,513 m³ (900,000 tons/annum) | Started on July 14, 1958; blown in on September 25, 1959. |
| No. 2 blast furnace | n.a. | Under construction in September 1959. |
| Steel plant | n.a. | Started in July 1958. |
| No. 1 open hearth | 660 tons/heat (1,300—1,500 tons/day) | Began operation on May 1, 1960. |
| No. 2 open hearth | n.a. | Under construction in June 1960. |
| No. 3 open hearth | n.a. | Under construction in June 1960. |
| Mixer | 1,300 tons | |
| Plate mill | 100,000—150,000 tons/annum (estimate) | Completed in April 1960. |

n.a. Not available.

Sources: *NCNA*, Paotow, December 16, 1958, October 5 and December 26, 1959, and January 8, 1960; *Kang-t'ieh* (Iron and Steel), Peking, No. 18, 1959, p. 859 and No. 23, 1959, p. 1126; and other sources.

## Importance of the Three Bases

The importance of the three bases in China's steel industry can be evaluated in terms of capacity and output. In view of the paucity of data, attention is to be focussed on iron-smelting, steel-refining and rolling in a few bench-mark years.

The blast furnace capacity by the end of 1953 for the economy as a whole was given by the State Bureau of Statistics at 7,739 cubic meters[64]. The 1957 and 1961 national capacity figures as well as those of the three key bases represent estimates based on heterogeneous data obtainable on individual furnaces. As some of the data show rated capacity in tons per day and others show capacity in cubic meters, it is necessary to convert to a consistent basis. Since the furnace volume is a more reliable capacity index, the given data in tons per day is multiplied by 1.5, a conversion factor Okazaki used in arriving at his national blast furnace capacity for 1957. Thus the estimated capacities for the key bases will be consistent with national totals. These estimates are presented in Column 2 of Table 5.6.

For 1953 and 1957, it should be noted, neither Wuhan nor Paotow had any installed capacity. Thus, these figures represent the smelting capacity of Anshan Steel alone. While in the first plan quinquennium, the smelting capacity of Anshan was expanding at a higher rate than that of the remaining producers in the industry, the situation was reversed from 1958 onward when the national aggregate capacity was inflated by the mushrooming of small furnaces. These formed the basis of small and medium *modern* furnaces built or rebuilt since 1959, the capacities of which have been included in the estimated 1961 total[65]. Consequently

Table 5.6. *Estimated Share of Key Bases in National Blast Furnace Capacity, 1953, 1957 and 1961 (in cubic meters)*

| Year | National | Key Bases | | Share of Key Bases (per cent) | | |
|------|----------|-----------|---|-------------------------------|---|---|
| | (1) | (2) | | (3) | | |
| 1953[a] | 7,739 | 3,970[c] | | 51.3 | | |
| 1957[a] | 13,021.5 | 7,728[c] | | 59.3 | | |
| 1961[b] | 53,360.5 | 20,148 | Anshan 13,866<br>Wuhan 4,335<br>Paotow 1,947 | 37.8 | Anshan 26.0<br>Wuhan 8.1<br>Paotow 3.6 | |

a. Year end.
b. Not specified.
c. Anshan Steel only.

Sources: Industrial Statistics Bureau, State Bureau of Statistics, *Wo-kuo kang-t'ieh, tien-li, mei-t'an, chi-hsieh, fang-chih, tsao-chih kung-yeh ti chin-hsi* (The past and present of China's iron and steel, electric power, coal, machine-making, textile and paper industries), Peking: Statistics Publishing House, 1958, p. 16; F. Okazaki, *Chugoku no tekkogyo to kikaikogyo no gijutsu suijun* (Technical level of the steel and machinery industry in China), Tokyo, 1962, pp. 15, 33, 43 and 53; *Liao-ning jih-pao*, Shengyang, January 13, 1959; and other sources.

64 *KTMCFT*, p. 16.
65 The so-called "backyard furnaces" are, however, excluded.

in 1961, when the capacity of the two new key bases was added to that of Anshan, their combined share was smaller than that of Anshan alone in either 1957 or 1953 (see Column 3 of Table 5.6).

China's overall open-hearth capacity has been estimated by Okazaki for the bench-mark years. While his estimates for 1953 and 1957 are acceptable, an independent estimate for 1961 has been made on the basis of individual furnace capacities. Thus estimated, the 1961 capacity comes to 8,062 tons per heat in comparison with Okazaki's 6,725 tons. The discrepancy between the two estimates, it is interesting to note, amounts precisely to the open-hearth capacity of No. 3 steel plant of Anshan Steel.

The year-end open-hearth capacity of Anshan for 1953 and 1957, and the combined capacity of the three key bases for 1961 represent estimates. The 1953 estimate is based on the capacity of No. 1 steel plant, which was the only one in operation at Anshan at that time. In estimating the 1957 and 1961 capacities, once again one encounters the problem of having to convert to rated from given actual capacity figures. For this conversion, it is necessary to identify furnaces where either the rated or the actual capacity is known, with those of which both types of capacity are given. For instance, No. 1 open hearth of Paotow Steel is known to have an actual capacity of 660 tons per heat. To estimate its rated capacity, it is identified with Nos. 23 and 24 open hearths of Anshan Steel both of which have the same actual capacity. Since the rated capacities of the latter two furnaces are known to be 500 tons each, it is reasonable to assume the same rated capacity for No. 1 open hearth at Paotow.

Where this identification process is impracticable, a conversion factor of 0.6122 is used[66]. The estimates thus derived for the key bases for the bench-mark years and for the 1961 national total are presented in Table 5.7 together with the 1953 and 1957 national totals estimated by Okazaki.

Table 5.7. Estimated Share of Key Bases in National Open-Hearth Capacity, 1953, 1957 and 1961 (in tons per heat)

| Year | National | Key Bases | | | Share of Key Bases (per cent) | | |
|------|----------|-----------|---|---|-------------------------------|---|---|
|       | (1)      | (2)       |   |   | (3)   |   |   |
| 1953a | 1,825   | 1,240c    |   |   | 67.9  |   |   |
| 1957a | 3,395   | 2,740c    |   |   | 80.7  |   |   |
| 1961b | 8,062   | 7,300     | Anshan | 4,550 | 90.5 | Anshan | 56.4 |
|       |          |           | Wuhan  | 2,250 |      | Wuhan  | 27.9 |
|       |          |           | Paotow | 500   |      | Paotow | 6.2  |

a. Year end.
b. Not specified.
c. Anshan Steel only.

Source: F. Okazaki, *Chugoku no tekkogyo to kikaikogyo no gijutsu suijun* (Technical level of the steel and machinery industry in China), Tokyo, 1962, pp. 57, 77, 83 and 96.

66 This is the same factor used by Okazaki in converting from actual to rated capacity of open hearths.

As can be seen from Column 3 of Table 5.7, the share of Anshan Steel in the economy's overall open-hearth capacity was much more prominent than that in blast furnace capacity for all three bench-mark years (1953, 1957 and 1961). The concentration of open hearths in the key steel bases is, perhaps, not unexpected, given the basic preference of the economic planners in China for the largest possible scale of operation. Second, the rate of expansion in open-hearth capacity during the first plan quinquennium was relatively higher in Anshan than for the rest of the steel industry. Finally, as in the case of blast furnace capacity, Anshan's share in national total open-hearth capacity declined in 1961, though not to the same extent. However, in contrast to the case of blast furnace capacity, the combined share of the three key bases showed a sizable increase. This can be explained by the fact that the campaign for small-scale production had only a slight effect on the open-hearth capacity, as it took mainly the course of converter steel. Thus the decrease in Anshan's share in the 1961 national total can be attributed preponderantly to the rising importance of Wuhan and Paotow; Wuhan Steel alone accounted for almost 28 per cent of the national total.

Turning from capacity expansion to output behavior, Table 5.8 presents Anshan's annual pig iron output and its share in the national total for the period 1949—1959. Anshan Steel was responsible for over three-quarters of China's pig iron production during 1952—1956. In 1957, Anshan's share declined, as there was probably no increase in capacity actually under operation. Although

*Table 5.8. Growth of Pig Iron Output at Anshan, 1949—1959*

| Year | Output | | Share of National Total (per cent) |
|------|--------|--|------------------------------------|
| | In thousand tons | Percentage increase | |
| | (1) | (2) | (3) |
| 1949 | 123 | — | 48.8 |
| 1950 | n. a. | — | n. a. |
| 1951 | n. a. | — | n. a. |
| 1952 | 1,460 | — | 75.7 |
| 1953 | 1,656 | 13.4 | 74.1 |
| 1954 | n. a. | — | n. a. |
| 1955 | 2,880 | — | 74.4 |
| 1956 | 3,888 | 35.0 | 80.6 |
| 1957 | 3,880 | -0.2 | 65.4 |
| 1958 | 4,150 | 7.0 | 43.5 |
| 1959 | 5,270 | 27.0 | 25.7 |
| 1949—1959 average | 2,913[a] | 45.6 | 47.5[a] |

n.a. Not available.
a. Computed for the years for which data are available.

Sources: Table 6.3; *Wen hui pao* (Cultural convergence), daily, Shanghai, September 23, 1959; *Ta kung pao*, Peking, December 31, 1957; *Nan-fang jih-pao*, October 1, 1956; *Jen-min jih-pao*, January 6 and December 26, 1957, and April 12, 1960; F. Okazaki, *Chugoku no tekkogyo to kikaikogyo no gijutsu suijun* (Technical level of the steel and machinery industry in China), Tokyo, 1962, p. 15; and other sources.

No. 3 blast furnace was rehabilitated in the latter part of 1957, two other furnaces (Nos. 8 and 9) were under major (cold down) repairs during the year.

The decline in Anshan's relative importance in the overall pig iron output of the country continued in 1958—1959, owing partly to the nation-wide steel campaign and partly to the beginning of production at the two new bases. Although the steel campaign also had the effect of raising Anshan's pig iron output in that 140 smaller blast furnaces (3—100 m³) were built in Anshan in the latter part of 1958 with an aggregate capacity of 4,440 m³ added, the effect on Anshan and other major bases was evidently far less than for the rest of the economy. Of the two new bases, Paotow's 1958 pig iron output is known to have been 12,000 tons and Wuhan's planned 1959 output 1.2 million tons[67].

Growth of Anshan's ingot steel output is shown in Table 5.9. It is interesting to note that while Anshan's output grew steadily during 1949—1959, its relative importance to the economy declined continually except in 1950 when its share increased. This exception is expected in view of the speedy rehabilitation of Anshan's No. 1 steel plant which had not been severely damaged by Soviet removals[68]. The dwindling share of Anshan in the overall ingot steel output from

Table 5.9. Growth of Ingot Steel Output at Anshan, 1949—1959

| Year | Output | | Share of National Total (per cent) |
|------|--------|--|------------------------------------|
| | In thousand tons | Percentage increase | |
| | (1) | (2) | (3) |
| 1949 | 106 | — | 67.1 |
| 1950 | 530 | 400.0 | 87.5 |
| 1951 | 700 | 32.1 | 78.1 |
| 1952 | 900 | 28.6 | 66.7 |
| 1953 | 1,100 | 22.2 | 62.0 |
| 1954 | n. a. | — | n. a. |
| 1955 | n. a. | — | n. a. |
| 1956 | n. a. | — | n. a. |
| 1957 | 2,950 | — | 55.1 |
| 1958 | 4,070 | 38.0 | 50.9 |
| 1959 | 5,050 | 24.1 | 37.8 |
| 1949—1959 average | 1,926a | 47.2 | 48.9a |

n.a. Not available.
  a. Computed for the years for which data are available.

Sources: Table 6.4; *Ta kung pao*, Hong Kong, December 4, 1952 and December 28, 1953; *Jen-min jih-pao*, December 26, 1957; *Ta kung pao*, Peking, December 31, 1957; and other sources.

67 *Chung-kung shih-nien* (A decade of Chinese communists), Hong Kong, p. 235; *Jen-min jih pao*, March 11, 1959.
68 In 1949, Nos. 2 and 3 open hearths were rehabilitated; by May 1950 all the six open hearths (two 150-ton and four 100-ton) and the three 300-ton tilting active mixers of No. 1 steel plant were restored and resumed production.

1957 on could be attributed, in part, to the rising relative importance of converter steel in ingot steel production, since the bulk of Anshan's ingot steel came from open hearths. As in the case pig iron, the beginning of produktion in the new bases also reduced Anshan's share; for instance, in 1959 ingot steel output was 500,000 tons (planned) at Wuhan and 20,000 tons at Paotow[69].

Data on the annual output of rolled products at Anshan, its growth and its share in the national total for the period 1952–1959 are presented in Table 5.10. Early rehabilitation of rolling facilities at Anshan in comparison with other steel centers accounts for its large and growing share in 1952–1953. In 1955 and, perhaps, in 1954, its relative importance declined owing to the more rapid expansion of rolling capacity elsewhere in 1954–1955, such as the Taiyuan Iron and Steel Works and the Chungking Iron and Steel Corportion. From 1956 on, the rising tendency resumed. This was expected because during 1952–1959 the annual average rate of increase came to 33.9 per cent for Anshan Steel and 31.7 per cent for the steel industry as a whole.

The above examination has clearly revealed the prominence of Anshan both in terms of capacity and output. With the rise of the two new steel bases, however, Anshan's pre-eminence tended to decline. Wuhan's output of major products became a threat to the position of Anshan Steel. Wuhan's output planned for 1960 amounted to 1.5 million tons each for pig iron and ingot steel, and 1.1 million tons for rolled products. The threat of Paotow Steel was, perhaps, more important. Its planned annual ingot steel output jumped from 1,470 thousand tons in 1961 to 3.5 million tons in 1962. Equally spectacular was its planned increase of rolled

Table 5.10. Growth of Rolled Steel Output at Anshan, 1952–1959

| Year | Output | | Share of National Total (per cent) |
|------|--------|--------|------|
| | In thousand tons | Percentage increase | |
| | (1) | (2) | (3) |
| 1952 | 520 | — | 39.6 |
| 1953 | 760 | 14.6 | 43.3 |
| 1954 | n. a. | — | n. a. |
| 1955 | 837 | — | 33.4 |
| 1956 | 1,456 | 74.0 | 37.1 |
| 1957 | 2,400 | 64.8 | 49.7 |
| 1958 | 3,600 | 50.0 | 52.4 |
| 1959 | 4,000 | 11.1 | 44.4 |
| 1952—1959 average | 1,895a | 33.9 | 43.9a |

n.a. Not available.
a. Computed for the years for which data are available.

Sources: Table 6.6; *Ta kung pao*, Peking, December 31, 1957; *Jen-min jih-pao*, December 15, 1956 and January 6, 1957; and other sources.

69 Paotow's output was for January-November 1959. *Chung-kung shih-nien, ibid.*; *Jen-min jih-pao*, March 11, 1959.

steel output from 1.1 million tons in 1961 to 2.5 million tons in 1962. The latter
may be compared with Anshan's planned 1960 output of 4.5 million tons[70].


## Concluding Remarks

The expansion of Anshan Steel and the rise of Wuhan and Paotow Steel
reveal that the communist economic planners were aiming at the latest technology
and the largest possible scale of operation. To achieve such an objective, Soviet
aid was indispensable, in view of China's lack of the necessary technical skills and
capacity. Thus, in the construction of the two new steel bases, Soviet aid extended
from prospecting, site selection, designing, supply of equipment down to actual
construction and installation. Similarly, forty-eight major capital construction
projects launched at Anshan Steel during 1953–1960 were Soviet-aid projects[71].

The importance of Soviet-aid projects to the growth of China's steel industry
can also be seen from their share in overall capacity expansion during the first
plan quinquennium. For the period as a whole, it was 92.1 per cent in iron
smelting, 82.1 per cent in steel refining and 90.4 per cent in rolling facilities[72]. If
1957 alone is considered, the importance of the aid projects declined. Their shares
in the expansion of smelting and refining capacities in 1957 dropped to 83.2 and
79.5 per cent respectively, although their share in rolling capacity expansion
became slightly higher (91.5 per cent)[73].

This decline coincided with a re-orientation of economic policy towards
greater self-reliance, which subsequently gave rise to a frantic movement for
building small-scale, labor-intensive industrial units using indigenous production
techniques. This represented an attempt to develop a second industrial front to
supplement the existing sector in which large-scale operation and modern technology remained the keynote. In the process of carrying out this campaign, however,
the large-scale modern industrial sector also became involved. Thus, in the key
steel bases, small and medium-sized equipment was installed. For example, in the
latter part of 1958, Anshan Steel constructed 140 blast furnaces of 3–100 m³,
with a total capacity of 4,440 m³, and 3,000 odd converters with an aggregate
daily output of 4,000 tons[74]. Similarly, Paotow Steel built in 1959 eight 13 m³
and six 55 m³ blast furnaces, and two 6-ton converters[75].

---

70 Data on the planned output of the three key steel bases for 1960–1962 were obtained
from a confidential source.
71 The 48 projects consisted of 3 iron mines, 8 ore-dressing and sintering plants, 6 blast
furnaces, 3 steel plants, 16 rolling mills, 10 coke oven batteries and 2 refractory plants.
*Jen-min jih-pao*, July 19, 1956.
72 Yang Ying-chieh, *Su-lien tui-yu wo-kuo ti-i-ke wu-nien chi-hua ti wei-ta yuan-chu*
(The great aid of the Soviet Union to the First Five-Year Plan of our country), Peking,
1956, p. 15.
73 *Ibid*.
74 *NCNA*, Anshan, December 15, 1958; *Liao-ning jih-pao*, Shengyang, January 13,
1959.
75 F. Okazaki, *op. cit.*, pp. 43 and 83.

The rationale for building such small furnaces was to meet, in part, the urgent construction needs of these bases, to maximize the immediate output, and to minimize current investment outlays[76]. This latter consideration also affected the capital construction schedule of key steel bases. For instance, the original plan for the construction of Wuhan Steel envisaged completion of the first-stage construction in 1961 with an annual ingot output of 1.5 million tons. This plan was revised in 1958 for completion in 1961 of both the first and second stages of construction with an annual ingot output of 3 million tons. The two-stage distinction was thus eliminated so that construction time and investment outlays could be minimized.

Many improvised measures used in capital construction at the key steel bases during the Leap Forward should be clearly recognized as nothing more than temporary emergency devices. They could not supplant the skills of modern technology. Hence, with the withdrawal of Soviet technical aid in the latter part of 1960 and the departure of Soviet experts together with blueprints of construction projects, capital construction in the steel industry, particularly at the three key bases, was abruptly interrupted. The decision made in January, 1961, at the Ninth Plenum of the Eighth Committee of the Chinese Communist Party to reduce the 1961 scale of capital construction in heavy industry and to consolidate available technical resources for selected key projects represented, in part, a recognition of the limitations of the make-do measures over an extended time period.

76 To minimize current investment outlays, the "contract investment" system was introduced, under which attention was focussed on the urgency and advantage of finding substitutes on the spot for materials which could not be supplied in time. This system, thus, made the concept of self-reliance applicable to an individual steel base.

# PART III
# PRODUCTION AND INVESTMENT

## Chapter 6

# OUTPUT OF MAJOR PRODUCTS

This chapter examines in physical terms the relative output behavior of the major sectors of the steel industry, and changes in the intra-industry output structure. Included in the major sectors are iron ore, coke, pig iron, ingot steel and rolled products. In addition, the output of ingots will be identified by the type of furnace so as to reveal the pattern of development in steel-refining.

Whereas data such as aggregate ingot steel output figures are readily obtainable, production statistics on coke and finished steel for certain years cannot be found in spite of a systematic effort at combing through all available publications. Thus the missing quantities have to be estimated so that a complete time series can be obtained for each of the major sectors.

### Iron Ore

Although official data on iron ore output are available for the years 1949 —1959, the 1958 figure disclosed in March 1959 represents a preliminary and unrevised figure. In August 1959 when official production statistics on pig iron and ingot steel were revised downward drastically, no similar revision of iron ore output was disclosed. It is thus necessary to estimate the ore output which would be consistent with the revised iron and steel figures. In view of the acute shortage in the supply of iron ores developed in 1958, it is not unrealistic to assume that there was no discrepancy between output and consumption in that year. The lack of information on iron ore input per ton of pig iron produced in 1958 requires a further assumption that it remained at the 1957 level. As the latter is known to be 3.26 tons and the revised pig iron output 9.53 million tons[1], the 1958 output of usable iron ore should, therefore, be in the neighborhood of 31 million tons, rather than the reported 36.8 million tons.

Since the official downward revision of iron and steel output quantities was based on quality standards, this estimate has accordingly eliminated the amount of low-grade ores which went mostly into the production of sub-standard pig iron subsequently rejected in the downward revision. Thus it is consistent not only with the revised pig iron and ingot steel output figures for that year, but also with the ore output quantities for earlier years in terms of iron content.

1 See Tables 6.2 and 6.3.

Table 6.1 presents official iron output data for 1949–1957, 1959 and 1960 (planned) together with the estimated output for 1958. In examining iron output data, it is difficult to identify the iron content. The usual communist practice of reporting output without indicating its iron content tends to reduce the usefulness of such data. Fortunately, it is possible to obtain some data on the national average input of iron ore per ton of pig iron output, where the iron content of the ore has been indicated. These input figures are shown in Table 6.2 along with the

*Table 6.1. Iron Ore Production, 1949–1960 (in thousand tons of 30–40% Fe content)*

| Year | Amount[a] | Index[b] (1952=100) |
|---|---|---|
| Pre-communist peak | 5,780 | 135 |
| 1949 | 589 | 14 |
| 1950 | 2,350 | 55 |
| 1951 | 2,703 | 63 |
| 1952 | 4,287 | 100 |
| 1953 | 5,821 | 136 |
| 1954 | 7,229 | 169 |
| 1955 | 9,597 | 224 |
| 1956 | 15,484 | 361 |
| 1957 | 19,370 | 452 |
| 1958 | 31,068[c] | 725 |
| 1959 | 39,674 | 925 |
| 1960 | 55,543[d] | 1296 |

a. Rounded.
b. Computed before rounding.
c. Estimated.
d. Planned.

Sources: Industrial Statistics Section, State Bureau of Statistics, *Wo-kuo kang-t'ieh, tien-li, mei-t'an, chi-hsieh, fang-chih, tsao-chih kung-yeh ti chin-hsi* (The past and present of China's iron and steel, electric power, coal, machine-making, textile and paper industries), Peking: Statistics Publishing House, 1958, pp. 11 and 19; *Kuan-ming jih-pao*, Peking, November 19, 1957; *Jen-min jih-pao*, September 15, 1958; *China News Service*, March 16, 1959; *Yeh-chin pao* (Metallurgy), Peking, No. 4, 1960, p. 6, and No. 6, 1960, p. 3.

iron ore–pig iron output ratios. The close resemblance of the two series strongly suggests that the ore output figures on the basis of which the ore-pig iron ratios are derived also carry an iron content of 30–40 per cent.

The extremely low level of output in 1949 (see Table 6.1) is more or less expected. As noted in Chapter 3, Soviet occupation forces stripped all iron mines of essential machinery and removed all ore concentration facilities in the Northeast. In addition, during their evacuation the nationalist troops inflicted serious damage to iron mines, particularly in Tayeh. The extensive removals and destruction coupled with the time-consuming task of rehabilitating mining and concentration installations made the recovery of ore production to its pre-communist peak level a rather slow process.

*Table 6.2. Comparison of Iron Ore-Pig Iron Output Ratio with Average Iron Ore Input Per Ton of Pig Iron Output, 1954—1957*

| Year | Iron Ore-Pig Iron Output Ratio | Input of Iron Ore (with 30 — 40% Fe) Per Ton of Pig Iron Produced (in tons) |
|---|---|---|
| 1954 | 2.32 | 2.31 |
| 1955 | 2.48 | 2.47 |
| 1956 | 3.21 | 3.21 |
| 1957 | 3.26 | 3.26 |

Sources: *Chi-hua yü t'ung-chi* (Planning and statistics), Peking, June 23, 1959, p. 15; Tables 6.1 and 6.3.

Although the output virtually quadrupled in 1950, it amounted to only about 40 per cent of the highest pre-communist level (see Table 6.1). The 1950 increase in output was attributable to the restoration of the First Ore-Dressing Plant[2], the First Sintering Plant and the First and Second Reduction Plants in Anshan, and of the Lungyen Iron Mines in Hopeh.

The highest pre-communist output level was reached in 1953. From 1954 onwards, iron ore production continued to increase at a high rate, consistently above 24 per cent annually. During the industrial upsurge of 1956 and the Great Leap of 1958, the annual increase was over 60 per cent. For the period 1954—1960, the annual average rate of increase came to 40.5 per cent.

Whether such a high development tempo can be sustained over an extended period of time depends ultimately on the available reserves. China's verified iron ore reserves at the end of 1958, according to the State Bureau of Statistics, amounted to 8 billion tons[3]. This figure which represents an increase of roughly 50 per cent over the pre-communist estimate does not appear to be unreasonable in view of the concentrated efforts of the communist regime on geological survey and the probability of discovering new deposits in a vast, underdeveloped country like China. In Chingtiehshan (Kansu province) alone, new iron ore reserves have been estimated to be over 200 million tons. Also, deposits of high-quality ores (with iron content of 50 — 60 per cent) have been discovered at Peiyunopo; the estimated reserves amount to 150 million tons[4]. In addition, substantial new iron ore deposits have been found in Wuan hsien of Hopeh, northwestern Honan, northern Sinkiang, and other places[5]. Thus in terms of availability, iron ore reserves pose no constraint to the development of the iron and steel industry.

On the other hand, China's iron ore deposits consist overwhelmingly of ores

2 The pre-war capacity of this plant was 400,000 tons per year.
3 State Bureau of Statistics, *Wei-ta ti shih-nien* (Ten great years), Peking, 1959, p. 12 (hereafter abbreviated as *WTSN*).
4 *CTCHK*, p. 721.
5 *NCNA*, Nanking, April 5, 1957; *NCNA*, Chengchow, August 1, 1958.

lean in iron content. Such ores require concentration before they can be charged
into a blast furnace. Their use thus pushes up the cost of iron production, even
though they are massive and can be mined by surface and open-cut equipment.
Rich ores, though available, occur mostly in veins and dykes and require under-
ground mining. These cost considerations place the Chinese steel industry at a
disadvantage.

## Pig Iron

Table 6.3 shows the output of pig iron from 1949—1960. Before examining the
output behavior, it should be made clear that the data presented in the table are
consistent. It is true that the figures prior to 1958 include the output of handicraft
as well as modern establishments. However, only native iron of usable quality
produced by handicraft workshops has been included; the inferior handicraft
output has already been eliminated[6]. Similarly, the sub-standard products of the
"backyard furnaces" which mushroomed during the year has been excluded from
the 1958 figure. In the course of 1959, small modern furnaces were developed,
capable of producing pig iron up to standard quality[7]. Consequently their output
was included in the 1959 and 1960 figures given in the table.

As can be seen in Table 6.3, pre-communist peak output was restored in 1952.
The growth in 1950 was spectacular, amounting to 288 per cent. Chiefly responsible for this substantial increase was the rehabilitation of Nos. 1 and 2 blast
furnaces at Penki, Nos. 1, 2 and 4 blast furnaces at Anshan, No. 1 blast furnace
at Shihchingshan and No. 1 blast furnace at Taiyuan. These furnaces began
operation either in the latter part of 1949 or early in 1950. The lower rate of
increase in 1951, on the other hand, can be attributed to the fact that of the blast
furnaces which were rehabilitated and went into operation during that year, only
No. 2 blast furnace at Shihchingshan was of sizable capacity (512 m³) while the
rest were relatively small, not exceeding 64 cubic meters each in capacity[8].

For the period 1949—1960, the lowest rate of growth in output was registered
in 1953. In that year, the over-enthusiasm that went with the launching of the
First Five-Year Plan prompted blast furnace workers to raise the smelting intensity beyond 1.1[9]. This practice, however, resulted in "lumping of slag" which
plagued a large number of blast furnaces throughout the country. Secondly, the
reconstruction of blast furnaces at Anshan which had been seriously damaged by

---

6 For the period 1952—1956, the proportion of usable native iron included never exceeded
2.7 per cent of the national total. *KTMCFT*, pp. 30 — 31.
7 In small modern furnaces, there is greater use of mechanical aids than in the case of
native furnaces. The skip is operated by a small winch and a motor. After the hopper is
charged, the bells are operated by a lever and wire rope from the ground. In addition,
there is some degree of sizing of raw materials, standardization of products and utilization of blast furnace gas.
8 For details, see Table 4.3 above.
9 Smelting intensity is measured by the amount in metric tons of coke consumed per
cubic meter of usable furnace volume in 24 hours.

*Table 6.3. Pig Iron Production, 1949—1960 (in thousand tons)*

| Year | Amount[a] | Index[b] (1952=100) |
|------|-----------|---------------------|
| Pre-communist peak | 1,801 | 93 |
| 1949 | 252 | 13 |
| 1950 | 978 | 51 |
| 1951 | 1,448 | 75 |
| 1952 | 1,929 | 100 |
| 1953 | 2,234 | 116 |
| 1954 | 3,114 | 162 |
| 1955 | 3,872 | 201 |
| 1956 | 4,826 | 250 |
| 1957 | 5,936 | 308 |
| 1958 | 9,530 | 494 |
| 1959 | 20,500 | 1,063 |
| 1960 | 27,500[c] | 1,426 |

a. Rounded.
b. Computed before rounding.
c. Planned.

Sources: Industrial Statistics Section, State Bureau of Statistics, *Wo-kuo kang-t'ieh, tien-li, mei-t'an, chi-hsieh, fang-chih, tsao-chih kung-yeh ti chin-hsi* (The past and present of China's iron and steel, electric power, coal, machine-making, textile and paper industries), Peking: Statistics Publishing House, 1958, pp. 11 and 19; State Bureau of Statistics, *Wei-ta ti shih-nien* (Ten great years), Peking, 1959, p. 84; *Jen-min jih-pao*, January 23, 1960; *Yeh-chin pao* (Metallurgy), Peking, No. 1, 1960, p. 29; *Ta-kung pao*, Hong Kong, March 31, 1960.

Soviet removals did not begin until 1952, and by 1953 only No. 8 blast furnace went into operation.

The highest rate of growth occurred in 1959 when the output of pig iron more than doubled. This is compared with a 60 per cent increase in 1958. Since the latter year marked the height of the steel campaign, one would have expected a higher rate of growth for that year. As a matter of fact, the preliminary official report gave the country's pig iron output at 13.69 million tons[10], and thus the 1958 growth rate would have been higher. But this incredible figure reported in the confused state of statistics was subsequently revised downward to 9.53 million tons to the exclusion of the sub-standard products of native furnaces. On the other hand, the above-mentioned development of small modern furnaces raised the 1959 output substantially[11].

10 State Bureau of Statistics, "Communiqué on the development of the national economy in 1958," *NCNA*, Peking, April 14, 1959.
11 Furnaces not exceeding 50 cubic meters in capacity contributed 11 million tons, or nearly 54 per cent of the 1959 output of pig iron. *Kang-t'ieh* (Iron and steel), semi-monthly, Peking, No. 1, 1960, p. 53; *Yeh-chin pao* (Metallurgy), weekly, Peking, No. 4, 1960, p. 9.

## Ingot Steel

Table 6.4 shows ingot steel output from 1949–1960 and its breakdown by furnace type from 1952–1960. The behavior of ingot steel output can be seen from the official statistics given in Column 1 of the table. For 1950 and 1951, the rate of increase was quite close to that in pig iron output. As the 1949 output level in comparison with the pre-communist peak was relatively higher in ingot steel than pig iron, the recovery of steel production was speedier. In fact, the pre-communist peak steel output of 923 thousand tons was almost reached in 1951. From that point on, ingot steel output continued to expand throughout the period under investigation, with the highest rate of increase registered in 1959. Here again, the output behavior resembled that of pig iron and for similar reasons.

Table 6.4. *Output of Ingot Steel and Breakdown by Furnace Type, 1949—1960* (in thousand tons)

| Year | Amount[a] | Open Hearth | | Electric Furnace | | Converter | |
|---|---|---|---|---|---|---|---|
| | | Amount | Percentage Share of Total | Amount[a] | Percentage Share of Total | Amount[a] | Percentage Share of Total |
| | (1) | (2) | (3) | (4) | (5) | (6) | (7) |
| 1949 | 158 | 130 | 82.1 | n. a. | — | n. a. | — |
| 1950 | 606 | 570 | 94.1 | n. a. | — | n. a. | — |
| 1951 | 896 | 650 | 72.6 | n. a. | — | n. a. | — |
| 1952 | 1,349 | 940 | 69.7 | 142 | 10.5 | 266 | 19.8 |
| 1953 | 1,774 | 1,140 | 64.3 | 223 | 12.6 | 410 | 23.1 |
| 1954 | 2,225 | 1,480 | 66.5 | 330 | 14.8 | 415 | 18.7 |
| 1955 | 2,853 | 1,670 | 58.5 | 417 | 14.6 | 766 | 26.9 |
| 1956 | 4,465 | 2,940 | 65.8 | 608 | 13.6 | 917 | 20.6 |
| 1957 | 5,350 | 3,570 | 66.7 | 983[e] | 18.4[e] | 797 | 14.9 |
| 1958 | 8,000[b] | 5,460 | 68.3 | 764[e] | 9.5[e] | 1,776 | 22.2 |
| 1959 | 13,350 | 6,590 | 49.4 | 2,034[e] | 15.2[e] | 4,726 | 35.4 |
| 1960 | 18,450 | 6,350[c] | 34.4[d] | 2,528[d] | 13.7[d] | 9,568[f] | 51.9 |

n.a. Not available.
  a. Rounded.
  b. Revised downward from 11.08 million tons.
  c. Estimated and rounded to the nearest ten thousand.
  d. Estimated.
  e. Derived.
  f. Planned.

Sources: Industrial Statistics Section, State Bureau of Statistics, *Wo-kuo kang-t'ieh, tien-li, mei-t'an, chi-hsieh, fang-chih, tsao-chih kung-yeh ti chin-hsi* (The past and present of China's iron and steel, electric power, coal, machine-making, textile and paper industries), Peking: Statistics Publishing House, 1958, pp. 11, 19 and 22; *Wei-ta ti shih-nien* (Ten great years), Peking, 1959, p. 84; *Kang-t'ieh* (Iron and steel), Peking, No. 18, 1959, pp. 805 and 813, and No. 9, 1960, p. 508; *Yeh-chin pao* (Metallurgy), Peking, December 28, 1959, p. 34, and No. 14, 1960, pp. 9—14; *NCNA*, Peking, January 22, 1960; *Hung-ch'i* (Red flag), February 1, 1961, p. 19; and *Communiqué* of the State Bureau of Statistics, January 22, 1960.

The output quantities of open-hearth steel shown in Column 2 of Table 6.4 was derived for the years 1949–1958 from a graph (presented in a technical journal put out jointly by the Ministry of Metallurgical Industry and China Metallurgical Society)[12], without which the breakdown of ingot steel production by furnace type would not have been possible. The 1959 output quantity can thus be derived from the known increase of 20.7 per cent over 1958. The output of open-hearth steel in 1960 is estimated on the basis of the known share of converter steel in the ingot steel output planned for 1960, and the average share of electric furnace steel in the ingot steel output for the period 1952–1959[13].

Data on the output quantities of electric furnace steel presented in Column 4 of Table 6.4 are obtained from the State Bureau of Statistics for 1952–1956, derived for 1957–1959, and estimated for 1960. The 1957–1959 quantities are derived from the known proportions of open-hearth and converter steels given in Column 3 and 7 of Table 6.4. The 1960 output, as indicated above, is estimated on the basis of the share of electric furnace steel in aggregate output of ingot steel during 1952–1959, which amounted to 13.7 per cent[14].

Output figures for converter steel for 1952–1956 shown in Column 6 of Table 6.4 represent the residues from the ingot steel totals after deducting open-hearth and electric furnace steels. The 1957–1959 quantities are derived from official percentage figures given in Column 7. The 1960 figure represents the planned quantity.

Even though the share of open-hearth steel was not large in comparison with leading steel-producing countries, it nevertheless constituted more than 60 per cent of ingot steel output for almost all years before 1959 as can be seen from Column 3 of Table 6.4. This predominance, however, began to wane after 1958. By 1960, even the output quantity fell. The declining relative importance of open-hearth steel was attributable chiefly to the shift in government policy in favor of converter steel for its smaller investment outlays, shorter gestation period and lower production costs[15]. Thus, the objectives of minimizing capital investment and maximizing immediate output could be achieved. This was in line with the Great Leap policy of exploiting fast-yielding investment opportunities by creating an additional production front consisting of innumerable small production units.

12 *Kang-t'ieh*, No. 18, 1959, p. 805.
13 The planned converter steel constituted 52 per cent of the 1960 planned ingot steel output of 18.4 million tons, and should therefore be 9,568 thousand tons, or 51.9 per cent of realized 1960 ingot steel output of 18.45 million tons. During 1952–1959, electric furnaces contributed 13.7 per cent of the ingot steel output; this is assumed to be the 1960 proportion. With the proportions of electric furnace and converter steel thus determined, the share of open-hearth steel is estimated at 34.4 per cent or approximately 6.35 million tons. *Yeh-chin pao*, April 18, 1960, pp. 9–14; Li Fu-chun's report to the Second Session of the Second National People's Congress on March 30, 1960.
14 This is indeed high in comparison with leading steel-producing countries. The relatively larger proportion of electric furnace steel prior to 1959 was attributable to technological constraint which made it difficult for the Chinese steel industry to produce high-quality steel in open hearths and converters.
15 For details, see Chapter 12.

Consequently, the relative importance of converter steel increased from 22.2 per cent in 1958 to 35.4 per cent in 1959 and to 51.9 per cent in 1960 (see Column 7 of Table 6.4). In contrast, the share of open-hearth steel declined from 68.3 per cent in 1958 to 49.4 per cent in 1959 and to 34.4 per cent in 1960 (see Column 3).

The policy of placing increasing emphasis on converter steel also affected the output behavior of electric furnace steel. As can be seen from Column 5 of Table 6.4, the rising trend in the importance of electric furnace steel was interrupted in 1958, when the policy shift was accompanied by an acute shortage of metal scrap resulting from the nation-wide all-out steel campaign. In 1959—1960, its relative importance was more or less stabilized at the level of the mid-1950's. The promotion campaigns for producing high-quality steel by converters waged in 1959 —1960 and the subsequent introduction of the L–D process[16] pointed to increasing competition with electric furnace steel.

## Finished Steel

In examining finished steel output, one is confronted with the extreme paucity of official statistics. The composition of finished steel is unknown. There is no quantitative information whatsoever on forgings or castings. Nor is there information on the output structure of rolled steel. Given this unsatisfactory state of statistics, the best one can do is to arrive at a time series of aggregate output of finished steel based on whatever official data are obtainable. Even such a modest attempt is handicapped by the inconsistency in available official statistics. Indices of finished steel output disclosed by the State Planning Commission, the State Bureau of Statistics, and the Ministry of Metallurgical Industry show considerable variance, as can be seen from Table 6.5. In fact, no identity whatsoever is found in the indices presented in the table for any single year.

The index series published in the official monthly of the State Planning Commission (Chi-hua ching-chi) is consistently higher than the others. The obvious explanation is that its base year output quantity is smaller. This is precisely the case. The text of the First Five-Year Plan published by the State Planning Commission in August 1955 gave the 1952 output of finished steel as 1.11 million tons[17]. If this base-year figure is applied to the 1955 index of 228 in the State Planning Commission series (see Column 4 of Table 6.5), the output quantity for that year becomes 2,530,800 tons. Comparing this figure with the one of 2,505 thousand tons announced by the State Bureau of Statistics in its 1955 Communiqué, the discrepancy is within a tolerable margin of one per cent.

Thus although the base-year quantities used by these two agencies were at

16 See Chapter 14.
17 Chung-hua jen-min kung-ho-kuo fa-chan kuo-min ching-chi ti ti-i-ke wu-nien chi-hua (The First Five-Year Plan of the People's Republic of China for the development of the national economy), Peking, 1955, p. 36.

*Table 6.5. Indices of Finished Steel Output, 1953—1956 (1952=100)*

| Year | State Bureau of Statistics | | Ministry of Metallurgical Industry | State Planning Commission |
|---|---|---|---|---|
| | Revised | Released Earlier | | |
| | (1) | (2) | (3) | (4) |
| 1953 | 133.7 | 134 | 134.1 | 139 |
| 1954 | 149.8 | 157a | 159.3 | 163 |
| 1955 | 190.9 | 201a | 200.3 | 228 |
| 1956 | 298.9 | 315a | 290.0 | 325 |

a. Derived from given data on annual percentage increases.

Sources: Annual *Communiqués* of State Bureau of Statistics for the years 1953—1956; Industrial Statistics Section, State Bureau of Statistics, *Wo-kuo kang-t'ieh, tien-li, mei-t'an, chi-hsieh, fang-chieh, tsao-chih kung-yeh ti chin-hsi* (The past and present of China's iron and steel, electric power, coal, machine-making, textile and paper industries), Peking: Statistics Publishing House, 1958, p. 20; *Chi-hua ching-chi* (Planned economy), Peking, No. 9, 1957, p. 12; Kang-t'ieh (Iron and steel), Peking, No. 18, 1959, p. 832.

considerable variance, by 1955 the difference had narrowed appreciably. This is in line with the general improvement from mid-1954 in the organization and operation of statistical services, particularly in state and joint industrial enterprises. More pertinent, perhaps, is the fact that after mid-1955 the State Planning Commission began to modify its concepts of indicators and methods of computation and classification in agreement with those of the State Bureau of Statistics (SBS)[18].

Relatively speaking, the Ministry of Metallurgical Industry index series follows closely that first released by SBS for the years 1953—1955. This close correspondence suggests a similar, if not identical, base-year quantity. The 1952 output quantity implied in the SBS series can be derived from the given data for 1955. Dividing the output of 2,505 tons by the corresponding index of 200.68 (before rounding), the base-year production is estimated at 1,248,256 tons. The close proximity of the 1955 output figure given by SBS to that implied in the statistics of the State Planning Commission strongly suggests the probability that the output quantity used by the Ministry of Metallurgical Industry in computing its 1955 index would be in that neighborhood. On the assumption that this output quantity is identical with the SBS figure before rounding (i. e. 2,504,817 tons), the base-year quantity of the Ministry of Metallurgical Industry series should be 1,250,533 tons, or 0.18 per cent higher than the SBS base-year figure estimated above. Such a negligible discrepancy can easily be attributed to rounding in computation with respect to both index series.

The base-year quantity of the revised SBS output index series shown in Column

18 For details, see Choh-Ming Li, *The Statistical System of Communist China,* Berkeley, 1962, pp. 23 — 26, 35 — 40.

1 of Table 6.5 has been given at 1,311,897 tons, representing a 5.1 per cent upward revision from the estimated base-year quantity of the earlier SBS series. The basis for this revision, however, has not been disclosed.

The speculation that it was due to an extension of coverage to include the output of handicrafts can easily be disproved. True, the presentation of the revised figure was accompanied by a note that the output of handicrafts had been included[19]. However, since the revised data on finished steel output were presented along with other production figures in the same table, the note need not be applicable to finished steel. Moreover, elsewhere in the same SBS publication where a breakdown of output by sector is given, the handicraft sector is absent in connection with finished steel, and yet the figures tally with the revised figure mentioned above[20]. Thus the note must refer to commodities other than finished steel. Although the basis for the revision remains unknown, it is clear that it is not due to the inclusion of handicraft output.

The 1953 output was revised from 1,627,660 to 1,754,161 tons, and the 1954 output ostensibly from 1,957,000 to 1,965,337 tons[21]. While the 1953 upward revision amounted to 7.8 per cent, the 1954 "upward revision" was merely 0.4 per cent. In view of the negligible difference, it is not at all clear whether the 1954 output figure was actually revised. This small difference could very well have arisen from the given annual percentage increase figures which have obviously been rounded. Whereas it is uncertain whether the 1954 output figure has been revised, there is little doubt that the 1955 and 1956 figures are unrevised. Their quantities of 2,505 and 3,921 thousand tons as disclosed in SBS *Communiqués* obviously represent the rounded figures of 2,504,817 and 3,920,975 tons subsequently released by SBS Industrial Statistics Section.

Table 6.6 presents finished steel output in physical quantities for the period under investigation. Data for 1949–1956 are given by SBS Industrial Statistics Section[22]; figures for 1957–1960 represent estimates. The Ministry of Metallurgical Industry series gives the 1957 and 1958 production indices as 386.5 and 549.4 respectively. The base-year (1952) quantity of this series has already been estimated to be 1,250,533 tons. Multiplying the indices by this figure will give 4,833,310 tons as the 1957 output and 6,870,428 tons as the 1958 output. The 1959 quantity is derived from the reported output increase of 31 per cent in the first half of the year, on the assumption that this rate of increase applies to the whole year[23]. This assumption appears reasonable considering that the average

19 *KTMCFT*, p. 19.
20 *Ibid.*, p. 30.
21 *Ibid.*, p. 20. The 1953 and 1954 unrevised output quantities are derived from the estimated base-year quantity and the given annual percentage increase figures.
22 The SBS revised figures have been used because they are more exact and show a sectoral breakdown. In addition, they were released much later than the State Planning Commission figure in physical quantity.
23 According to *CNS*, Peking, August 20, 1959, the rate of increase in output during the first half of 1959 was 31 per cent over the corresponding period in 1958.

Table 6.6. *Output of Finished Steel, 1949—1960 (in thousand tons)*

| Year | Amount[a] | Index[ab] (1952=100) |
|------|-----------|----------------------|
| Pre-communist peak | 686 | 52 |
| 1949 | 141 | 11 |
| 1950 | 464 | 35 |
| 1951 | 808 | 62 |
| 1952 | 1,312 | 100 |
| 1953 | 1,754 | 134 |
| 1954 | 1,965 | 150 |
| 1955 | 2,505 | 191 |
| 1956 | 3,921 | 299 |
| 1957 | 4,833[c] | 368 |
| 1958 | 6,870[c] | 524 |
| 1959 | 9,000[c] | 686 |
| 1960 | 11,510[c] | 877 |

a. Rounded.
b. Computed from data before rounding.
c. Estimated.

Sources: Industrial Statistics Section, State Bureau of Statistics, *Wo-kuo kang-t'ieh, tien-li, mei-t'an, chi-hsieh, fang-chih, tsao-chih kung-yeh ti chin-hsi* (The past and present of China's iron and steel, electric power, coal, machine-making, textile and paper industries), Peking: Statistics Publishing House, 1958, pp. 11 and 20; *CNS*, Peking, August 20, 1959; *Kang-t'ieh* (Iron and steel), Peking, No. 18, 1959, p. 832.

annual rate of increase from 1952 to 1958 came to 31.8 per cent. The 1960 output of 11.51 million tons is estimated on the basis of the trend of 1952—1959[24].

While the output quantities given in Table 6.6 are in broad agreement with the figures given in Yuan-li Wu's study[25], it may be of interest to note that he has made a separate tentative re-estimate of finished steel output as follows[26]:

| Year | Output ('000 tons) |
|------|--------------------|
| 1952 | 805 |
| 1953 | 1,124 |
| 1954 | 1,293 |
| 1955 | 1,648 |
| 1956 | 1,735 |
| 1957 | 1,884 |
| 1958 | 2,655 |
| 1959 | 4,071 |
| 1960 | 5,664—7,345 |

24 Derived from the following equation which represents a projection of the output figures for 1952—1959:

$$\text{Log } Y_c = 3.515,369 + 0.060,630 \, t$$

where $Y_c$ represents finished steel output taken to the nearest thousand tons. The estimate is computed by setting $t = 9$ for 1960.
25 *The steel Industry in Communist China*, New York 1965, pp. 284—285. The discrepancies for 1957—1960 are within a margin of roughly 12 per cent.
26 *Ibid.*, pp. 288—290.

This represents, as Wu puts it, a bold attempt to adjust the output of finished steel. The boldness lies in his assumptions that official output data on finished steel include semi-finished steel and that the *capacity* ratio of semi-finished to finished steel for Anshan is the same as the *output* ratio of semi-finished to finished steel for the industry as a whole.

An even bolder attempt has been made by Frederick M. Cone[27]. To estimate China's rolled steel output, he relates the increase in output to imports of complete plants for the expansion of the steel industry. As such imports are unknown, he assumes that one half of China's imports of complete plants fall in this category. Unfortunately China's imports of complete plants are also unknown. On the basis of Alexander Eckstein's estimates of such imports from USSR and non-communist countries, Cone arbitrarily blows it up by one quarter to take in the unknown quantity of such imports from other communist countries. However, as Eckstein's estimates cover the years 1955—1959, Cone extrapolates backward from 1955 to 1952 on the basis of imports of machinery and equipment from USSR and non-communist countries from 1952—1955. Inasmuch as imports are given in value terms, he asumes the import cost per ton of rolled steel output to be US$250. By further assuming the 1952 rolled steel output to be 1.1 million tons and allowing one year lag between the import of complete plants and the increase in output, he comes up with the following rolled steel output estimates:

| Year | Output ('000 tons) | Year | Output ('000 tons) |
|------|--------------------|------|--------------------|
| 1952 | 1,100 | 1957 | 3,000 |
| 1953 | 1,280 | 1958 | 3,600 |
| 1954 | 1,600 | 1959 | 4,260 |
| 1955 | 2,000 | 1960 | 5,360 |
| 1956 | 2,400 |      |       |

While this represents an interesting exercise, the accuracy of these estimates cannot be ascertained.

The output behavior of finished steel can be seen from Table 6.6. From 1950 —1952, the annual rate of increase did not fall below 62 per cent. This high rate of increase reflected chiefly the speedy rehabilitation work. By 1952, while the rolling mill capacities at Penki and Taiyuan were fully restored, rolling capacity recovery at Anshan amounted to 83 per cent. In view of the fact that the pre-communist rate of capacity utilization for the industry as a whole came to less than 60 per cent, it is not surprising that the pre-communist peak output was surpassed in 1951 (see Table 6.6). As expected, the rate of growth slowed down somewhat after 1952. In contrast to the output behavior of ingot steel or pig iron, the growth rate of finished steel was higher in 1958 than in 1959. This contrast

---

27 *Chinese Industrial Growth: Brief Studies of Selected Investment Areas,* Santa Monica, 1969, pp. 29—36.

signifies that the 1958 steel campaign left less of an imprint in the finishing sector than either the refining or the smelting sector.

The growth of finished steel output was accompanied by a considerable increase in the variety of products. With type and specification both taken into account, the number of products rose from 484 in 1953 to 3,997 in 1957[28]. In spite of the increase in variety, however, the Chinese steel industry lacked at that point the capacity to produce certain special steels and the facilities for cold rolling and heavy forging. Consequently, China had to rely on imports for such products[29]. On the other hand, she had been exporting small quantities of finished steel since 1954[30], reflecting the capability of the Chinese steel industry to meet the country's need for ordinary steels.

### Metallurgical Coke[31]

Although the official coke production figure is obtainable only for 1952, it is possible to derive the output quantities from given percentage figures or occasional indices for the other years except 1955, 1956 and 1960. Coke output for these years can be estimated on the basis primarily of pig iron production and the national average coke rate. The latter is obtainable for 1955 and 1956, but not for 1960. To obtain 1960 coke output, it is therefore necessary to estimate first the average coke rate for that year.

The coke rates of large and medium blast furnaces in the country's more important iron-smelting centers for March 1960 are shown in Table 6.7, with an average coke rate of 0.8699 ton. For lack of other data, this is assumed to be the annual average. While the 1960 average coke rate of small furnaces is not known, the 1959 average was reported to be 1.293 ton[32]. It was also reported that output by small furnaces constituted 51.1 per cent of the overall pig iron production in 1959[33]. Assuming no change during 1960 either in the average coke rate of small furnaces or in the proportion of their contribution to the total national output, the 1960 weighted average coke rate for blast furnaces of all sizes is estimated at 1.0861 ton.

---

28 *KTMCFT*, p. 26.
29 For China's imports of finished steel, see Appendix 6—A at the end of this chapter.
30 China's exports of finished steel during 1954—1959 are given below. It should be noted that with the exception of 1958 and 1959, exports were less than one per cent of domestic output.

| Year | Tons |
|------|------|
| 1954 | 1,000 |
| 1955 | 21,000 |
| 1956 | 34,000 |
| 1957 | 44,000 |
| 1958 | 92,000 |
| 1959 | 139,000 |

31 Referring to coke used in the metallurgical industry.
32 *Yeh-chin pao*, No. 1, 1960, p. 19.
33 *Ibid.*, No. 4, 1960, p. 7.

The national average coke rates for 1955 and 1956 are known to be 1.41 and 1.32 ton respectively[34]. Applying these and the above-estimated coke rates to the pig iron output quantities for their corresponding years (given in Table 6.3) yields the following annual coke input in pig iron production:

| Year | Coke Input (in tons) |
|------|----------------------|
| 1955 | 5,350,950 |
| 1956 | 6,305,640 |
| 1960 | 29,867,750 |

Pig iron, however, is not the only product which uses metallurgical coke as an input. It is also used in the production of open-hearth and converter steels. The aggregate consumption of coke in such production can be derived from the average amount of coke used per ton of steel output and steel output quantities. The pertinent data are presented in Table 6.8.

Table 6.7. Coke Rate of Large and Medium Blast Furnaces in Major Iron-Smelting Centers, March 1960

| Name of Enterprise | Average Coke Input Per Ton of Pig Iron Output (in tons) |
|--------------------|--------------------------------------------------------|
| Penki: No. 1 Plant | 0.610 |
| No. 2 Plant | 0.711 |
| Maanshan: No. 1 Plant | 0.794 |
| Anshan | 0.656 |
| The Shanghai No. 1 Steel Plant | 0.867 |
| Taiyuan: No. 1 Iron Smelting Plant | 0.929 |
| Shihchingshan | 0.731 |
| Paotow: No. 1 Plant | 0.911 |
| Wuhan | 0.733 |
| Lungyen: No. 1 Plant | 1.192 |
| No. 2 Plant | 1.435 |

Source: Yeh-chin pao (Metallurgy), Peking, No. 14, 1960, p. 14.

Adding the aggregate coke input in steel production shown in Column 7 of Table 6.8 to the amount of coke consumed in pig iron production gives the known overall coke consumption for each of the three years. These consumption estimates are presented in Table 6.9 as coke output quantities, on the assumption that consumption in those years was identical with output. This assumption is not unrealistic in view of the chronic shortage of coke in China. To alleviate the shortage, coke production was stepped up in 1958 and 1959 especially through

34 Chi-hua yü t'ung-chi (Planning and statistics), monthly, Peking, No. 9, June 23, 1959.

small units, which according to Wang Ho-shou (Minister of Metallurgical Industry) were responsible in 1959 for 75 per cent of the national total output[35].

## Relative Output Behavior

From the changes in the output of major products given in Table 6.10, a general pattern of their output behavior emerges. Nearly all the major products (considering ingot steel as one product) were increasing more or less steadily between

Table 6.8. Estimated Coke Input in the Production of Open-hearth and Converter Steels, 1955, 1956 and 1960

| Year | Average Coke Input Per Ton of Steel Output (in kilograms) | | Ingot Steel Production (in tons) | | Aggregate Coke Input | | |
|---|---|---|---|---|---|---|---|
| | Open-hearth | Con-verter | Open-hearth | Con-verter | Open-hearth Converter (in kilograms) | | Both (in tons) |
| | (1) | (2) | (3) | (4) | (5)=(1)x(3) | (6)=(2)x(4) | (7)=(5) +(6) |
| 1955 | 1.71 | 139 | 1,670,000 | 766,070 | 2,855,700 | 106,483,730 | 109,339 |
| 1956 | 1.81 | 140 | 2,940,000 | 917,390 | 5,321,400 | 128,434,600 | 133,756 |
| 1960 | 1.81 | 140 | 6,354,350 | 9,568,000 | 11,501,374 | 1,339,520,000 | 1,351,021 |

Sources: Table 6.4; Yeh-chin pao (Metallurgy), Peking, No. 1, 1958, p. 34.

Table 6.9. Metallurgical Coke Output Estimates, 1949—1960 (in thousand tons)

| Year | Amount[a] | Index[a][b] (1952 = 100) |
|---|---|---|
| 1949 | 539.6 | 19 |
| 1950 | 1,216.0 | 43 |
| 1951 | 1,945.6 | 68 |
| 1952 | 2,860.0 | 100 |
| 1953 | 3,603.6 | 126 |
| 1954 | 4,540.5 | 159 |
| 1955 | 5,460.3 | 191 |
| 1956 | 6,439.4 | 225 |
| 1957 | 8,008.0 | 280 |
| 1958 | 13,342.0 | 467 |
| 1959 | 24,015.6 | 840 |
| 1960 | 31,218.8 | 1092 |

a. Rounded.
b. Computed before the rounding of estimates.

Sources: Kang-t'ieh (Iron and steel), Peking, No. 18, 1959, p. 794; Ta-kung pao, Hong Kong, December 14, 1951; Annual Communiqués of State Bureau of Statistics for 1953 and 1954; Yeh-chin pao (Metallurgy), Peking, No. 4, 1960, p. 26.

35 Hung-ch'i (Red-flag), semi-monthly, Peking, No. 9, 1962, p. 2.

Table 6.10. Rate of Increase in Output of Major Products, 1952–1960 (per cent)

| Year | Iron Ore | Coke | Pig Iron | Ingot Steel | | | | Finished Steel |
|------|----------|------|----------|-------|-------------|-----------|------------------|----------------|
|      |          |      |          | Total | Open-hearth | Converter | Electric furnace |                |
| 1953 | 35.8 | 26.0 | 15.8 | 31.5 | 21.2 | 54.1 | 57.2 | 33.7 |
| 1954 | 24.2 | 26.0 | 38.8 | 25.4 | 29.8 | 1.0 | 47.6 | 12.0 |
| 1955 | 32.8 | 20.3 | 24.4 | 28.3 | 12.8 | 84.7 | 26.4 | 27.4 |
| 1956 | 61.3 | 17.9 | 24.6 | 56.5 | 76.0 | 19.8 | 45.8 | 56.5 |
| 1957 | 25.1 | 24.8 | 23.0 | 19.8 | 21.4 | -13.1 | 61.6 | 23.3 |
| 1958 | 60.4 | 66.6 | 60.5 | 49.5 | 52.9 | 122.8 | -22.3 | 42.1 |
| 1959 | 27.7 | 80.0 | 115.1 | 66.9 | 20.7 | 166.1 | 166.2 | 31.0 |
| 1960 | 40.0 | 30.0 | 34.1 | 38.2 | -3.6 | 102.5 | 24.3 | 27.9 |
| Average (1952–60) | 37.7 | 34.8 | 39.4 | 38.7 | 27.0 | 56.5 | 43.3 | 31.2 |

Sources: Tables 6.1, 6.3, 6.4, 6.6 and 6.9.

1952 and 1956. In the latter year, under the impetus of the nation-wide industrial upsurge the pace was quickened notably for iron ore, ingots and rolled steel. The decline in growth rate in 1957 was common to all products except coke. During the Leap Forward years, the highest rate of increase for most products was registered in 1959 rather than 1958 when the mass steel campaign was at its zenith. This was attributable, as indicated previously, to the fact that while large amounts of sub-standard products were excluded from the 1958 production statistics, improvements in the output quality of modernized small-scale capital equipment enhanced output quantities in 1959.

Within this general pattern, however, there were variations in the output behavior of individual products. Their annual average growth rates, for instance, ranged from 27 per cent in the case of open-hearth steel to 56.5 per cent for converter steel. That the latter should grow twice as fast as the former can be attributed mainly to government policy of promoting a particular pattern of steel-refining in order to maximize both the short-run output and the marginal efficiency of investment[36].

Variations in the output behavior of individual products reveal further that smelting and refining were developing more rapidly than either mining or rolling. As it was technically difficult for the expansion in productive capacities of coke and iron ore to keep pace with the rapid increases of smelting and refining capacities, shortages particularly in the supply of coke constituted a bottleneck in the steel industry. The inability of rolling, casting and forging capacities to increase as rapidly, on the other hand, resulted in a continuous decline in the output ratio of finished products to ingot steel. It fell from 90.3 per cent in 1957 to 85.9 per cent in 1958, 67.4 per cent in 1959 and 62.3 per cent in 1960[37]. This clearly pointed to the need for an intensive development of the finishing sector, which constituted another bottleneck in the Chinese steel industry.

36 This will be further discussed in Chapter 12.
37 Based on data given in Tables 6.4 and 6.6.

# APPENDIX 6 — A

*Table 6—A.1. Manganese Ore Production, 1949—1966 (in tons)*

| Year | Amount |
|------|--------|
| 1949 | 673 |
| 1950 | 87,812 |
| 1951 | 112,231 |
| 1952 | 190,591 |
| 1953 | 195,043 |
| 1954 | 172,201 |
| 1955 | 276,544 |
| 1956 | 524,070 |
| 1957 | 583,592[a] |
| 1958 | 873,038[a] |
| 1959 | 1,457,391[a] |
| 1960 | 2,014,438[a] |
| 1961 | 800,000[b] |
| 1962 | 800,000[b] |
| 1963 | 1,000,000[b] |
| 1964 | 1,000,000[b] |
| 1965 | 1,000,000[b] |
| 1966 | 1,000,000[b] |

a. Estimated on the basis of the relationship between manganese output and ingot steel output. The regression equation of manganese output on steel output data for the years 1949—1956 is given by

$$Yc = 10.922,419X - 0.076,162$$

where Yc stands for the computed manganese output taken to the nearest ten thousand tons and X ingot steel output to the nearest million tons.

b. Estimated by K. P. Wang of US Bureau of Mines; the method of estimation is not known.

Sources: Industrial Statistics Section, State Bureau of Statistics, *Wo-kuo kang-t'ieh, tien-li, mei-t'an, chi-hsieh, fang-chih, tsao-chih kung-yeh ti chin-hsi* (The past and present of China's iron and steel, electric power, coal, machine-making, textile and paper industries), Peking: Statistics Publishing House, 1958, pp. 11 and 19; K.P. Wang, "The Mineral Resource Base of Communist China," *An Economic Profile of Mainland China*, New York, 1968, p. 174; US Bureau of Mines, *Minerals Yearbook 1966*, Washington, 1967, Vol. I — II, p. 990.

## APPENDIX 6 — B

## IMPORTS OF FINISHED AND SEMI-FINISHED STEEL

Figures for China's imports of finished and semi-finished steel during 1950 —1962 are presented in Table 6 — B.1. Annual imports were fairly stable between 1950 and 1957, and increased sharply in 1958. The sharp increase was attributable more to the relaxation of UN embargo on export of strategic goods to China than to the heightened demand under the impetus of the Leap Forward movement. As can be seen from the table, steel imports tripled in 1958 and the increase amounted to over one million tons. Of this increase, more than 95 per cent came from non-communist countries, notably West Germany, France, Belgium, Luxemburg, Italy, Japan and the United Kingdom. West Germany alone was responsible for half of the increase, with the six remaining countries responsible for the other half. In terms of products, plates, sheets, tubes and tinplates accounted for the bulk of the increase.

As noted previously, China's output of finished steel increased in 1958 by two million tons. The latter coupled with the phenomenal rise in imports resulted in an over-supply of finished steel. Consequently the need for imports was lessened in the ensuing years. As shown in Table 6—B.1, imports in 1959 and in 1960 were lowered to the 1955—1956 level, which came to roughly half of the 1958 quantity. However, further drops in steel imports in 1961 and 1962 were attributable chiefly to the downturn of general economic activity resulting from the aftermath of the Great Leap, the natural calamities and the withdrawal of Soviet aid.

Table 6—B.1 also shows changes in the sources of China's steel imports. From 1950—1956, communist countries contributed 67—99 per cent of the total. Their predominance, however, began to decrease in 1957 when UN embargo was relaxed. With further substantial relaxation in 1958, the non-communist countries became the major source of imports. These countries supplied one half to three quarters of China's steel imports during 1958—1962. In addition to the non-communist countries mentioned above, Australia became an important supplier in this period. In 1959, for instance, Australia was responsible for one seventh of China's steel imports.

A breakdown of China's steel imports from 1950—1962 is given in Table 6—B.2. The prominence of plates was maintained throughout this period. The proportion of plates in the overall imports of finished and semi-finished steel reached as much as 37 per cent in 1956, but in general ranged between one fifth and one third. Prior to 1956, the prominence of steel sections exceeded that of plates. The former's importance among steel imports, however, declined from 1956 onwards. The imports of railway-track material showed a similar pattern of behavior. The reverse is true for sheets, the imports of which increased more than five-fold in 1957. From then on, the relative importance of this category rivaled that of plates. Similarly, the imports of tubes and fittings became relatively important after 1957.

Imports of finished steel were indispensable to China's industrialization. Owing to technological constraint, the Chinese steel industry still lacked the capacity to produce certain special steels. Available data show that in 1956 it was only able to turn out 58, 53 and 69 per cent of the variety of steel required in the production of aircraft, tanks and automobiles respectively[1]. As long as the deficiency of variety remains, China is likely to continue relying on imports as a source of finished steel supply.

*Table 6—B.1. Imports of Finished and Semi-finished Steel, 1950—1962*

| Year | Total ('000 tons) | Non-Communist Sources (per cent) | Communist Sources (per cent) |
|---|---|---|---|
| 1950 | 632.6 | 32.9 | 67.1 |
| 1951 | 588.6 | 5.7 | 94.3 |
| 1952 | 506.0 | 1.9 | 98.1 |
| 1953 | 739.0 | 7.5 | 92.5 |
| 1954 | 554.4 | 3.5 | 96.5 |
| 1955 | 714.7 | 1.2 | 98.8 |
| 1956 | 658.9 | 10.8 | 89.2 |
| 1957 | 503.5 | 28.0 | 72.0 |
| 1958 | 1579.7 | 74.0 | 26.0 |
| 1959 | 757.3 | 62.8 | 37.2 |
| 1960 | 791.3 | 63.2 | 36.8 |
| 1961 | 184.8 | 61.6 | 38.4 |
| 1962 | 166.5 | 53.4 | 46.6 |

Source: UN Economic Commission for Europe, *Statistics of World Trade in Steel,* Geneva, 1961, 1962 and 1963, and New York, 1964.

1 The deficiency in variety can also be seen by comparison with the Soviet Union. In 1955, for example, the variety of finished steels China was capable of producing amounted to less than 30 per cent of that produced in the Soviet Union. *KTMCFT*, p. 33.

Table 6—B.2. Imports of Finished and Semi-finished Steel Products, 1950—1962 (in thousand tons)

| Year | Ingots & Semis | Railway-Track Material | Heavy & Light Sections | Wirerods | Strip | Plates | Sheets | Tubes & Fittings | Wire | Tinplate | Wheels, Tyres & Axles | Total |
|---|---|---|---|---|---|---|---|---|---|---|---|---|
| 1950 | 55.0 | 78.8 | 199.5 | 19.6 | 1.8 | 205.7 | 6.3 | 40.8 | 3.2 | 15.7 | 6.2 | 632.6 |
| 1951 | 52.7 | 126.1 | 198.6 | 13.4 | 1.4 | 149.5 | 14.6 | 27.5 | 0.4 | 1.4 | 3.0 | 588.6 |
| 1952 | 53.4 | 123.3 | 169.7 | 12.7 | 2.7 | 110.1 | 3.3 | 27.3 | 1.6 | 0.3 | 1.6 | 506.0 |
| 1953 | 133.4 | 146.4 | 192.8 | 10.6 | 4.9 | 193.1 | 14.1 | 36.1 | 6.7 | 0.9 | — | 739.0 |
| 1954 | 123.0 | 90.6 | 144.8 | 12.0 | 5.5 | 115.6 | 16.2 | 42.0 | 2.5 | 0.8 | 1.4 | 554.4 |
| 1955 | 71.2 | 193.7 | 164.4 | 16.5 | 3.0 | 137.3 | 32.6 | 65.3 | 4.1 | 7.3 | 19.3 | 714.7 |
| 1956 | 101.9 | 74.5 | 102.0 | 18.2 | 4.5 | 242.4 | 14.8 | 66.9 | 3.6 | 17.5 | 12.6 | 658.9 |
| 1957 | 88.8 | 32.8 | 39.7 | 15.4 | 3.3 | 137.8 | 91.9 | 52.1 | 2.8 | 33.2 | 5.7 | 503.5 |
| 1958 | 113.8 | 21.0 | 64.3 | 25.8 | 7.7 | 531.7 | 455.4 | 277.5 | 2.2 | 76.2 | 4.1 | 1579.7 |
| 1959 | 22.8 | 46.3 | 33.7 | 2.9 | 7.4 | 219.0 | 137.4 | 193.7 | 1.1 | 39.4 | 53.6 | 757.3 |
| 1960 | 28.3 | 60.9 | 65.1 | 11.2 | 9.9 | 148.5 | 206.9 | 177.3 | 4.6 | 29.4 | 52.2 | 791.3 |
| 1961 | — | 0.1 | 10.4 | 0.8 | 7.4 | 16.8 | 56.4 | 52.8 | 1.1 | 10.5 | 28.5 | 184.8 |
| 1962 | 0.1 | — | 11.8 | — | 4.6 | 32.3 | 43.4 | 37.2 | 0.7 | 13.6 | 22.8 | 166.5 |

Note — The data refer to the following countries: Australia, Austria, Belgium-Luxemburg, Canada, Federal Republic of Germany, France, Hungary, Italy, Japan, Netherlands, Norway, Poland, South Africa, Sweden, USSR, UK, USA, and Yugoslavia.

Source: UN Economic Commission for Europe, Statistics of World Trade in Steel, Geneva, 1961, 1962 and 1963, and New York, 1964.

*Chapter 7*

# CAPITAL INVESTMENT AND GROSS OUTPUT

The present chapter examines first the amount and proportion of the economy's investment resources that were allocated to the steel industry. This reflects the importance economic planners in China attached to the industry. It then looks into the gross output of the steel industry in order to see its importance in aggregate industrial output and national product.

## Capital Investment

Capital investment as used in communist China includes fixed investment and investment in geological surveys, engineering design, technical training, research and development. Data on annual capital investment in the steel industry for 1950–1952 have been disclosed by the Industrial Statistics Section of the State Bureau of Statistics[1]. No annual investment figures are obtainable for the steel

*Table 7.1. Estimated Capital Investment in the Steel Industry, 1950–1958*
  *(in thousand yuan at current prices)*

| Year | Amount of Investment | |
| | Within the State Plan | The Entire Industry[a] |
| --- | --- | --- |
| | (1) | (2) |
| 1950 | 86,750 | 94,254 |
| 1951 | 52,800 | 66,000 |
| 1952 | 189,684 | 222,917 |
| 1953 | 395,681 | 486,252 |
| 1954 | 489,853 | 592,379 |
| 1955 | 735,269 | 792,326 |
| 1956 | 787,473 | 833,068 |
| 1957 | 1,040,196 | 1,138,078 |
| 1958 | — | 2,884,726 |

a. Rounded. Including investment outside the state plan.

Sources: Industrial Statistics Section, State Bureau of Statistics, *Wo-kuo kang-t'ieh, tien-li, mei-t'an, chi-hsieh, fang-chih, tsao-chih kung-yeh ti chin-hsi* (The past and present of China's iron and steel, electric power, coal, machine-making textile and paper industries), Peking: Statistics Publishing House, 1958, pp. 9 and 14; *Ta-kung pao*, Hong Kong, August 20, 1957; *Jen-min jih-pao*, September 23 and 26, 1959.

1 *KTMCFT*, p. 9.

industry in subsequent years. However, annual investment increases from 1953 –1956 in the metallurgical industry are known[2]. Since iron and steel predominate in the metallurgical industry, the latter's investment increases can be justifiably used as a basis for estimating investment in the steel industry for these years. Estimates for 1953–1956 are shown in Column 1 of Table 7.1, together with the given data for earlier years.

These estimates enable us to compare the importance of the steel industry with other leading heavy industries, such as machine-building and electric power in terms of their claims on the economy's investment resources. The percentage shares of the three industries in the aggregate capital investment are shown below[3]:

| Year | Steel | Machine-building | Electric power |
| --- | --- | --- | --- |
| 1953 | 6.1 | 4.9 | 4.0 |
| 1954 | 6.5 | 6.1 | 5.2 |
| 1955 | 8.5 | 6.6 | 6.2 |
| 1956 | 5.6 | 5.2 | 5.2 |

The consistently higher claim of the steel industry on resources can be attributed to the strategic importance of steel in the communist model of industrialization and the policy of self-sufficiency in basic industrial materials.

For the period 1950–1958, it has been reported that investment in the steel industry amounted to 15.8 per cent of the overall industrial investment of 45 billion yuan[4]. Investment in steel thus came to roughly 7.11 billion yuan. This total, however, appears to differ in coverage from the available or estimated annual investment figures for the years 1950–1956. Whereas the latter figures bear reference only to investment included in the state plan, the investment total for 1950–1958 apparently includes also investment outside the state plan. This difference in coverage appears primarily from the close correspondence between the above-mentioned amount of overall industrial investment and the amount of industrial investment disclosed by the State Bureau of Statistics[5]; and the known coverage of the latter, which extends to investment both within and outside the state plan.

Consequently, in order to make use of the 1950–1958 aggregate investment in steel to derive the amount for 1957–1958, it is necessary first to widen the coverage of the annual figures given or estimated for 1950–1956. For this purpose, there are fortunately available two series of capital investment data: one on the overall capital investment of the economy and the other on the capital investment

---

2 The annual percentage increases are: 1953 — 108.6; 1954 — 23.8; 1955 — 50.1; and 1956 — 7.1. *Ta-kung pao*, Hong Kong, August 20, 1957.
3 Official data on the capital investment of the Chinese economy are given in Table 7.2. Capital investments in the machine-building and electric power industries respectively are (in million *yuan* at current prices) 320 and 262 for 1953, 460 and 392 for 1954, 570 and 535 for 1955, 730 and 724 for 1956. *KTMCFT*, pp. 54 and 116.
4 Presumably at current prices. *Jen-min jih-pao*, September 23 and 26, 1959.
5 *WTSN*, p. 48; *KTMCFT*, p. 9.

within the state plan. The two series are presented in Table 7.2 together with their ratios. On the assumption that the proportion of capital investment outside the state plan applies equally to the economy as a whole and to the steel industry, these ratios enable us to estimate the total investment of the industry. Such estimates are shown in Table 7.1 (Column 2) along with investment within the state plan.

By widening the coverage of the annual investment figures for 1950–1956, it becomes possible to derive the investment amount for 1957–1958 from the given aggregate investment for 1950–1958. Since the latter amounts to 7.11 billion yuan, capital investment during 1957–1958 should be 4.02 billion yuan. Investment in 1957 can be estimated on the basis of the planned investment for that year and the extent of plan fulfillment during 1953–1956. Here the assumption is that the extent of plan fulfillment in the final year was the same as that during the first four years of the First Five-Year Plan. With the data given in Table 7.3, the ratio of aggregate realized investment to the aggregate planned figure for 1953–1956 is computed to be 1.18. Multiplying the 1957 planned investment by this ratio yields 1.04 billion yuan. This estimated realized investment is presented in Column 1 of Table 7.1.

An 18 per cent overfulfillment of the investment plan by the steel industry in 1957 does not appear to be excessive in view of the moderate increase of 6 per

Table 7.2. *Capital Investment for the Entire Economy, 1950—1957*
  *(in million yuan at current prices)*

| Year | Amount of Investment | | Ratio |
| | Throughout the Economy | Within the State Plan | |
|---|---|---|---|
| | (1) | (2) | (3) = (1) / (2) |
| 1950 | 1,130 | 1,040 | 1.09 |
| 1951 | 2,350 | 1,880 | 1.25 |
| 1952 | 4,360 | 3,710 | 1.18 |
| 1953 | 8,000 | 6,510 | 1.23 |
| 1954 | 9,070 | 7,500 | 1.21 |
| 1955 | 9,300 | 8,630 | 1.08 |
| 1956 | 14,800 | 13,990 | 1.06 |
| 1957 | 13,830 | 12,640 | 1.09 |

Source: *Wei-ta ti shih-nien* (Ten great years), Peking, 1959, pp. 46—47.

cent in planned investment for that year (see Column 1 of Table 7.3). In addition, a certain amount of reshuffling in the allocation of investment resources was effected during 1957. Investment in the machine-building industry was reduced in view of the serious material input shortages which resulted in much idle capacity in the industry in 1957. Some of the investment resources thus released were logically allocated to the steel industry in order to alleviate in due time the shortages of material input of the machine-building industry. Seen in this light, it is not surprising that the extent of overfulfillment of planned investment in the steel industry during 1957 was larger than for the economy as a whole[6].

Since the 1957 estimate bears reference only to investment within the state plan, its coverage needs to be widened to include investment outside the state plan so that the appropriate amount is to be deducted from the biennial total obtained above. Thus the estimated 1957 investment is multiplied by the factor 1.09 (see Column 3 of Table 7.2), yielding 1,138,078 thousand yuan. Deducting this latter figure from the biennial total gives 2,884,726 thousand yuan as the estimated 1958 investment for the *entire* steel industry. This figure shows a 153.5 per cent increase over 1957. The substantially higher rate of increase is not surprising in view of the tremendous importance attached to steel in 1958. The 1957 and 1958 investment estimates are presented in Column 2 of Table 7.1 along with investment figures for earlier years.

### Investment at 1952 Prices

The above investment estimates are made in terms of current prices. It is necessary to convert them to a constant price basis in order to show the investment behavior over time. For consistency with communist Chinese statistics, 1952 is taken as the base year. For this conversion, the wholesale price indices for construction materials in Shanghai are used for 1950–1951, and Liu-Yeh estimates

Table 7.3. *Planned and Realized Capital Investment in the Steel Industry, 1953—1957 (in thousand yuan at current prices)*

| Year | Planned Investment | Realized Investment | Percentage Ratio of Realized to Planned Investment |
|------|------|------|------|
| | Within the State Plan | | |
| | (1) | (2) | (3) |
| 1953 | 300,300 | 395,681 | 132 |
| 1954 | 282,200 | 489,853 | 174 |
| 1955 | 630,140 | 735,269 | 117 |
| 1956 | 832,782 | 787,473 | 95 |
| 1957 | 883,470 | 1,040,196 | 118[a] |

a. Percentage ratio of the aggregate realized investment to the aggregate planned figures for the years 1953 — 1956.

Sources: Industrial Statistics Bureau, State Bureau of Statistics, *Wo-kuo kang-t'ieh, tien-li, mei-t'an, chi-hsieh, fang-chih, tsao-chih kung-yeh ti chin-hsi* (The past and present of China's iron and steel, electric power, coal, machine-making, textile and paper industries), Peking: Statistics Publishing House, 1958, p. 14; and Table 7.1.

6 The 1957 planned investment in capital construction for the economy at large was overfulfilled by 11 per cent. *Ta-kung pao*, Peking, July 2, 1957; *Jen-min jih-pao*, February 4, 1958.

on changes in investment costs, for 1952–1957[7]. For 1958, investment costs are assumed to follow the wholesale price behavior and remain unchanged. The index numbers used and the converted investment figures for the entire steel industry are presented in Table 7.4.

The drastic reduction in the volume of investment in 1951 is worth noting. It can be attributed to the reduced rehabilitation requirements of the steel industry.

Table 7.4. *Estimated Capital Investment in the Steel Industry[a], 1950–1958*
       *(in thousand yuan at 1952 prices)*

| Year | Index of Investment Costs (1952 = 100) | Amount of Investment[b] | Percentage Increase over Preceding Year |
|------|------|------|------|
|  | (1) | (2) | (3) |
| 1950 | 62.3[c] | 151,291 | — |
| 1951 | 82.7[c] | 79,807 | -47.2 |
| 1952 | 100.0 | 222,917 | 179.3 |
| 1953 | 106.5 | 456,575 | 104.8 |
| 1954 | 102.0 | 580,764 | 27.2 |
| 1955 | 96.7 | 819,365 | 41.1 |
| 1956 | 90.4 | 921,535 | 12.5 |
| 1957 | 90.4 | 1,258,936 | 36.6 |
| 1958 | 90.4 | 3,191,069 | 153.5 |

a. Including investment outside the state plan.
b. Rounded.
c. Costs of construction materials in Shanghai.

Sources: Column 1 from *Shang-hai chieh-fang ch'ien-hou wu-chia tzu-liao hui-pien* (A collection of price data in Shanghai before and after the liberation), Shanghai, 1958, p. 455; Ta-chung Liu and Kung-chia Yeh, *The Economy of the Chinese Mainland: National Income and Economic Development, 1933–1959*, Princeton University Press, Princeton, New Jersey, 1965, p. 235. Column 2 computed from data given in Column 1 of this table and Column 2 of Table 7.1.

By mid-1950, rehabilitation work at Anshan on installations damaged during the civil conflict was largely completed. The task of restoring the equipment and installations completely removed by Soviet troops could not be undertaken without the preliminary task of design and preparation, which even under normal circumstances would be time-consuming. The outbreak of the Korean War merely extended this preparatory period and minimized the investment needs.

In addition, the outbreak of military hostilities created a possibility that An-shan and other iron and steel centers might be exposed to land and air attacks. It

7 *Shang-hai chieh-fang ch'ien-hou wu-chia tzu-liao hui-pien* (A collection of price data in Shanghai before and after the liberation), Shanghai, 1958, p. 455; Ta-chung Liu and Kung-chia Yeh, *The Economy of the Chinese Mainland: National Income and Economic Development, 1953–1959*, Princeton University Press, Princeton, New Jersey, 1965. p. 235.

was natural for the rehabilitation work in these localities to be reduced or suspended. Thus, while the amount of government investment at 1952 prices in industry as a whole went up 26 per cent in 1951, the amount of investment in the steel industry decreased by 47 per cent (see column 3 of Table 7.4). In fact, the share of the steel industry in the 1951 overall industrial investment was smaller than any other year during 1950—1958.

With the cessation of hostilities in Korea in the latter part of 1951, the 1952 government investment in the steel industry was nearly tripled whereas overall government industrial investment at 1952 prices scarcely doubled. This reallocation of investment resources was in keeping with the level of rehabilitation activity planned for the steel industry. The planned 1952 volume of capital construction for Anshan, for instance, was five times above the amount accomplished in the preceding year[8].

With the launching of the First Five-Year Plan in 1953, the demand for new construction was added to that for reconstruction. As envisaged in the Plan, new construction projects amounted to 29.6 per cent of the investment in the steel industry. The latter, in turn, constituted 12.8 per cent of the planned overall industrial investment for the quinquennium. Although this represented a smaller proportion in comparison with the Soviet Union[9], it was raised to 15.3 per cent in the implementation of the Plan. Annual variation of actual from planned proportions of steel investment in overall industrial investment during the first plan period are shown in Table 7.5. In all years except 1956[10], the actual proportion was higher than planned. This reflected the greater over-fulfillment of planned investment in the steel industry vis-à-vis the industrial sector as a whole, since the planned overall industrial investment was also over-fulfilled[11]. Obviously the higher proportion of realized investment meant a certain amount of reallocation of investment resources in favor of steel.

## Gross Output

Economic planners in China poured a good deal of investment resources into the steel industry primarily to speed up its growth. The latter is shown in Table 7.6, which presents the gross output of the steel industry from 1950—1960[12]. Before examining this growth, however, it may be of interest to look briefly into Chinese

8 CTCHK, p. 166.
9 Under the First Five-Year Plan of the Soviet Union, the investment in steel accounted for 15 per cent of the overall industrial investment. KTMCFT, p. 14.
10 Even in 1956, the planned investment in the steel industry was slightly over-fulfilled.
11 Except 1955.
12 The figures for 1950—1956 represent official statistics and those for 1957—1960 are estimated. For details concerning the estimates, see R. Hsia, "Capital Investment and Output of the Steel Industry," Contemporary China, Vol. VI, Hong Kong, 1968, pp. 29—31.

official statistics on the gross output of the steel industry, since there has been some doubt as to how such statistics are derived[13].

Barring evidence to the contrary, it would be reasonable to assume that the "factory method" generally used in computing gross industrial output was also applied in the case of the steel industry. According to this method, the gross value of an industry is the sum of the value of the final products of all the enterprises

Table 7.5. Investment in Steel Industry as a Proportion of Overall Industrial Investment: Planned and Realized, 1953—1957 (per cent)

| Year | Planned | Realized |
|------|---------|----------|
| 1953 | 10.6 | 17.1 |
| 1954 | 7.9 | 15.5 |
| 1955 | 13.5 | 18.4 |
| 1956 | 14.7 | 12.2 |
| 1957 | 14.2 | 15.7 |
| 1953—57 | 12.8 | 15.3 |

Sources: Industrial Statistics Section, State Bureau of Statistics, *Wo-kuo kang-t'ieh, tien-li, mei-t'an, chi-hsieh, fang-chih, tsao chih kung-yeh ti chin-hsi* (The past and present of China's iron and steel, electric power, coal, machine-making, textile and paper industries), Peking: Statistics Publishing House, 1958, p. 14; *Wei-ta ti shih-nien* (Ten great years), Peking, 1959, p. 48; and Table 7.1.

Table 7.6. Gross Output of the Steel Industry, 1950—1960 (in thousand yuan at 1952 prices)

| Year | Gross Output |
|------|--------------|
| 1950 | 609,521 |
| 1951 | 911,784 |
| 1952 | 1,369,594 |
| 1953 | 1,871,333 |
| 1954 | 2,327,556 |
| 1955 | 2,896,611 |
| 1956 | 4,124,915 |
| 1957 | 5,190,947 |
| 1958 | 6,647,284 |
| 1959 | 10,338,713 |
| 1960 | 12,340,000 |

Sources: Industrial Statistics Section, State Bureau of Statistics, *Wo-kuo kang-t'ieh, tien-li, mei-t'an, chi-hsieh, fang-chih, tsao-chih kung-yeh ti chin-hsi* (The past and present of China's iron and steel, electric power, coal, machine-making, textile and paper industries), Peking: Statistics Publishing House, 1958, pp. 10, 30—31; R. Hsia, "Capital Investment and Output of the Steel Industry," *Contemporary China*, Vol. VI. Hong Kong, 1968, p. 31.

13 F. M. Cone, *Chinese Industrial Growth: Brief Studies of Selected Investment Areas*, Santa Monica, California, 1969, p. 19; Y. L. Wu, *The Steel Industry in Communist China*, New York, 1965, Chapter 4.

within the industry. The final products include, however, intermediate goods which are involved in inter-enterprise transactions[14]. To this extent double-counting is present in official gross output statistics. For the steel industry, in addition, double-counting is permitted for internal transfers of certain goods produced and consumed within the enterprise, such as iron ore, coke, and ingot moulds[15].

With the output quantities of iron ore, coke as well as finished steel given in Chapter 6 and their "average" prices estimated by Liu-Yeh and Wu[16], it is possible to attempt some rough estimates of the gross output of the steel industry in accordance with the factory method. In presenting these estimates in Table 7.7, it must be emphasized that the price data are unweighted thus concealing the heterogeneous nature of these products, especially finished steel. The prices are also unsatisfactory in that they do not reflect temporal changes. Nevertheless, as can be seen from the table, the estimates come reasonably close to the official statistics. For 1950, they are practically identical. For 1951, 1954 and 1955, the discrepancy is less than 10 per cent. For the remaining years, it varies between 14 and 17 per cent. For the years 1950–1956 as a whole, it amounts to 11 per cent. In view of the unsatisfactory price data, such discrepancies are well within the margin of tolerance. It, therefore, appears that official statistics on the gross output of the steel industry may well have been computed according to the factory method.

Table 7.7. Comparison of Estimated and Official Gross Output of Steel, 1950–1956 (in million 1952 yuan)

| Sector | 1950 | 1951 | 1952 | 1953 | 1954 | 1955 | 1956 |
|---|---|---|---|---|---|---|---|
| Iron ore | 91.7 | 105.4 | 167.2 | 227.0 | 281.9 | 374.3 | 603.9 |
| Finished steel | 464.0 | 808.0 | 1,312.0 | 1,754.0 | 1,965.0 | 2,505.0 | 3,921.0 |
| Coke | 53.5 | 85.6 | 125.8 | 158.6 | 199.8 | 240.3 | 283.3 |
| Total (estimated) | 609.2 | 999.0 | 1,605.0 | 2,139.6 | 2,446.7 | 3,119.6 | 4,808.2 |
| Official total | 609.5 | 911.8 | 1,369.6 | 1,871.3 | 2,327.6 | 2,896.6 | 4,124.9 |

Sources: T.C. Liu and K.C. Yeh, *The Economy of the Chinese Mainland: National Income and Economic Development 1933–1959*, Princeton, 1965, p. 462; Y.L. Wu, *The Steel Industry in Communist China*, New York, 1965, p. 311; and Tables 6.1, 6.3, 6.4, 6.6, 6.9, 6-A.1, and 7.6.

In terms of gross output, the industry was growing at an annual average rate of 31.6 per cent from 1952–1960. This high rate of growth was attributable to the low incremental capital-output ratio (ICOR) as well as the sizable capital investment. On the basis of official output statistics and adjusted investment data

14 Ke Po, "Kung-yeh tsan-liang tung-chi" (Industrial output statistics), *Tung-chi kung-tso tung-hsun* (Bulletin on statistical work), Peking, No. 11, 1956, p. 31.
15 *Ibid.*, p. 32.
16 Estimated prices (in 1952 yuan) per ton were: 1,000 for finished steel, 44 for coke (T. C. Liu and K. C. Yeh, *The Economy of the Chinese Mainland: National Income and Economic Development 1933–1959*, Princeton, 1965, p. 462); and 39 for iron ore (Y.L. Wu, op. cit., p. 311).

(presented in Table 7.6 and 7.4 respectively) and allowing a one-year gestation lag, ICOR values of the steel industry for the years 1951–1956 are computed as follows[17]:

| Year | ICOR |
| --- | --- |
| 1951 | 0.5 |
| 1952 | 0.2 |
| 1953 | 0.4 |
| 1954 | 1.0 |
| 1955 | 1.0 |
| 1956 | 0.7 |

The exceedingly low ICOR values of the earlier years reflect the predominance of rehabilitation in investment expenditures. Conceivably a small amount of investment in rehabilitation can bring about a relatively large expansion in operative capacity. Such low ICOR values can be attributed, to a large extent, to the minimization of investment expenditures for rehabilitating plant equipment and installations by means of (1) assigning high priorities to the rehabilitation of the least damaged equipment, (2) "cannibalizing" the remaining parts of the more severely damaged equipment, (3) staging mass movements to recover the parts and installations which were looted during the nationalist-communist conflict, and (4) low wage payments through the "public supplies" system under which construction workers were provided only with daily necessities.

Even the ICOR values for the later years are low in comparison with other countries. The ICOR values of the Indian steel industry, for example, range from 3.5 to 4.0 for the corresponding period[18]. The low ICOR values of the Chinese steel industry can be attributed, in part, to a more intensive use of labor, relatively lower wage rates and the treatment of involuntary increases in inventories. Other things being equal, the ICOR value would be lower if the rate of equipment utilization is increased by a more intensive use of labor. The pertinence of relatively lower wage rates lies in reducing investment costs. Similarly the Chinese communist practice of excluding involuntary increases in inventories from capital investment tends to underrate the latter and thus lower the ICOR value.

After examining the growth of the steel industry, it would be significant to show its importance relative to national income. On the assumption that "grossness" in its annual gross output remained unchanged during 1950–1960, the industry's relative importance, as can be seen from Table 7.8, increased more than four-fold during this period. With the exclusion of the rehabilitation years, it almost quadrupled between 1952 and 1960. The rise in the importance of the steel industry within the industrial sector, though not as pronounced, was nevertheless considerable. It doubled from 1950–1957 (see Table 7.9). This reflects the prominence of steel in the priority scale of Chinese planners.

---

17  $ICOR_{t+1} = I_t/(O_{t+1} - O_t) = I_t/\triangle O_{t+1}$, where I and O stand for capital investment and gross output respectively.
18  M. I. T., India Project. See B. Higgins, *Economic Development*, London, 1959, p. 646.

*Table 7.8. Importance of Steel Industry in the Economy, 1950—1960*

| Year | Ratio of Gross Output of Steel Industry to Net Domestic Product (per cent) |
|---|---|
| 1950 | 1.4 |
| 1951 | 1.8 |
| 1952 | 2.0 |
| 1953 | 2.6 |
| 1954 | 3.0 |
| 1955 | 3.5 |
| 1956 | 4.3 |
| 1957 | 5.0 |
| 1958 | 4.6 |
| 1959 | 5.8 |
| 1960 | 7.9 |

Sources: T.C. Liu, "The Tempo of Economic Development of the Chinese Mainland, 1949—1965," *An Economic Profile of Mainland China,* New York, 1968, p. 50; Table 7.6; and other sources.

*Table 7.9. Share of Steel Industry in Gross Industrial Output, 1950—1957*

| Year | Per Cent |
|---|---|
| 1950 | 3.1 |
| 1951 | 3.4 |
| 1952 | 4.1 |
| 1953 | 4.3 |
| 1954 | 4.4 |
| 1955 | 5.3 |
| 1956 | 5.8 |
| 1957 | 6.6 |

Sources: *Wei-ta ti shih-nien* (Ten great years), Peking, 1959, p. 76; and Table 7.6.

# POST-1960 GROSS OUTPUT

On the basis of data given in Tables 6.6, 7.6 and 14.1, some conjectural estimates of the annual gross output of the steel industry can be attempted for the years 1961–1965. These estimates are presented in Table 7-A.1. Rough as they are, with these estimates it is possible to have a general idea of the importance of the steel industry to the economy in the 1960's. As can be seen from Table 7-A.2, the industry's importance continued to increase from 1961–1965. By 1965, the ratio of its gross output to net domestic product reached 10.2 per cent, as compared with 2 per cent in 1952.

*Table 7—A.1. Estimated Gross Output of the Steel Industry, 1961—1965*
*(in million yuan at 1952 prices)*

| Year | Gross Output |
|------|--------------|
| 1961 | 8,623 |
| 1962 | 9,696 |
| 1963 | 10,769 |
| 1964 | 11,843 |
| 1965 | 12,916 |

Sources: Based on data given in Tables 6.6, 7.6 and 14.1.

*Table 7—A.2. Importance of Steel Industry in the Economy, 1961—1965*

| Year | Ratio of Gross Output of Steel to Net Domestic Product (per cent) |
|------|------------------------------------------------------------------|
| 1961 | 6.8 |
| 1962 | 9.7 |
| 1963 | 10.0 |
| 1964 | 10.1 |
| 1965 | 10.2 |

Sources: T.C. Liu, "The Tempo of Economic Development of the Chinese Mainland, 1949–1965," *An Economic Profile of Mainland China,* New York, 1968, p. 50; and Table 7-A.1.

# PART IV
# PRODUCTIVITY

## Chapter 8

# PRODUCTIVITY OF CAPITAL EQUIPMENT
## *BLAST FURNACES*

In an economy with a relative abundance of labor and an extreme scarcity of capital equipment, emphasis is naturally placed on the productivity of the latter. In the Chinese steel industry, therefore, attention has been focused on the productivity of furnaces. This chapter examines and analyses changes in the productivity of blast furnaces, with particular reference to (1) the quality and quantity of inputs, (2) the production techniques, (3) the outgoing quality level (defined as the proportion of products up to quality standards), and (4) human factors.

### *Productivity*

The productivity of a blast furnace is measured in China as in Soviet Russia, by the coefficient of the utilization of the useful furnace capacity. Prior to September 1958, the coefficient was derived by dividing the volume of useful furnace capacity in cubic meters by the daily output in tons. On September 21, 1958, the Ministry of Metallurgical Industry issued a directive which changed the coefficient from measuring the volume of useful capacity required per ton of output to measuring the quantity of output per cubic meter of useful capacity[1]. In other words, the revised practice in deriving the blast furnace coefficient was to divide the daily output in tons by the volume of useful furnace capacity in cubic meters. Thus, a coefficient of 1.5, for example, means 1.5 tons of pig iron per cubic meter of useful furnace volume per day. In this study, all blast furnace coefficients are expressed according to this usage for consistency.

National average data on blast furnace coefficients for the years 1949—1959 as given in Chinese official sources are presented in Table 8.1. In examining changes in furnace productivity, it should be noted that the coverage of the data presented has not been made explicit by official sources. However, these national average figures come extremely close to those for the nation's large and medium-sized furnaces. The 1958 national average coefficient for such furnaces has been reported by Wang Ho-shou, Minister of Metallurgical Industry, to be 1.487[2]. This may be

---

1 *Jen-min jih-pao*, September 25, 1958. The volume of useful capacity of a blast furnace is measured from the centerline of the iron notch to the bottom of the large bell in the open position.
2 *Kung-jen jih-pao*, Peking, April 25, 1959.

compared with the 1.490 figure in Column 1 of Table 8.1, which is supposedly the national average coefficient for all blast furnaces in operation throughout the country. That the national average coefficient should be slightly higher is somewhat puzzling because it implies that furnaces in operation not included in the large and medium-sized groups had a higher productivity. Such an inference, however, is contrary to the known performance of small furnaces. Their coefficients averaged 0.560 for the first quarter of 1958 and 0.900 for November of the same year[3].

*Table 8.1. Average Blast Furnace Coefficient in China, 1949—1959 (ton/m³/24 hrs.)*

| Year | Coefficient | Index (1952 = 100) |
|------|-------------|--------------------|
| 1949 | 0.617 | 60.3 |
| 1950 | 0.758 | 74.0 |
| 1951 | 0.858 | 83.8 |
| 1952 | 1.024 | 100.0 |
| 1953 | 1.035 | 101.1 |
| 1954 | 1.080 | 105.5 |
| 1955 | 1.150 | 112.3 |
| 1956 | 1.305 | 127.4 |
| 1957 | 1.321 | 129.0 |
| 1958 | 1.490 | 145.5 |
| 1959 | 1.560 | 152.3 |

Sources: Industrial Statistics Section, State Bureau of Statistics, *Wo-kuo kang-t'ieh, tien-li, mei-t'an chi-hsieh, fang-chih, tsao-chih kung-yeh ti chin-hsi* (The past and present of China's iron and steel, electric power, coal, machine-making, textile and paper industries), Peking: Statistics Publishing House, 1958, p. 10; *Kang-t'ieh* (Iron and steel), No. 18, 1959, pp. 796 and 798; *Chi-hua ching-chi* (Planned economy), No. 4, 1958, p. 23; *Chugoku nenkan* (China yearbook), Tokyo: China Research Institute, 1959, p. 210; *Jen-min jih-pao*, August 8, September 9, 1958; April 15, 1959 and February 6, 1960; and *Wei-ta ti shih-nien* (Ten great years), Peking, 1959, p. 97.

The 1958 national average of 1.490, on the other hand, could well be a rounded figure for the average of large and medium-sized furnaces indicated by Wang Ho-shou. This finds support in the available coefficient data for 1957. In that year, the average coefficient was 1.368 for large furnaces and 1.274 for medium-sized furnaces[4]. Thus the 1957 national average of 1.321 appears to be a simple average of the coefficient values of the two groups.

The extreme closeness of the national average figures to those for the nation's large and medium-sized furnaces points to the likelihood that the coefficients of small furnaces were excluded in the national average. To the extent that the proportion of small furnaces in the overall capacity was increased from 1958 onwards, the exclusion of their productivity from national average coefficients tends to accentuate the upward bias of the given data.

3 *Yeh-chin pao* (Metallurgy), Peking, weekly, No. 1, 1960, p. 6.
4 *Chi-hua ching-chi* (Planned economy), Peking, monthly, No. 4, 1958, p. 23.

At this point, it is necessary to question the terms large, medium-sized and small furnaces. In spite of the general practice in China of classifying blast furnaces into these three categories, such terms have not been defined consistently in terms of cubic meters of furnace volume. This lack of clear definition brought about a state of confusion regarding the classification of furnaces, particularly since 1958 when blast furnaces of all descriptions mushroomed in the country. A cursory look at the state of confusion in the designation of large, medium-sized and small furnaces should therefore be of interest.

Within the short period May-August 1959, the term small blast furnace was given three different interpretations. First, all furnaces with a volume below 55 m³ were classified as small[5]. Second, those furnaces whose volumes ranged from 3 m³ to under 54 m³ fell within the small category[6]. Last, small blast furnaces included those with a volume from 6.5 m³ to 100 cubic meters[7]. The difference between 54 m³ and 55 m³ is small enough to be overlooked. The setting of a lower limit was to exclude the tiny furnaces whose products were of little use. Thus the first two interpretations may be considered as reconcilable. The third interpretation appears to be an expedient measure for enhancing the importance of small furnaces in the overall capacity structure, in view of the far greater aggregate capacity of furnaces of 54 m³ to 100 m³ than that of furnaces of 3 m³ to 6.5 cubic meters[8]. The upward revision of the lower limit to 6.5 m³, although not serving the purpose of raising the importance of small furnaces in the overall capacity structure, was perhaps intended to give a better impression of their performance as a group.

On the other hand, the third interpretation might be construed as a revision of blast furnace classification in view of the time sequence in the disclosure of the divergent specifications. But the fact that late in 1960, 3 m³ was still used as one of the standardized sizes for blast furnace designs[9] is indeed puzzling. Could it be that the state of confusion regarding blast furnace classification was prevailing as late as the latter part of 1960?

The demarcation between medium-sized and large furnaces remains to be examined. Here again divergent interpretations prevailed. On the one hand, a vague demarcation of 200 − 300 m³ was given[10]. This interpretation may have stemmed from the fact that the largest furnace size of standardized designs within the medium-sized group was 255 m³. However, the largest among the selected sizes

---

5 *Jen-min jih-pao*, May 21, 1959.
6 *Iron and Steel Industry in China: Survey of a Report of the Indian Steel Delegation*, New Delhi: Ministry of Steel, Mines and Fuel, May 1959, p. 4.
7 Report by Chou En-lai to the Executive Committee of the Second National People's Congress on August 26, 1959. *Jen-min jih-pao*, August 29, 1959.
8 No detailed breakdown of blast furnace capacity is available for 1959. The aggregate capacity of furnaces of 54 — 100 m³ is known to have amounted to 2,966 m³ or 7.3 per cent of the national total in 1961. The aggregate capacity of furnaces under 6.5 m³ for the same year is known to have been 213 m³ or 0.5 per cent of the national total. F. Okazaki, *op. cit., passim*.
9 *Hung-ch'i* (Red flag), No. 18, 1960, p. 25.
10 *Jen-min jih-pao*, May 21, 1959.

for design purposes cannot be construed as the upper limit for the medium-sized furnaces.

On the other hand, No. 2 blast furnace of the Penki Iron and Steel Works was identified as a medium-sized furnace in an official publication of the State Planning Commission[11]. The time reference given was 1957, in which year the capacity of Penki's No. 2 furnace was 400 m³. This volume appears to approximate the upper limit for medium-sized furnaces, judging by the fact that No. 1 blast furnace at Shihchingshan with a capacity of 413 m³ was classified as a large furnace.

It is thus necessary to bear in mind the nature of the data presented in Table 8.1 in examining the behavior of blast furnace productivity during 1949–1959. As can be seen from the table, the average coefficient value increased continuously throughout this period. The growth averaged 9.7 per cent per annum for the period, and 6.2 per cent with 1949–1952 excluded. The exceptionally high rate of increase in 1950 merely reflected the low level of productivity in 1949, when rehabilitation was limited to the least damaged and less efficient furnaces. The 1949 coefficient was, in fact, comparable to that of 1936 before the construction of the more efficient furnaces in Anshan and Penki[12], although the pre-1949 average coefficient reached 0.890[13].

The high rate of increase in blast furnace productivity in the rehabilitation period can also be attributed to improvements in production techniques. The use of full blast coupled with speedier and better-coordinated charging, for instance, was responsible for raising the coefficient of No. 4 blast furnace at Anshan. And this method was immediately popularized[14].

The rate of increase in furnace productivity in 1953 and 1954 would have been higher, had it not been for (1) the fact that a good many blast furnaces in the country were plagued by the "lumping of slag" as a result of raising the smelting intensity above 1.1[15], and (2) the inability of the labor force to cope with the complexity of the newly installed Soviet equipment.

The relatively high rate of productivity increase in 1956 is understandable in the context of the general step-up of industrial production which called for a maximum utilization of all available capital equipment in order to fulfill the ambitious targets. The extent of blast furnace operation in Anshan Steel, for instance, increased from 96.6 per cent in 1950 to 99.3 per cent in 1956. Lengthening of actual operating time tends to raise the coefficient, which is computed on the basis of nominal operating time (i. e. calendar year minus cold down time). The actual operating time can, therefore, be increased by reducing the time and

11 *Chi-hua ching-chi* (Planned economy), Peking, monthly, No. 4, 1959, p. 23.
12 The 1936 national average coefficient was 0.520. *KTMCFT*, p. 6. Examples of the more efficient blast furnaces constructed after 1936 are Nos. 4 — 9 at Anshan and Nos. 3 and 4 at Penki. See Table 2.2 in Chapter 2.
13 *Kang-t'ieh* (Iron and steel), Peking, semi-monthly, No. 18, 1959, p. 796.
14 *Ibid.*
15 Smelting intensity is measured in tonnage of the amount of coke consumed per cubic meter of useful furnace volume in 24 hours.

frequency required for hot down and other minor repairs. In 1956, the capacity loss due to repair time for all the blast furnaces in the country was 13.611 $m^3$/24 hrs. less than in 1955[16].

The recuperation necessary after the high tempo of 1956 was reflected in a substantially smaller rise in furnace productivity in 1957. This, in turn, made possible another sharp increase in furnace productivity in 1958. It is worth noting that the national average coefficient most probably did not include the coefficients of the large number of small furnaces which sprang up in that year.

For a closer examination of blast furnace productivity and its rising trend in the period under study, it is necessary to look into the input structure.

## Inputs and Productivity

The quantity and quality of material inputs per ton of pig iron output constitute one of the determinants of furnace productivity. Normally, an improvement in input quality is accompanied by a decrease in input quantity per unit of output to yield greater productivity. However, the relationship between input quality and furnace productivity is often obscured by other factors. In the case of iron ore input, for instance, both the average iron content of ore and the quantity consumed per ton of pig iron output declined from 1952–1957. The continued decline in ore consumption, as shown in Column 1 of Table 8.2, may be explained in part by the rising national average percentage of sinter in the furnace feed from 27.8 in 1955 to 29.7 in 1956 and 38.0 in 1957[17]. At the same time, the average Fe content of ores charged directly into blast furnaces[18] declined (see Column 2 of the table). The deterioration in the Fe content of the raw ore intended as direct furnace feed was obviously the cause for the increasing use of sinter.

The deterioration in ore quality, on the other hand, was indicative of higher coke consumption and lower output. It was observed that *ceteris paribus*, a decrease of one per cent in the Fe content of ores would result in a 2 per cent increase in coke consumption and a 2 per cent decrease in output[19].

The decrease in the average Fe content of ore became more pronounced in 1958 when the overwhelming emphasis of the Leap Forward on quantitative achievements encouraged the production of low quality ores. In fact, ore deterioration became a serious problem. Thus the Ministry of Metallurgical Industry in 1959 issued a regulation forbidding the use of ore with less than 40 per cent Fe content in blast furnaces[20].

The quantity and quality of coke input similarly affects furnace productivity. Table 8.3 presents the amount of coke consumed per ton of pig iron output for the

16 *Kang-t'ieh*, No. 18, 1959, p. 802.
17 *Ibid.*, p. 800.
18 Including raw ore treated in sinter plants adjacent to blast furnaces.
19 *Chi-hua yü t'ung-chi* (Planning and statistics), Peking, monthly, No. 9, 1959, p. 16.
20 *Ibid.*

*Table 8.2. Iron Ore Consumption by Blast Furnace, 1952—1957*

| Year | Ore Consumption per Ton of Conversion Iron in Terms of 100% Fe Content (Kilograms) | Average Fe Content of Ore Charged Directly into Blast Furnaces* (per cent) |
|------|------|------|
|      | (1) | (2) |
| 1952 | n. a. | 57.35 |
| 1953 | 1,037 | 56.58 |
| 1954 | 1,004 | 56.18 |
| 1955 | 986 | 54.73 |
| 1956 | 984 | 53.25 |
| 1957 | n. a. | 50.88 |

* Including raw ore treated in sinter plants adjacent to blast furnaces.
n.a. Not available.

Source: *Chi-hua yü t'ung-chi* (Planning and statistics), Peking, Monthly, No. 9, 1959, p. 16.

period 1952—1957. The rate shown in Column 1 refers to the gross weight of coke per ton of pig iron output. That in Column 2, on the other hand, represents the corresponding weight of coke void of "breeze," ash, moisture and other impurities.

As noted above, the amount of coke input depends, to some extent, on the Fe content of the ore used. But the quality of coke itself is a more important factor. Coke quality varies inversely with the amount of its sulphur and ash content. An increase of 0.1 per cent in sulphur content, for instance, raised coke consumption by 1.8 – 2.4 per cent and lowered output by 3 per cent. An increase of one per cent in ash content, similarly, raised coke consumption by 3 per cent and lowered output by 3 per cent[21].

The chronic shortage of coke in China demanded a maximum economy in its consumption. Raising its quality was therefore an urgent task. To this end, an increasing amount of coke went through washing plants to have its sulphur and ash content reduced. From 1952 to 1957, the amount of washed coke used in the steel industry quadrupled[22]. Correspondingly, the ash content was reduced from 13.7 per cent in 1952 to 12.8 per cent in 1957, and the sulphur content from 0.8 per cent to 0.7 per cent over the same period[23]. Such quality improvements accounted, in part, for the decreasing trend in the coke rate revealed in Table 8.3. The slight rise in the coke rate in 1957, on the other hand, could be attributed to the substantial ore deterioration in that year, as can be seen from Column 2 of Table 8.2.

21 *Ibid.*
22 *Kang-t'ieh*, No. 18, 1959, p. 794.
23 *Ibid.*

*Table 8.3. Coke Consumption Per Ton of Conversion Iron, 1952—1957 (in tons)*

| Year | Coke Rate | Carbon Equivalent |
|------|-----------|-------------------|
|      | (1)       | (2)               |
| 1952 | 1.50      | n. a.             |
| 1953 | 1.46      | 1.008             |
| 1954 | 1.44      | 0.916             |
| 1955 | 1.41      | 0.876             |
| 1956 | 1.32      | 0.808             |
| 1957 | 1.40      | n. a.             |

n.a. Not available.

Sources: *Chi-hua yü t'ung-chi* (Planning and statistics), Peking, Monthly, No. 9, 1959, p 16 and *Kang-t'ieh* (Iron and steel), No. 18, 1959, p. 798.

## Technique and Productivity

While the quantity and quality of material inputs, among other factors, determine furnace productivity, they are often the result of changes in production techniques. This section examines major changes in iron-smelting technique which took place in China, and their effect on furnace productivity. Most of these changes represented mere adaptations of techniques known to other countries, particularly the Soviet Union.

*Blast temperature* — Raising the temperature to which the blast is preheated and at which the furnace operates is a precondition for increasing smelting intensity. It is, therefore, an essential measure for lowering the coke rate and raising furnace productivity. The relationship between the blast temperature and the coke rate at Anshan Steel for the period 1953—1958 is shown in Table 8.4. Except for 1953[24], the blast temperature showed a continual increase and the coke rate a continual decrease. At the Shihchingshan Iron and Steel Works, similarly, the increase in the temperature of its No. 2 blast furnace from 680°C to 720°C was accompanied by a 2.2 per cent decrease in the coke rate and a 2.5 per cent increase in productivity[25].

*Blast moisture control* — In order to increase the volume of the blast and control its temperature, it is necessary to stabilize its moisture. This can be achieved by adding a certain amount of steam in the blast. Such an experiment was carried out at Anshan Steel in 1954. The addition of 20 − 25 grams of steam to each cubic meter of blast (the temperature of which was preheated to 760 − 810°C) raised the productivity of No. 7 blast furnace by 5 per cent[26]. Early in

24 The average blast temperature at Anshan Steel was lowered in 1954 to avoid the "lumping of slag" which, as pointed out previously, resulted from raising smelting intensity above 1.1. However, the relationship does not appear to be distorted, since the coke rate went up in 1954.
25 *Kang-t'ieh*, No. 18, 1959, p. 801.
26 *KTMCFT*, p. 24.

Table 8.4. Blast Temperature and Coke Rate at Anshan, 1953—1958

| Year | Blast Temperature (deg. C) | Coke Rate (index) |
|------|-----------------------------|-------------------|
| 1953 | 671 | 100.0 |
| 1954 | 653 | 100.2 |
| 1955 | 763 | 92.7 |
| 1956 | 857 | 80.3 |
| 1957 | 860 | 77.5 |
| 1958 | 900 | 71.4 |

Source: *Kang-t'ieh* (Iron and steel), Peking, No. 18, 1959, p. 801.

1955, this technique was extended to ten blast furnaces in the country, all of which reported favorable effects on furnace productivity and coke consumption[27].

*Charging technique* — Improvement in charging the mix into the furnace lies in increasing the amount of the charge and distributing the burden more evenly throughout the furnace. This improved technique was disseminated to all the iron-producing enterprises in 1954. By improving furnace charging, the Taiyuan Iron and Steel Works raised the average utilization coefficient of its No. 2 blast furnace from 0.890 for the first quarter to 1.158 for the second quarter of 1954. The higher productivity of the furnace resulted in a 23 per cent increase in its output. Similarly, the use of this improved method of charging at Anshan Steel brought about an output increase of 34 per cent, a 23.2 per cent decrease in coke rate, an increase in the carbon dioxide content of blast furnace gas from 8.3 to 10.8 per cent, and a decrease in the frequency of "dump" failures from 7 to 3 times every 10 days[28].

Table 8.5. Anshan Blast Furnace Data, June and November 1958

| Item | June | November |
|------|------|----------|
| Utilization coefficient (ton/m$^3$/24 hrs) | 1.672 | 1.859 |
| Smelting intensity (ton/m$^3$/24 hrs) | 1.142 | 1.351 |
| Coke rate (ton/ton of output) | 0.672 | 0.705 |
| Sinter in burden (per cent) | 100 | 100 |
| Top pressure (kg/cm$^2$) | 0.40 | 0.80 |
| Blast temperature (deg. C) | 821 | 806 |

Source: *Kang-t'ieh* (Iron and steel), Peking, No. 18, 1959, p. 801.

27 Of the ten blast furnaces, six were at Anshan, two at Shihchingshan and two at Penki.
28 *Kang-t'ieh*, No. 18, 1959, p. 800.

*Self-fluxing sinter* — The use of self-fluxing sinter represented an important change in production technique for raising blast furnace productivity. The basicity ratio ($CaO/SiO_2$) of sinter produced in China prior to 1955 was below 0.5. By the end of 1955, however, it was raised to 1.0. The experience of Anshan Steel reveals that when the charge consists of 60 per cent sinter, the increase of basicity from 0.6 to 1.0 resulted in a 5 — 7 per cent increase in furnace productivity, a 4 — 5 per cent decrease in coke rate, and a 60 — 70 kilogram reduction in limestone consumption per ton of iron output[29]. While maintaining the basicity ratio at above 1.2, the sinter was subsequently changed into the shape of pellets for the additional advantages of more complete utilization in the burning process, more amenable to the agglomeration of powdery ore, and a minimal loss of basicity in shipment.

*Top pressure* — The technique of using high top pressure was introduced in 1956. In Anshan Steel, the Penki Iron and Steel Works and Wuhan Steel, the use of high top pressure tended to intensify the smelting process, lower the coke rate, reduce waste in blast furnace gas, and enlarge the volume of air blast forced through the furnace. Table 8.5 gives top pressures of an unidentified blast furnace at Anshan Steel in June and November 1958, along with its other technical data. While the effect of top pressure on coke rate may have been counteracted to a small degree by the slight reduction in blast temperature, its effects on smelting intensity and productivity are unobscured. An increase of 0.1 $kg/cm^2$ in top pressure raised productivity by 3 per cent.

*Smelting intensity* — Early attempts at raising the smelting intensity beyond 1.2[30] resulted in a nation-wide phenomenon of "lumping of slag" which plagued a number of blast furnaces in 1953 and 1954. The subsequent practice was to keep the smelting intensity within 1.1 — 1.2. During the 1958 steel drive, however, the Penki Iron and Steel Works took the lead in raising the smelting intensity of its blast furnace beyond this limit. Such a decision was based on its experiment regarding the proper relationship between the permeablitity of gas in the mix and the volume of air blast forced through the furnace. This experiment invalidated not only the earlier belief that smelting intensity could not be raised much beyond 1.0, but also the prevailing conviction that any increase in the smelting intensity was bound to raise the coke rate. Thus, while the smelting intensity of the blast furnaces at the 1st Penki Iron and Steel Plant was raised gradually from 1.013 to 1.550, the average utilization coefficient of these furnaces increased from 1.392 to 2.436[31]. The nation-wide adoption of high smelting intensity was chiefly responsible for the increase in the average coefficient of

29 *Ibid.*, pp. 799 — 800. The use of self-fluxing sinter had the additional advantage of practically eliminating the "lumping of slag."
30 Smelting intensity, as pointed out previously, is expressed by the amount of coke (in tons) consumed per cubic meter of useful furnace volume in 24 hours.
31 The smelting intensity was 1.013 in 1957 and 1.550 in April-May 1959; the average coefficient was 1.392 in the first quarter of 1958 and 2.436 in May 1959. *Kang-t'ieh*, No. 18, 1959, p. 799.

furnaces over 100 m³ in 1959. In addition, it lowered the average coke rate by as much as 100 kilograms[32].

## Outgoing Quality Level and Productivity

The outgoing quality level, as defined above, is the proportion of products up to quality standards expressed as a percentage. While the outgoing quality level depends on the quality of material inputs and changes in production technique, it is one of the determinants of blast furnace productivity. *Ceteris paribus*, the higher the outgoing quality level, the higher the coefficient of furnace utilization, inasmuch as the latter takes into account only the proportion of products which is up to the quality standards. A change in coefficients, on the other hand, need not bring about a corresponding change in outgoing quality level.

Usable data on the outgoing iron quality level are obtainable only from 1959 onwards. Perhaps the mass steel campaign had elevated the importance of pig iron quality. The average outgoing quality level for large and medium-sized blast furnaces came to 94.5 per cent in June 1959[33]. Available data on the monthly average outgoing quality level of the major pig iron producers for the last quarter of 1959 and the first quarter of 1960 are presented in Table 8.6, along with their monthly average coefficients.

In view of the differences in input quality and production methods as well as possible variation in standards, it is more sensible to examine changes in productivity and outgoing quality level within individual producing units. The relationship between these two variables is more apparent in some cases than others. In No. 1 Plant of the Penki Iron and Steel Works, for example, the correlation is almost perfect (see Row 1 of Table 8.6). The same thing can be said of the Shihchingshan Iron and Steel Corporation, the Maanshan Iron and Steel Works, No. 2 Plant of the Lungyen Iron and Steel Works and Paotow Steel (see Rows 4, 5, 9, and 12 of Table 8.6).

In the cases of Wuhan Steel, the Chungking Iron and Steel Corporation and the Tayeh Iron and Steel Works, the relationship between furnace productivity and outgoing quality level, though not as apparent, nevertheless existed. For example, as can be seen from Row 7 of Table 8.6, the average monthly coefficient of the Chungking Iron and Steel Corporation followed its average outgoing quality level closely in the last quarter of 1959, but continued to decline in January 1960 in spite of an improvement in the average outgoing quality level.

The relationship between the two variables in the remaining cases was obscured by other factors. For changes in coefficients attributable to causes other than outgoing quality level, naturally no corresponding changes in the latter could be expected. In No. 1 Plant of the Lungyen Iron and Steel Works, for example, the

32 *Yeh-chin pao*, No. 4, 1960, p. 7.
33 *Jen-min jih-pao*, August 1, 1959.

two variables moved in an opposite direction (see Row 8 of Table 8.6). Evidently forces raising furnace productivity were such in March 1960, that a small decline in outgoing quality level failed to register any effect.

*Table 8.6. Outgoing Quality Level and Blast Furnace Productivity, Large and Medium-sized Furnaces of Major Producers, 1959—1960*

| Producing Unit | Outgoing Quality Level (per cent) | | | | Coefficient of Utilization (tons/m³/day) | | | |
|---|---|---|---|---|---|---|---|---|
| | Sept. (1959) | Dec. | Jan. (1960) | March | Sept. (1959) | Dec. | Jan. (1960) | March |
| | (1) | (2) | (3) | (4) | (5) | (6) | (7) | (8) |
| 1. Penki (No. 1 Plant) | 99.72 | 99.19 | 99.66 | 99.02 | 2.718 | 2.497 | 2.555 | 2.413 |
| 2. Penki (No. 2 Plant) | 99.45 | 99.66 | 99.79 | 99.86 | 2.160 | 2.259 | 2.162 | 1.513 |
| 3. Anshan | 94.06 | 92.85 | 93.26 | 92.67 | 1.639 | 1.635 | 1.597 | 1.783 |
| 4. Shihchingshan | 96.78 | 98.57 | 99.33 | 99.97 | 1.239 | 1.359 | 1.545 | 1.832 |
| 5. Maanshan | 89.31 | 90.22 | 85.61 | n. a. | 1.513 | 1.667 | 1.377 | 1.378 |
| 6. Wuhan | 78.29 | 87.95 | 89.05 | 91.30 | 1.245 | 1.256 | 1.149 | 1.350 |
| 7. Chungking | 100.00 | 97.37 | 98.52 | n. a. | 1.986 | 1.274 | 1.105 | n. a. |
| 8. Lungyen (No. 1 Plant) | n. a. | 73.55 | 78.24 | 69.22 | 0.975 | 0.793 | 0.727 | 0.958 |
| 9. Lungyen (No. 2 Plant) | n. a. | 45.63 | 58.41 | n. a. | 1.109 | 0.741 | 0.796 | 0.761 |
| 10. Tayeh | 88.70 | 96.25 | 78.89 | n. a. | 1.942 | 1.493 | 1.480 | n. a. |
| 11. Taiyuan | 72.94 | 95.07 | 97.47 | 77.03 | 1.855 | 1.422 | 1.524 | 0.965 |
| 12. Paotow | 100.00 | n. a. | n. a. | 96.79 | 0.996 | n. a. | n. a. | 0.883 |

Sources: *Ye-chin pao* (Metallurgy), Peking, Weekly, No. 42, 1959; No. 4, 1960, p. 38; No. 7, 1960, p. 38; and No. 14, 1960, p. 14.

The data in Table 8.6 also indicate a wide discrepancy between the individual producers in terms of both productivity and outgoing quality level. Variation in the latter ranges from 45.6 to 100.0 (see Rows 7, 9 and 12). More pronounced is the difference in productivity which ranges from 0.727 to 2.718 (see Rows 1 and 8). Such wide differences point to the potential of increasing the aggregate output by pulling the coefficients of the less efficient to the level of the advanced. In fact, to tap this potential was the objective of government policy. The promotion of inter-firm emulation campaigns among the blast furnace workers during 1959—1960 was one of its effective implementation measures.

## Emulation Campaign and Productivity

The effect of human factors on productivity should not be overlooked, particularly in a communist country where the authorities can resort to various means, ranging from formal directives to physical rewards or mere titles of prestige, to stimulate production. Indeed, it is difficult to distinguish voluntary co-operation from mere obedience on the part of workers as a result of these manipulations.

The relevance of human factors to furnace productivity can be illustrated by reference to an emulation campaign, which was a common practice to bring about a larger output. During such a campaign launched in the spring of 1959 among big blast furnace workers, No. 9 furnace team of Anshan through greater phsyical and mental exertion was able to raise its furnace coefficient from an average of 2.051 in April to 2.187 in May in order to maintain its leading position. This rapid increase in furnace productivity was said to have been stimulated by the fact that No. 3 blast furnace team, also of Anshan and a close second in April, managed to raise its furnace coefficient to 2.170 by the beginning of May. This example is perhaps indicative of the relevance of human factors to furnace productivity.

### Productivity of Small Blast Furnaces

As pointed out at the beginning of this chapter, the term "small blast furnace" has been subjected to different interpretations with respect to furnace volume. In this section, the term will be taken to refer to furnaces with a volume of 100 $m^3$ or less, the latest official upper limit for small furnaces.

Prior to the steel drive of 1958, productivity of small furnaces was comparable to that of large or medium-sized ones. In 1957, for example, the coefficient of small blast furnaces came to 1.144 as against 1.274 for medium-sized ones and 1.368 for large ones[34]. With the launching of the mass steel campaign in 1958, however, "backyard furnaces" mushroomed. The number of furnaces increased from some 12,000 in June to half a million within three months; by the end of 1958, some two million such furnaces had been built or rebuilt[35]. Such rapid growth ruled out any possibility of obtaining data on the average productivity of small furnaces in 1958. However, judging by the monthly average coefficient of 0.5 in January 1959 (with "backyard furnaces" excluded)[36], the 1958 productivity of small furnaces as a group must have declined considerably more.

The monthly average coefficients of small blast furnaces for March, July, September and December of 1959 were reported to be respectively 0.560, 0.643, 0.852 and 0.900 ton/$m^3$/24 hrs[37]. While the accuracy of such data cannot be ascertained, the rising productivity of small blast furnaces during 1959 appears to be reasonable in view of the replacement of small native furnaces in most parts of the country by modern furnaces of somewhat larger size[38].

34 *Chi-hua ching-chi*, No. 4, 1958, p. 23.
35 *Hung-ch'i*, February 1, 1961, p. 19.
36 *Yeh-chin pao*, No. 8, 1960, p. 7.
37 *Ibid.; Jen-min jih-pao*, October 24, 1959, and March 27, 1960.
38 Small *modern* blast furnaces differ from small *native* furnaces notably in the following aspects:
a) While the volume of most small *native* furnaces was below one cubic meter, that of small *modern* furnaces is generally not under 6.5 cubic meters.

## Technique and Small Blast Furnace Productivity

The importance of small blast furnaces to China cannot be overestimated. In 1959, their combined capacity amounted to nearly two-thirds of the nation's total blast furnace capacity and accounted for 11.05 million tons, or 53.9 per cent of the overall pig iron output[39]. Furthermore, it was possible and plausible to raise the productivity of small furnaces by improving production techniques. The more important of such improvements will be examined below.

*Use of lime in lieu of limestone* — This change was directed at lowering the coke rate, improving output quality and raising productivity. To begin with, the use of lime (CaO) in place of limestone ($CaCO_3$) as a flux eliminates the necessity of having to convert $CaCO_3$ into CaO before it enters the smelting zone. Since the decomposition of limestone does not take place at a temperature less than $500°C$[40], its elimination makes possible a saving in fuel consumption, thus lowering the coke rate. In addition, as coke normally contains a certain amount of sulphur, less coke input lowers the sulphur content of the mix (provided, of course, the sulphur content of ores is not increased). This tends to improve the quality of pig-iron produced. Finally, since the decomposition of limestone involves the formation of carbon dioxide ($CO_2$), its elimination means less $CO_2$ in the furnace gas, allowing more complete reduction of ores to metallic iron. This is a distinct advantage.

This technique is particularly effective for small furnaces because of the low iron content of their ore input and the high sulphur content of their native coke input. The experience of the Tangshan Iron Plant shows that the use of lime in lieu of limestone in its 13 m³ blast furnace resulted in 67 per cent increase in productivity and a 37 per cent decrease in coke rate[41]. Similarly, the Maanshan Iron and Steel Works in Anhwei reported that by employing this technique, No. 2 "Red Flag" small blast furnace increased its productivity by 36 per cent and lowered its coke rate by 25 per cent[42].

*Sizing of ore and coke* — The beneficial effect of regulating the size of raw materials toward greater uniformity has been demonstrated by the Limin Iron Plant in Hunan. By reducing the size of coke from 25 — 60 mm to 5 — 20 mm and restricting the ore size to the range of 5 — 12 mm, the 7 m³ blast furnace at Limin achieved a higher permeability of the mix and a greater stability in the temperature at which the furnace was operating. When this technique was applied simultaneously with the methods of enlarging the volume of air blast and increasing the

---

38 (cont'd)
b) Unlike *native* furnaces, small *modern* furnaces generally have a casing of steel plate for the bosh and tuyere jacket zone.
c) There is greater use of mechanical aids in handling raw materials in the case of small *modern* furnaces than in the case of *native* furnaces.
39 *Kang-t'ieh*, No. 18, 1959, p. 798; *Yeh-chin pao*, No. 11, 1960, p. 10.
40 The decomposition of $CaCO_3$ normally takes place at a temperature of $800°C$.
41 *Kang-t'ieh*, No. 18, 1959, p. 799.
42 *Yeh-chin pao*, No. 4, 1960, p. 20.

furnace temperature, the coefficients of some small furnaces went up substantially and their coke rate was considerably lowered[43].

*Use of multitubular air preheater* — This was introduced by the People's Iron Plant in Yu *hsien*, Hunan Province. The essence of having multitubes was to maintain a reasonably uniform temperature in the preheater, keeping the difference within 150°C[44]. In addition, such a device makes it possible to preheat the blast to 600 — 800°C., thus raising smelting intensity. Hence this device is effective in increasing the productivity of small furnaces and lowering their coke rate.

### Outgoing Quality Level and Small Blast Furnace Productivity

As pointed out previously, the outgoing quality level reflects the quality of material inputs. Since small furnaces generally use ores of low iron content and coke of high sulphur content, their low average outgoing quality level is expected. In April 1959, for instance, it was merely 30 per cent[45]. It was raised to the relatively decent level of 80 per cent in December 1959, as a result of the greater attention to coke washing and ore dressing as well as the above-discussed changes in production technique[46].

The low average outgoing quality level of small furnaces had a significant effect on furnace productivity. Their relationship with each other and with the coke rate can be seen from the monthly data for September and November 1959 on small blast furnaces in selected provinces presented in Table 8.7. In the case where both the coke rate and the outgoing quality level have similar effects on productivity, the relationship between the latter variables can readily be seen. For example, the increase in the productivity of small furnaces in Anhwei and Honan follows an increase in outgoing quality level and a decrease in coke rate (see Rows 1 and 2). Conversely, following a decrease in outgoing quality level and an increase in coke rate, the productivity of small furnaces in Chekiang declines (see Row 3). The relationship between outgoing quality level and furnace productivity, however, becomes less apparent in the case where coke rate and outgoing quality level produce different effects. Thus, productivity may follow changes in the outgoing quality level as in Shantung (see Row 4), or follow changes in the coke rate as in Kiangsu, Hunan and Shansi (see Rows 5 — 7).

### Scale and Productivity

The above findings on blast furnace productivity confirm the economies of scale: the productivity of large and medium-sized furnaces are substantially higher

43 *Ibid.*
44 *Kang-t'ieh*, No. 6, 1959, pp. 190 — 197.
45 *Jen-min jih-pao*, November 22, 1959.
46 *Yeh-chin pao*, No. 4, 1960, p. 6.

Table 8.7. *Data on Small Blast Furnaces in Selected Provinces, September and November 1959*

| Province | Utilization Coefficient (tons/m³/24 hrs.) | | Outgoing Quality Level (per cent) | | Coke Rate (tons/ton of conversion iron) | |
|---|---|---|---|---|---|---|
| | September | November | September | November | September | November |
| | (1) | (2) | (3) | (4) | (5) | (6) |
| 1. Anhwei | 1.120 | 1.296 | 89.78 | 93.34 | 1.190 | 1.163 |
| 2. Honan | 0.760 | 0.918 | 79.39 | 93.60 | 1.610 | 1.213 |
| 3. Chekiang | 1.104 | 0.979 | 93.88 | 87.90 | 1.113 | 1.223 |
| 4. Shantung | 1.070 | 1.177 | 74.20 | 76.80 | 1.170 | 1.185 |
| 5. Kiangsu | 1.115 | 1.162 | 84.51 | 82.03 | 1.137 | 1.110 |
| 6. Hunan | 0.800 | 0.874 | 86.60 | 81.33 | 1.340 | 1.286 |
| 7. Shansi | 0.833 | 0.820 | 81.27 | 86.50 | 1.165 | 1.316 |

Sources: *Yeh-chin pao* (Metallurgy), Peking, weekly, No. 42, 1959; No. 51, 1959, p. 7.

than that of small ones. As an illustration, take the figures for September 1959. The average coefficients of small blast furnaces in seventeen provinces varied from 0.601 in Fukien to 1.120 in Anhwei[47]. The range of the coefficients for large and medium-sized furnaces in twelve producing units, on the other hand, was from 0.975 at the Lungyen Iron and Steel Works to 2.718 at the Penki Iron and Steel Works[48]. The contrast in the productivity of the two groups can be more clearly shown by the national average over a longer period. The average coefficient for the first half of 1959, for example, came to 1.562 for large and medium-sized furnaces and 0.700 for small ones[49].

Given the relatively low coefficients of small furnaces, their importance in the nation's overall capacity and the ease with which they can be multiplied, it would be more effective to raise the productivity of small rather than large furnaces in order to maximize the immediate aggregate output. Consequently, the average coefficient of small furnaces increased at a higher rate than that of large and medium-sized furnaces. The latter increased from 1.490 in 1958 to 1.560 in 1959[50] whereas the former increased from 0.701 in August 1959 to 0.852 in September of the same year[51]. Thus the average coefficient of small furnaces showed a much greater rate of increase in a month than the average coefficient of large and medium furnaces in a year. In spite of the previous reservation regarding the national average figures (particularly those for small furnaces), the contrasting rates of increase appear to be reasonable in view of the greater possibility of improving the production methods and equipment designs of small furnaces.

47 In addition to the monthly average coefficients of small blast furnaces in the seven provinces presented in Column 1 of Table 8.7, those for the remaining ten provinces in September 1959 are as follows:

| Province | Coefficient (ton/m³/24 hrs.) |
| --- | --- |
| Yunnan | 1.009 |
| Hupeh | 0.972 |
| Kweichow | 0.970 |
| Kwangtung | 0.965 |
| Kiangsu | 0.870 |
| Szechwan | 0.729 |
| Hopeh | 0.720 |
| Liaoning | 0.692 |
| Kwangsi | 0.632 |
| Fukien | 0.601 |

Source: *Yeh-chin pao*, No. 42, 1959.
48 See Column 5 of Table 8.6.
49 *Jen-min jih-pao*, September 5, 1959.
50 See Column 1 of Table 8.1.
51 *Jen-min jih-pao*, October 24, 1959, and March 27, 1960.

## Chapter 9

# PRODUCTIVITY OF CAPITAL EQUIPMENT
## *OPEN HEARTHS, CONVERTERS AND ELECTRIC FURNACES*

This chapter examines and analyzes changes in the productivity of open hearths, converters and electric furnaces. Special attention will be directed to the improvements in steel-refining techniques which have affected furnace productivity in China, even though such improved techniques may have originated elsewhere.

### *Open-Hearth Productivity*

The open-hearth productivity coefficient measures the amount of output per square meter of furnace floor in twenty-four hours. It is derived by dividing the average daily output of an open hearth by the area of the furnace floor. Table 9.1 presents data on the national annual average open-hearth coefficients for the period 1949—1959. As can be seen from the table, there was a consistent increase in open-hearth productivity throughout this period. The annual average

*Table 9.1. Average Open-Hearth Coefficient in China, 1949—1959 (tons/m²/24 hrs.)*

| Year | Coefficient | Index (1952 = 100) |
|------|-------------|---------------------|
| 1949 | 2.423 | 50.7 |
| 1950 | 3.306 | 69.1 |
| 1951 | 3.840 | 80.3 |
| 1952 | 4.782 | 100.0 |
| 1953 | 4.910 | 102.7 |
| 1954 | 5.160 | 107.9 |
| 1955 | 6.070 | 126.9 |
| 1956 | 6.670 | 139.5 |
| 1957 | 7.210 | 150.8 |
| 1958 | 7.659 | 160.2 |
| 1959 | 8.210 | 171.7 |

Sources: Industrial Statistics Section, State Bureau of Statistics, *Wo-kuo kang-t'ieh tien-li, mei-t'an, chi-hsieh, fang-chih, tsao-chih kung-yeh ti chin-hsi* (The past and present of China's iron and steel, electric power, coal, machine-making, textile and paper industries), Peking: Statistics Publishing House, 1958, pp. 10 and 25; *Kang-t'ieh* (Iron and steel), Peking, No. 18, 1959, pp. 787 and 790; *Wei-ta ti shih-nien* (Ten great years), Peking, 1959, p. 97; *Jen-min jih-pao*, August 8 and December 22, 1958; February 6, 1960.

rate of increase came to 13 per cent[1]. As in the case of blast furnace productivity, the relatively high rates of increase were registered in the rehabilitation years, notably 1950. The favorable effect of the practice of overcharging the furnace (in excess of its rated capacity) introduced in 1950 combined with the low level of 1949 productivity[2] to yield the highest rate of increase. The practice of overcharging the furnace remained a potent force in raising open-hearth productivity in subsequent years.

The high rate of increase in open-hearth productivity during the rehabilitation period can also be explained, in part, by reductions in the frequency of hot repairs as well as the time required for each repair. Since the open-hearth productivity coefficient bears reference to the nominal time which includes hot down time, the effect was equivalent to lengthening the actual operating period or increasing the rate of utilization. For example, the 1950 rate of open-hearth utilization was 60.1 per cent at No. 1 Plant of Anshan Steel, 60.9 per cent at the Tientsin Steel Plant and 37.6 per cent at No. 3 Shanghai Steel Plant. By the end of 1952, however, 80 per cent was the lowest rate of open-hearth utilization in all steel plants[3].

Unlike blast furnace productivity, open-hearth productivity did not show a high rate of increase in 1956 or 1958. Instead, it showed a notably high rate of increase in 1955 when certain new techniques were introduced in open-hearth operation. The use of chrome-magnesite firebricks lengthened the life-span of open hearths and reduced the frequency of hot repairs. In addition, during his visit to Anshan Steel in mid-1955, Krezhnikov (a Soviet steel worker) demonstrated the possibility of reducing the heat time for each cast despite a continual increase in the size of the charge. Through faster charging and higher temperature, he was able to cut down the heat time for a large open hearth at Anshan to 5 hours and 35 minutes, amounting to only 60 per cent of the heat time specified by the Ministry of Metallurgical Industry[4]. Further demonstrations by Krezhnikov at the Taiyuan Iron and Steel Works, the Chungking Iron and Steel Works and other places soon resulted in a distinct reduction in heat time. Thus during the last quarter of 1955, the heat time for all the open hearths in the country was reported to have been shortened by 12–30 per cent[5]. Between 1949 and 1959, the annual coefficient value more than tripled, as can be seen from Table 9.1. Largely responsible for this increase in productivity were changes in production techniques.

---

1 With the rehabilitation years (1949–1952) excluded, the annual average rate becomes 8 per cent. This rate of increase is comparable to that in the Soviet Union during the period 1928–1937. By 1956, China's open-hearth productivity caught up with the Soviet level attained in 1954. For the Soviet data, see M. G. Clark, *op. cit.*, p. 254.
2 The 1949 average coefficient of open hearths was 2.42 as compared with the highest pre-communist level of 3.22. F. Okazaki, *Chugoku no kikaikogyo no gijutsu suijun* (Technical level of the steel and machinery industry in China), Tokyo, 1962, p. 97.
3 *Kang-t'ieh* (Iron and steel), Peking, No. 18, 1959, p. 806.
4 *Chung kung-yeh t'ung-hsin* (Heavy industry bulletin), Peking, May 11, 1956, p. 24.
5 *Ibid.*

## Technique and Open-Hearth Productivity

Changes in open-hearth operating technique in the period under study were along the lines of enlarging the tonnage capacity of the furnace and raising the smelting intensity. The more important of such changes will be examined below.

*Charging in excess of rated furnace capacity* — With the introduction of this practice in Anshan Steel in 1950, the capacity of its tilting open hearth was raised from 180 to 200 tons. To apply this technique successfully, however, required modification of the furnace structure. Thus the furnace remodelling enabled the 10-ton open hearth of No. 3 Shanghai Steel Plant to expand its capacity from 14 tons in 1954 to 19 tons in 1956 and 45 tons in 1958[6].

Redesigning of the interior of the furnace in order to accommodate a bigger charge lay essentially in deepening the bath, heightening the roof, and trifurcating the tapping apparatus. It was in the latter direction that the open-hearth operators in China made their noted contribution. A major limiting factor to increasing the charge is the capacity of the casting cranes. To eliminate this bottleneck, the Soviet experience was to bifurcate the spout and tap steel into two ladles. While this practice was widely followed in the open-hearth shops in China, the Taiyuan Iron and Steel Works in March 1958 succeeded in developing a three-ladle steel-tapping method by trifurcating the spout. With this innovation, the Taiyuan No. 3 open hearth with an original rated capacity of 49 tons increased its charging capacity to 130 tons, resulting in a 47.5 per cent increase in its productivity and a 4.5 per cent decrease in per-ton production costs[7].

*Reducing the heat time* — In spite of the continual increase in the size of the charge, most of the open hearths in the country were able to cut down the heat time. At No. 3 Shanghai Steel Plant, for instance, whereas the average size of the charge was raised from 14 tons in 1954 to 41 tons in 1958, the average heat time for each cast was lowered from 5 hours 30 minutes to 5 hours and 6 minutes. Similarly, at No. 1 Plant of Anshan Steel, the average heat time was reduced from 10 hours 34 minutes in 1950 to 8 hours 42 minutes in 1958. This 18 per cent cut in the heat time was accompanied by a 39 per cent increase in the average output per heat[8].

The heat time was shortened essentially by increasing the firing rate (measured in million kilogram-calories per square meter of the furnace floor in an hour). With the increase in the size of the charge, the firing rate for the furnace must increase in order to provide an amount of heat required for the bigger charge. The increase in the firing rate, at the same time, raises the temperature of the furnace, cuts down the heat time, and consequently pushes up furnace productivity. The relationship between the firing rate and productivity can be illustrated by the

---

6 *Kang-t'ieh*, No. 6, 1959, pp. 190 — 197.
7 Ministry of Metallurgical Industry, *Kuan-yu t'ai-yuan kang-t'ieh ch'ang san-ts'ao-ch'u-kang ti pao-kao* (Report on the three ladle steel-tapping experiment of the Taiyuan Iron and Steel Works), March 1958; *Kang-t'ieh*, No. 23, 1959, p. 1126.
8 *Kang-t'ieh*, No. 18, 1959, p. 809.

experience of No. 3 Shanghai Steel Plant. The firing rate for its open hearths was 1.05 x 10⁶ kilogram-calories per square meter per hour in 1958, or twice that for the furnaces in other steel centers. Their average utilization coefficient reportedly reached 14.3, in comparison with the 1958 average coefficient of 7.7 for all the open hearths in the country[9].

The method of heating the open hearth was improved by injecting outside air through compressed air jets in the gas port. By using this measure, Anshan Steel was able to cut down the heat time by 20 – 30 minutes and increase productivity by 4.0–4.5 per cent[10]. This method was widely adopted in the country. Another improvement was to add a small amount of tar in the furnace ends to impart luminosity to the flame. This technique could also cut down the heat time by 20 – 30 minutes.

A third improvement was to use hot metal in the charge. Prior to 1954, mixers were used to provide hot metal in the charge only at Anshan Steel and the Taiyuan Iron and Steel Works. In 1954, the Chungking Iron and Steel Works experimented with the use of remelting furnaces to provide hot metal in the charge[11]. By 1956, this method was introduced in open-hearth shops in Tientsin, Shanghai and Tayeh. The effectiveness of this method can be illustrated by the experience of No. 3 Shanghai Plant. In July 1956 before this method was introduced, the average heat time was 5 hours 24 minutes. Its application shortened the heat time to 4 hours 2 minutes, or by 18.5 per cent. Similarly, the introduction of this method at No. 1 Shanghai Plant reduced the heat time by one hour[12]. In 1959, remelting furnaces were used in nearly all the open-hearth shops in China.

*Use of magnalium roof bricks* — The relevancy of such bricks to productivity lies in prolonging the life of the roof and increasing the firing rate for the furnace. In 1955, the Refractory Plant of Anshan Steel succeeded in manufacturing chrome-magnesite bricks. The new bricks were subsequently used in the roofs of all open hearths at Anshan Steel with the result of lengthening roof life two and a half times.

Further extension in the use of chrome-magnesite bricks was restricted by scarce domestic supply of chrome and its inadequate imports to meet the needs of the fast-growing steel industry. Accordingly, research towards finding a substitute for the scarce chrome was undertaken jointly by the Metal Research Institute of the Academy of Sciences, the Iron and Steel Research Institute of the Ministry of Metallurgical Industry, Anshan Steel and the Chungking Iron and Steel Works. The joint research efforts resulted in the successful manufacture of superior magnalium bricks from alumina and magnesite, with which China is richly endowed. The use of such bricks in Anshan Steel lengthened roof life to 520 heats

9 *Ibid.*, pp. 787 and 809; Table 9.1.
10 Reported by the Anshan Chapter of the All-China Metallurgical Society in April 1958.
11 Such remelting furnaces essentially fulfil the functions of mixers.
12 *Kang-t'ieh*, No. 6, 1957, p. 13.

or 14 per cent longer than the roof made of chrome-magnesite bricks[13]. This coupled with general improvement in temperature control and furnace design made it possible to prolong the life span of open hearths, reduce the frequency of their hot repairs and thus enhance their productivity[14].

## Converter Productivity

The productivity of a converter is measured by a coefficient of utilization of its useful capacity. As in the case of a blast furnace, it is derived by dividing the average daily output of a converter in tons by its volume in cubic meters. Consistent data on the annual average converter coefficients are obtainable for the years 1952–1956. Such data are presented in Table 9.2. As can be seen from the table, the coefficient value tripled in these years, although in 1956 the excessive demand for pig iron by open hearths was met at the relative expense of converters. The 1956 output of open-hearth steel increased 76 per cent, while that of converter steel increased less than 20 per cent[15]. Converter steel was in a worse situation in 1957, since pig iron of standard quality was in short supply[16]. The dwindled supply affected the converter coefficient as well as output. As open hearths had priority over converters in the use of iron of standard quality, some converters had to resort to sub-standard iron as input. Thus average converter productivity in 1957 was bound to decline.

Converter productivity remained low during 1958–1959 in comparison with the 1952–1956 level. The 1958 annual average converter coefficient was only 5.00 tons/m$^3$/24 hrs. By the end of 1959, the national average was reported to be 13.00[17]. Judging by the coefficient value of 10.00 planned for 1960[18], the annual average for 1959 could not have been above this level. The drastic decline in converter productivity since 1957 requires some explanation.

During the mass steel campaign, a huge number of small, native converters sprang up over the country. The extremely low productivity of these converters was bound to pull down the national average. Second, the mass steel campaign created a need for converters to treat the low-quality iron (with $0.07 - 1.6$ per cent phosphorus content and $0.3 - 1.0$ per cent sulphur content)[19] produced by small native furnaces. This had a double-barrelled unfavourable effect on converter productivity. While the low-quality iron input lowered the coefficient, its excessive phosphorus content called for basic lining, which further reduced furnace productivity. The coefficient of an acid converter could easily double that of a

13 *Ibid.*, No. 9, 1958, p. 19; *Jen-min jib-pao*, September 23, 1959.
14 As pointed out previously, cold-down time is excluded in measuring productivity.
15 See Table 6.4 in Chapter 6.
16 *Yeh-chin pao*, No. 4, 1958, p. 16.
17 *Yeh-chin pao*, No. 15, 1960, p. 15.
18 *Honan jih-pao*, January 26, 1960.
19 *Kang-t'ieh*, No. 18, 1959, pp. 813 and 818.

*Table 9.2. Average Converter Coefficient in China, 1952—1956 (tons/m³/24 hrs.)*

| Year | Coefficient | Index (1952 = 100) |
|------|-------------|--------------------|
| 1952 | 13.11 | 100.0 |
| 1953 | 21.80 | 166.3 |
| 1954 | 30.38 | 231.7 |
| 1955 | 32.97 | 251.5 |
| 1956 | 40.40 | 308.2 |

Source: Industrial Statistics Section, State Bureau of Statistics, *Wo-kuo kang-t'ieh, tien-li, mei-t'an, chi-hsieh, fang-chih, tsao-chih kung-yeh ti chin-hsi* (The past and present of China's iron and steel, electric power, coal, machine-making, textile and paper industries), Peking: Statistics Publishing House, 1958, p. 25.

basic converter. In 1958, for example, the coefficient of a basic converter at the Tangshan Steel Plant reached 35.1 whereas that of an acid converter at No. 1 Shanghai Steel Plant reached 78.6[20]. The need to treat low-quality iron, in addiion, led to the development of basic side-blown converters.

### Side-blown Converters

Although the theory of steel making in side-blown converters had been widely known, China was the first country to apply it on a large scale. Experiments in the use of side-blown converters were carried out at the Tangshan Steel Plant as early as August 1951. Although this process was adopted for regular production in January 1952, its importance was increased only in 1958 as a result of the mushrooming of "backyard" iron-smelting furnaces. The side-blown converter enjoyed a distinct advantage over the more common bottom-blown type in that it could effectively remove phosphorus and, to a lesser extent, sulphur without requiring high-pressure blowers. In addition, the converters, the blowers, the ancillary pid side teeming equipment as well as refractories could all be made in China.

In the course of developing the side-blown converter, a number of improvements in production technique were made to cope with the low-quality iron input, notably the use of a keep-slag process and cupolas.

*The keep-slag process* — Under the suggestion of Philipchenko, a Soviet metallurgist, this technique was developed to cope with the problem of refining iron with high phosphorus and sulphur content. The method was to retain one-half to two-thirds of the slag of the requisite quality, composition and characteristics in the converter prior to the addition of hot metal; the removal of phosphorus and sulphur from the metal was brought about by the addition of suitable fluxes. In

---

20 *Ibid.*, p. 814. The wide discrepancy in coefficient value is attributable to the relatively higher rate of air intake of the acid converter, the rate of air intake being measured in cubic meters per cubic meter of converter capacity per minute.

addition to lime, a certain amount of oxide of iron was also used as flux since it aided in producing a fluid slag and also gave a slightly higher yield of steel. With this technique, 56 — 80 per cent of the phosphorus content and 30 — 40 per cent of the sulphur content could be removed[21]. In fact, the keep-slag process as applied to side-blown converters was so effective in dephosphorization that there was hardly any need for the afterblow, which was indispensable for bottom-blown converters.

*Raising iron input temperature* — An effective means for providing sufficient heat in the converter was to raise the temperature of iron input in cupolas. While such a measure ensured output quality[22], it shortened the heat time and reduced the blowing losses as well as raw material consumption.

Three major improvements were made toward increasing iron input temperature. First, the size of charging boxes was reduced to achieve a more even distribution of the charge in the cupola. With this simple change, the Tangshan Steel Plant was able to raise the temperature of molten iron from the cupola by 50°C. Second, the air intake of the cupola was preheated to 200–300°C. Experiments at the Hsinhsing Steel Plant indicated that when the air temperature reached 150°C and 300°C, the temperature of molten iron rose by 50°C and 100°C respectively[23]. Finally, the number of tuyeres in the cupola was increased from one or two rows to three rows so as to allow faster melting and raise molten iron temperature. By 1959, the above changes were effected in most of China's converter shops.

In addition to raising the temperature of iron input to 1,350 — 1,410°C, the use of cupolas served to remove as much as 80 per cent of its sulphur content. In fact, their use made it possible for the basic side-blown converters to turn out steel with a sulphur content of 0.055 per cent, thus meeting the quality requirements of the Ministry of Metallurgical Industry[24].

## Electric Furnace Productivity

The electric furnace coefficient shows the quantity of output for a given amount of electrical energy input, and is expressed in tons/1000 KVA[25]. For a given

21 *Ibid.*, p. 815.
22 Sufficient internal heat must be generated in the foreblow of a converter to ensure the quality of the product. With insufficient heat, phosphorus would oxidize before the metal, thus lengthening the oxidization process and turning out inferior steel with gas cavities.
23 *Jen-min jih-pao*, December 12, 1958.
24 *NCNA*, Wuhan, November 27, 1958; *Jen-min jih-pao*, August 1, 1959. Prospects for further improving the quality and for increasing the variety of converter steel were particularly bright in view of the successful experiments undertaken by the Tayeh Iron and Steel Works with the assistance of the Iron and Steel Research Institute. These experiments were conducted on the mixing of converter steel with ferro-alloys melt in the electric furnace and with the electric furnace slag. Thus mixed in the ladle, while the slag promoted further desulphurization and oxidization of the converter steel, alloys from the electric furnace reacted with it to form alloy-steels. As a result, the quality of converter steel was improved and its variety increased.
25 KVA stands for kilovolt-amperes.

output, therefore, a decrease either in heat time or in electrical energy input represents an increase in furnace productivity. Annual average electric furnace coefficient data for the years 1952–1958 are presented in Table 9.3. As can be seen from the table, the coefficient value nearly tripled over the period. This high rate of increase in productivity was attributable chiefly to the introduction of new smelting techniques, notably the use of oxygen and coal gas on preheated charge and the use of tourmaline to yield the desired reducing slag. Also effective in raising furnace productivity were the adoption of (1) transformers with a larger capacity coupled with more effective cooling systems to allow a larger energy input per unit weight of charge; (2) mechanized charging, introduced in 1954 and in use in 80 per cent of China's electric furnace shops by 1956[26]; and (3) larger electrodes with automatic control.

The installation of charging machines was accompanied by a change to charging through the top. While this practice speeded up the charging process, it also facilitated certain changes in furnace structure to take in a bigger charge, such as raising the position of the door and reducing the thickness of the side bricks. Additional changes in furnace structure included deepening and widening of the bath and heightening of the walls. In the Dairen Steel Plant, for example, increasing the bath diameter from 2,140 to 2,460 mm and depth from 350 to 780 mm

*Table 9.3. Average Electric Furnace Coefficient in China, 1952–1958 (tons/1000 KVA)*

| Year | Coefficient | Index (1952 = 100) |
|------|-------------|--------------------|
| 1952 | 7.40 | 100.0 |
| 1953 | 10.20 | 137.8 |
| 1954 | 13.12 | 177.3 |
| 1955 | 15.00 | 202.7 |
| 1956 | 18.12 | 244.9 |
| 1957 | 18.62 | 251.6 |
| 1958 | 22.11 | 298.8 |

Sources: Industrial Statistics Section, State Bureau of Statistics, *Wo-kuo kang-t'ieh, tien-li, mei-t'an, chi-hsieh, fang-chih, tsao-chih kung-yeh ti chin-hsi* (The past and present of China's iron and steel, electric power, coal, machine-making, textile and paper industries), Peking: Statistics Publishing House, 1958, p. 25; *Kang-t'ieh* (Iron and steel), Peking, No. 18, 1959, pp. 787 and 823.

raised the tonnage capacity from 5 to 15. By mid-1959, furnaces with a rated capacity of 15 tons were reported to take a charge of 66 tons[27]. Increased charge was an important factor in raising furnace productivity provided, of course, the heat time was not increased in the same proportion.

In the Dairen Steel Plant, however, the increased charge was accompanied by a reduction of the heat time per unit weight of charge, as can be seen from Table

26 *Kang-t'ieh*, No. 18, 1959, pp. 822 and 824.
27 *Ibid.*, p. 823.

9.4. This was possible because oxygen was used in the smelting process[28] and the power factor of the transformer raised[29]. Experiments on the use of oxygen in 1954 revealed that not only did it reduce the heat time per unit of output, but also cut down power consumption per unit of output. In 1958, approximately 80 per cent of China's electric furnaces were using oxygen[30]. In the case of the Dairen Steel Plant, the use of oxygen led to a 30.4 per cent increase in productivity and 27.5 per cent decrease in power consumption[31]. Similarly in the Penki Steel Plant, while the heat time per ton of output was reduced from 16 minutes in 1957 to 10 minutes in the last quarter of 1958, power consumption per ton of output was lowered from 742 to 492 KWH[32].

*Table 9.4. Indices of Quantity of Charge and Heat Time for DC-5M Electric Furnaces at Dairen Steel Plant, 1956—1959 (1955＝100)*

| Year | Quantity of Each Charge | Heat Time Per Ton of Charge |
|------|------------------------|-----------------------------|
| 1956 | 121.0 | 76.5 |
| 1957 | 131.0 | 65.0 |
| 1958 | 154.5 | 46.3 |
| 1959a | 191.0 | 34.0 |

a. For the first quarter only.

Source: *Kang-t'ieh*, (Iron and steel), Peking, No. 18, 1959, p. 823.

Further experiments were carried out at the Penki Steel Plant combining the use of oxygen and coal gas on preheated charge, with the result of reducing the heat time by 25.3 per cent and power consumption by 23.7 per cent[33]. When the Plant used this process for regular production early in 1959, better results were obtained. As can be seen from Columns 2 and 4 of Table 9.5, the corresponding reductions amounted to 33.2 and 33.3 per cent.

Electric furnace productivity was further improved through the converter-electric furnace process. The chief advantage of such a duplex process was a drastic reduction or complete elimination of the time required for melting and oxidizing in the electric furnace. As this time requirement normally amounted to half of the heat time for an electric furnace using cold charge, its elimination shortened the heat time from $3^{1}/_{2} - 4$ hours to $2 - 2^{1}/_{2}$ hours, as in the case of the Penki Steel Plant[34]. Thus in 1958 the coefficient of electric furnaces fed by con-

28 The use of oxygen in the smelting process should not be taken to imply the L-D process. The latter was not introduced in China until the mid-1960's. See Chapter 14.
29 By raising the proportion of available electrical energy which could be converted into heat, the potentiality of the transformer was more fully tapped.
30 *Kang-t'ieh*, No. 18, 1959, p. 791.
31 *Ibid.*, p. 824.
32 *Ibid.*, p. 823.
33 *Ibid.*, p. 824.
34 *Jen-min jih-pao*, March 3, 1960.

verter steel exceeded 35 tons, as compared with the overall average of 22.1 tons[35]. With this method, power consumption per unit of output was halved and the life of electrodes lengthened[36]. In addition, it helped to alleviate the shortage of steel scrap, which had been accentuated by the introduction of continuous steel casting.

The duplexing production technique, however, required a high degree of synchronization in operating the two types of furnaces, in order to ensure that the charge for the electric furnace was always ready when needed. If the electric furnace had to wait for its feed, the linings would start to cool off. This cooling and reheating would not only prolong the heat time and reduce the daily output quantity, but also shorten the life of the furnace and lower the quality of its product.

Table 9.5. *Effect of Oxygen, Coal Gas and Preheated Charge on Heat Time and Power Consumption for Electric Furnaces at the Penki Steel Plant Early in 1959*

| Process | Heat Time | | Power Consumption | |
|---|---|---|---|---|
| | Minutes/Ton of Steel | Index | KWH/Ton of Steel | Index |
| | (1) | (2) | (3) | (4) |
| Cold charge | | | | |
| Without oxygen | 11.3 | 100.0 | 492 | 100.0 |
| With oxygen | 10.6 | 93.8 | 430 | 87.4 |
| With oxygen and coal gas | 8.5 | 75.2 | 345 | 70.1 |
| Preheated charge | | | | |
| With oxygen | 9.2 | 81.4 | 374 | 76.0 |
| With oxygen and coal gas | 7.55 | 66.8 | 328 | 66.7 |

Source: *Kang-t'ieh* (Iron and steel), Peking, No. 18, 1959, p. 824.

35 *Ke-hsüeh t'ung-pao* (Science bulletin), semimonthly, Peking, No. 5, 1959, p. 138; Table 9.3.
36 *Yeh-chin pao*, No. 12, 1956, p. 30.

## Chapter 10

# PRODUCTIVITY OF LABOR

Although the productivity of capital equipment examined in the two preceding chapters is of more immediate concern to a capital-poor overpopulated economy, the importance of labor productivity to such an economy should not be overlooked. Labor productivity in the steel industry, therefore, constitutes the subject of enquiry in this chapter. Because of the paucity of data, the period of investigation is confined to 1952–1957. For the same reason, labor productivity is measured by average output per man-year. Such a measurement obviously cannot reflect variations in the actual working hours stemming from any irregular attendance or overtime work. In addition, the amount of fixed assets per production worker will be examined in relation to labor productivity.

## Size of Labor Force

Two series of employment data are obtainable for the steel industry: total employees and production workers. The latter include only those engaged directly in the production process, such as engineers, technicians, skilled and unskilled workers. Total employees, on the other hand, cover production workers as well as those employees not directly engaged in the production process, such as management personnel, clerical staff, janitors, guards, etc. Table 10.1 presents the two series of employment data for the steel industry. While figures for 1952–1956 are obtained from official sources, those for 1957 represent estimates[1].

Column 5 of Table 10.1 shows a general rising trend of production workers as a proportion of total employment. The notable decline of this proportion in 1953 was due to a larger increase in non-production workers. In that year, while production workers rose 14.3 per cent, non-production workers increased 30.2 per cent. Adherence to the general government policy of minimizing non-production workers in industrial establishments in the following year, however, led to a 15 per cent increase in the production labor force while total employment went up less than 3 per cent (see Columns 2 and 4 of Table 10.1).

---

1 The method of estimation is given in Appendix 10 — A.

Productivity of Labor

Table 10.1. Employment in the Steel Industry, 1952—1957

| Year | All Employees | | Production Workers | | |
|------|------|------|------|------|------|
| | Persons | 1952 = 100 | Persons | 1952 = 100 | Percentage of All Employees |
| | (1) | (2) | (3) | (4) | $(5) = \dfrac{(3)}{(1)} \times 100$ |
| 1952 | 211,587 | 100.0 | 134,415 | 100.0 | 63.5 |
| 1953 | 254,109 | 120.1 | 153,605 | 114.3 | 60.4 |
| 1954 | 261,521 | 123.6 | 177,327 | 131.9 | 67.8 |
| 1955 | 276,902 | 130.9 | 185,647 | 138.1 | 67.0 |
| 1956 | 304,269 | 143.8 | 209,153 | 155.6 | 68.7 |
| 1957 | 332,094 | 157.0 | 228,150 | 169.7 | (68.7) |

Source: Industrial Statistics Section, State Bureau of Statistics, Wo-kuo kang-t'ieh, tien-li, mei-t'an, chi-hsieh, fang-chih, tsao-chih kung-yeh ti chin-hsi (The past and present of China's iron and steel, electric power, coal, machine-making, textile and paper industries), Peking: Statistics Publishing House, 1958, p. 27 and Appendix 10-A.

*Productivity in Value Terms*

The data on employment together with the gross output figures given in Chapter 7 make it possible to derive labor productivity for total employees and for production workers. These productivity figures are presented in Table 10.2. The annual average rate of increase in labor productivity over the period 1952 –1957 came to 17.4 per cent for production workers and 19.3 per cent for all employees. The divergence stems from the higher rate of increase in production workers, as pointed out above. The relatively higher rate of productivity increase for all employees should not obscure the fact that the productivity of production workers more than doubled during the first plan quinquennium. The index of the latter series, as shown in Column 4 of Table 10.2, stood at 223.3 in 1957 with 1952 as the base year.

This impressive increase in labor productivity was attributable to a number of factors such as improved production technique, greater intensity and better organization of work, and higher capital-labor ratio. Any improvement in production technique is bound to raise labor productivity because it involves higher skill and better design of equipment. For example, the practice of adding steam in the blast introduced in 1954 decidedly increased the output per blast furnace worker at Anshan, Shihchingshan and Penki. The frequent launching of emulation campaigns in the steel industry was intended to increase the intensity and improve the organization of work. Thus by resorting to faster charging, the open-hearth workers at Anshan, Taiyuan and Chungking managed to raise their productivity. The amount of fixed assets per production worker will be examined later in the chapter.

The productivity increase of production workers in the steel industry compares favorably with that of production workers in the industrial sector as a whole. For the years 1952–1956 for which data are available, labor productivity in the steel industry was not only persistently higher than, but also tended to outrun, that for the entire industrial sector, as can be seen from the productivity ratios given below[2]:

| Year | Productivity Ratio of Steel Industry to Entire Industrial Sector |
|:---:|:---:|
| 1952 | 1.2659 |
| 1953 | 1.3513 |
| 1954 | 1.2655 |
| 1955 | 1.3702 |
| 1956 | 1.5889 |

The increasing gap between the two productivity series reflected the prominence of the steel industry in the industrialization strategy of the communist regime which emphasized modern technology and large-scale operation during the first plan quinquennium.

2 Derived from data given in *KTMCFT*, p. 27 and Table 10.2.

*Table 10.2. Labor Productivity in the Steel Industry, 1952–1957*

| Year | All Employees | | Production Workers | |
|---|---|---|---|---|
| | Yuan Per Employee (at 1952 prices) | Index (1952 = 100) | Yuan Per Worker (at 1952 prices) | Index (1952 = 100) |
| | (1) | (2) | (3) | (4) |
| 1952 | 6,473 | 100.0 | 10,189 | 100.0 |
| 1953 | 7,364 | 113.8 | 12,183 | 119.6 |
| 1954 | 8,900 | 137.5 | 13,126 | 128.8 |
| 1955 | 10,461 | 161.6 | 15,603 | 153.1 |
| 1956 | 13,557 | 209.4 | 19,722 | 193.6 |
| 1957 | 15,631 | 241.5 | 22,752 | 223.3 |

Sources: Tables 7.6 and 8.1.

*Table 10.3. Productivity of Blast Furnace Workers, 1952–1956*

| Year | Ministry of Metallurgical Industry | | Anshan Steel | | Productivity Ratio of Anshan to Metallurgical Ministry |
|---|---|---|---|---|---|
| | Tons Per Man-Year | Index (1952 = 100) | Tons Per Man-Year | Index (1952 = 100) | $(5) = \frac{(3)}{(1)}$ |
| | (1) | (2) | (3) | (4) | |
| 1952 | 261.4 | 100.0 | 870.6 | 100.0 | 3.3305 |
| 1953 | 273.0 | 104.4 | 1,044.4 | 120.0 | 3.8256 |
| 1954 | 335.9 | 128.5 | 1,249.8 | 143.6 | 3.7208 |
| 1955 | 446.4 | 170.8 | 1,616.9 | 185.7 | 3.6221 |
| 1956 | 625.7 | 239.4 | 2,678.1 | 307.6 | 4.2802 |

Source: Industrial Statistics Section, State Bureau of Statistics, *Wo-kuo kang-t'ieh, tien-li, mei-t'an, chi-hsieh, fang-chih, tsao-chih kung-yeh ti chin-hsi* (The past and present of China's iron and steel, electric power, coal, machine-making, textile and paper industries), Peking: Statistics Publishing House, 1958, p. 20.

*Physical Productivity*

In the production of pig iron and open-hearth steel which are more or less homogeneous commodities, productivity can also be measured in physical quantities. Table 10.3 presents available data on pig iron output per blast furnace worker within the enterprises under the jurisdiction of the Ministry of Metallurgical Industry, together with similar data for Anshan Steel during 1952–1956. Data on the productivity of open-hearth workers at Anshan and all enterprises under the Ministry for the same period are given in Table 10.4. In this connection, some observations can be made.

First, productivity increase during this period was at a higher rate for blast furnace workers than for all production workers in the steel industry. Output per production worker in the steel industry, as shown in Column 4 of Table 10.2, rose 93.6 per cent for the period. Output per blast furnace worker, on the other hand, went up 139.4 per cent for the same period (see Column 2 of Table 10.3). Second, in this period productivity was increasing at an annual average rate of 32 per cent for Anshan blast furnace workers as against 24 per cent for all blast furnace workers under the Ministry of Metallurgical Industry. As a result, the superior productivity of Anshan workers became more and more pronounced, as indicated by the productivity ratios given in Column 5 of Table 10.3. Lastly, a comparison of Tables 10.3 and 10.4 reveals that productivity increase was slower for open-hearth workers than for blast furnace workers (see Columns 2 and 4 of both tables). It also shows that the superior productivity of Anshan's open-hearth workers was not as prominent as that of its blast furnace workers (see Column 5 of both tables). These observations confirm the communist development policy during this period of emphasizing large-scale modern equipment, particularly in the smelting sector. As pointed out in Chapter 4, rehabilitation of blast furnaces at Anshan was accompanied by enlargement of capacity and automation of the productive process.

*Fixed Assets Per Worker*

Data on the amount of fixed assets per production worker in the steel industry for the years 1952–1956 are presented in Table 10.5. The amount of fixed assets per worker is undoubtedly one of the key determinants of labor productivity. However, an examination of the data presented in Tables 10.5 and 10.2 reveals no apparent relationship between the two variables in the period concerned. This is not surprising in view of the many other variables involved. Furthermore, there is the consideration of time required to train the labor force to operate the newly installed equipment[3].

3 No. 3 steel plant at Anshan may be cited as an example. According to the Ministry of Metallurgical Industry, the low output level was attributable to the high proportion of some 80 per cent of new workers in its labor force and their low productivity. After a year's intensive training of the new labor force, the daily output of the plant increased 50 per cent. *Yeh-chin pao*, No. 50, 1959, p. 4.

*Table 10.4. Productivity of Open-Hearth Workers, 1952–1956*

| Year | Ministry of Metallurgical Industry | | Anshan Steel | | Productivity Ratio of Anshan to Metallurgical Ministry |
| | Tons Per Man-Year | Index (1952 = 100) | Tons Per Man-Year | Index (1952 = 100) | $(5) = \dfrac{(3)}{(1)}$ |
| | (1) | (2) | (3) | (4) | |
| 1952 | 236.1 | 100.0 | 416.6 | 100.0 | 1.7645 |
| 1953 | 242.0 | 102.5 | 476.5 | 114.4 | 1.9690 |
| 1954 | 285.7 | 121.0 | 654.5 | 157.1 | 2.2909 |
| 1955 | 353.6 | 149.8 | 743.8 | 178.5 | 2.1035 |
| 1956 | 470.9 | 199.4 | 956.4 | 229.6 | 2.0310 |

Source: Industrial Statistics Section, State Bureau of Statistics, *Wo-kuo kang-t'ieh, tien-li, mei-t'an, chi-hsieh, fang-chih, tsao-chih kung-yeh ti chin-hsi* (The past and present of China's iron and steel, electric power, coal, machine-making, textile and paper industries), Peking: Statistics Publishing House, 1958, p. 20.

Within the steel industry, the amount of fixed assets per worker for the sub-sectors varied considerably. As can be seen from Table 10.6, the amount of fixed assets per production worker in iron and manganese mining came to merely a fraction of that in smelting and refining. This implies the wide prevalence of manual operation in the mining sector. However, the relatively rapid rise in the level of technology in mining during the period 1952–1954 was reflected in the sharp decline in the relative discrepancy between the two series.

In examining per-worker fixed assets in relation to labor productivity, one should not overlook such intangible factors as the attitudes of workers, labor incentives, organization of work and welfare. The effect of these forces can be considerable, although they do not lend themselves readily to quantitative treatment. This is particularly true in a communist country where ingenious human engineering techniques have been devised to enhance the morale of workers by giving public recognition to their achievements or by arousing their competitive spirit and sense of participation. For instance, the honor of becoming a labor hero or the distinction of being awarded a special merit certificate or even a red banner is oftentimes sufficient to induce workers to greater physical and mental exertion, which will undoubtedly affect labor productivity.

*Table 10.5. Fixed Assets Per Production Worker in the Steel Industry, 1952–1956 (at 1952 prices)*

| Year | Yuan Per Worker | Index (1952 = 100) |
|---|---|---|
| 1952 | 9,251 | 100.0 |
| 1953 | 9,241 | 99.9 |
| 1954 | 11,662 | 126.1 |
| 1955 | 13,302 | 143.8 |
| 1956 | 12,781 | 138.2 |

Source: Industrial Statistics Section, State Bureau of Statistics, *Wo-kuo kang-t'ieh, tien-li, mei-t'an, chi-hsieh, fang-chih, tsao-chih, kung-yeh ti chin-hsi* (The past and present of China's iron and steel, electric power, coal, machine-making, textile and paper industries), Peking: Statistics Publishing House, 1958, p. 18.

*Table 10.6. Fixed Assets Per Production Worker in Mining and Smelting Sectors of the Steel Industry, 1952—1956 (yuan per worker at 1952 prices)*

| Year | Iron and Manganese Mining | Smelting and Refining |
|---|---|---|
| 1952 | 1,203 | 11,166 |
| 1953 | 1,887 | 10,151 |
| 1954 | 4,407 | 12,385 |
| 1955 | 4,057 | 14,244 |
| 1956 | 3,775 | 13,420 |

Source: Industrial Statistics Section, State Bureau of Statistics, *Wo-kuo kang-t'ieh, tien-li, mei-t'an, chi-hsieh, fang-chih, tsao-chih kung-yeh ti chin-hsi* (The past and present of China's iron and steel, electric power, coal, machine-making, textile and paper industries), Peking: Statistics Publishing House, 1958, p. 18.

# DERIVATION OF EMPLOYMENT AND PRODUCTION LABOR FORCE OF THE STEEL INDUSTRY

## 1957

Data on labor productivity are incomplete for the period under investigation. Although data on output value of the steel industry for the period 1952 — 1957 have been estimated in Chapter 7, data on employment and production labor force are available only for the years 1952–1956. Thus, one needs to estimate the number of employees and production workers in the steel industry in 1957 in order to derive their productivity.

The method of estimating the volume of 1957 employment is presented in Table 10–A.1. In view of the stable relationship between the volume of employment in the steel industry and that in the industrial sector as a whole during 1952–1956, it is assumed that this relationship continued to hold in 1957. It is further assumed that the exact relationship was determined by the 1952 — 1956 average so as to avoid assigning undue weights to any particular year. The share

*Table 10-A.1. Employment of the Steel Industry, 1952—1957 (persons)*

| Year | Industrial Sector[a] | Steel Industry | Percentage Share of Steel Industry |
|------|------|------|------|
| | (1) | (2) | $(3) = \dfrac{(2)}{(1)} \times 100$ |
| 1952 | 5,263,000 | 211,587 | 4.0 |
| 1953 | 6,188,000 | 254,109 | 4.1 |
| 1954 | 6,408,000 | 261,521 | 4.1 |
| 1955 | 6,477,000 | 276,902 | 4.3 |
| 1956 | 7,170,000 | 304,269 | 4.2 |
| 1957 | 7,907,000 | 332,094 | (4.2) |
| 1952–1956 Average | 6,301,000 | 261,678 | 4.2 |

a. Rounded to the nearest thousand.

Sources: Industrial Statistics Section, State Bureau of Statistics, *Wo-kuo kang-t'ieh, tien-li, mei-t'an, chi-hsieh, fang-chih, tsao-chih kung-yeh ti chin-hsi* (The past and present of China's iron and steel, electric power, coal, machine-making, textile and paper industries), Peking: Statistics Publishing House, 1958, p. 27; *Wei-ta ti shih-nien* (Ten great years), Peking, 1959, p. 162; *T'ung-chi kung-tso* (Statistical work), Peking, No. 14, 1957, p. 13; and *T'ung-chi yen-chiu* (Statistical research), Peking, No. 9, 1958, p. 5.

of employees in the steel industry thus came to 4.2 per cent of the overall industrial employment in 1957, or 332,094 persons (see Columns 3 and 2).

Estimation of the 1957 production labor force in the steel industry is based on this 1957 employment figure on the assumption that the proportion of production workers in the overall employment in 1957 remained unchanged from 1956. Since this proportion was given at 68.7 per cent by official sources[1], the number of production workers in the steel industry in 1957 is estimated to be approximately 228,150 persons.

1 *KTMCFT*, p. 27.

# PART V
# PATTERN OF GROWTH

*Chapter 11*

# INSTITUTIONAL TRANSFORMATION

The overall economic plan of the communist regime in China contains the twin goals of socialization and industrialization. The economic importance of the former stems from the regime's conviction that "production relations"[1] tend to restrain productive forces. As Mao Tse-tung put it, "When production relations become a barrier to the development of productive forces, the former have to be changed."[2] Such a conviction can be interpreted to mean (1) that socialization eliminates the need for indirect control measures and thus facilitates development planning, and (2) that the morale of laborers will be raised when working for socialized industry. Since it is not feasible to establish a simple causal relationship between institutional changes and growth in output, this chapter examines the socialization of the steel industry in terms of the different forms of ownership.

*Types of Ownership*

As stipulated in Article 26 of the *Common Programme*, the Chinese economy consisted of five components: (1) the state-owned sector, (2) the cooperative sector, (3) the sector of individual peasants and handicraftsmen, (4) the private capitalist sector, and (5) the state capitalist sector. As the last refers to the sector in which the state collaborates with private capitalists, it is also identified as the joint state-private sector in this study. Official data on the socialization of the steel industry are classified according to these five categories.

This classification is presumably based on the form of ownership of the means of production. However this criterion alone cannot distinguish between sectors 2, 3 and 4, inasmuch as all these sectors pertain to private ownership. If the collective form of private ownership should be distinguished from the individual form of private ownership as in the case of sectors 2 and 3, the private capitalist sector then becomes a mixture of both.

This inconsistency is, however, less apparent in a country where the doctrine of class struggle requires a sharp distinction between workers and capitalists. Since the private capitalist sector was doomed, there was no further need to classify it

---

1 The term "production relations" refers essentially to the pattern of ownership of the means of production.
2 *Mao Tse-tung hsüan-chi* (Selected works of Mao Tse-tung), Volume I, Peking, 1952 (Second edition), p. 314.

according to individual or collective ownership. On the other hand, since collectivization was the designated path for the socialization of handicraftsmen, it was necessary to provide a cooperative sector.

In addition to ideological considerations, the separation of individual handicraftsmen from private capitalists served a practical purpose. Individual handicraftsmen were widely scattered, and could not be readily organized through government control measures alone. Some reliance on their own initiative was necessary for the transformation of their sector. Collective ownership thus became an indispensable intermediate step in its socialization.

The private capitalist sector, on the other hand, consisted of relatively large-scale enterprises more important to the national economy and amenable to government supervision. Through rigid control over the capitalist enterprises, the government could force them into joint state-private form of ownership as a transition to their ultimate nationalization. This designated path for socializing the private capitalist sector accounted for the rapid growth of the state-capitalist sector, as data on the steel industry will show.

### Transformation Process

Table 11.1 gives an overall view of the socialist transformation of the steel industry. It shows the relative changes in output value of the five sectors during 1949−1956. The essence of socialization, as indicated previously, was to transform all the other sectors into the state sector. This process, however, is not immediately apparent from a glance at the table for several reasons.

The first is the unusually large share of the state sector from the very beginning. As can be seen from Column 1 of the table, this sector was responsible in 1949 for 82.5 per cent of the output of the steel industry. In contrast, for the modern industrial sector as a whole, only 34.7 per cent of its output value came from the

Table 11.1. Percentage Distribution of Output Value of the Steel Industry by Institutional Sector, 1949—1956

| Year | State-Owned | Joint State-Private | Private Capitalist | Handicraft | Cooperative |
|------|-------------|---------------------|--------------------|------------|-------------|
|      | (1)         | (2)                 | (3)                | (4)        | (5)         |
| 1949 | 82.5        | 3.0                 | 14.2               | 0.3        | —           |
| 1950 | 85.3        | 3.3                 | 11.1               | 0.3        | —           |
| 1951 | 82.8        | 4.4                 | 12.5               | 0.3        | —           |
| 1952 | 84.5        | 5.6                 | 9.6                | 0.3        | —           |
| 1953 | 81.7        | 6.9                 | 11.1               | 0.3        | —           |
| 1954 | 82.0        | 10.9                | 6.6                | 0.4        | 0.1         |
| 1955 | 82.0        | 13.4                | 4.0                | 0.4        | 0.2         |
| 1956 | 81.7        | 17.8                | —                  | 0.3        | 0.1         |

Sources: Tables 7.6 and 11-A.1.

state sector. The early predominance of this sector in the steel industry was attributable to the inheritance of the communist regime rather than its deliberate policy. During the war, the National Resources Commission controlled almost two-thirds of the steel production in unoccupied China. When the war ended, important iron and steel works in the liberated area of China Proper were handed over to the nationalist government by the Japanese. After the departure of Soviet troops, the major steel bases in the Northeast first served as military targets in the ensuing civil war, and subsequently fell under the control of the communist government.

A second reason for the more or less stable share of the state sector shown in Column 1 of Table 11.1 is found in the socialization plan for the private capitalist sector, which required that this sector be transformed first into the joint state-private sector. This also explains the steadily increasing relative importance of the joint sector, as can be seen from Column 2 of the table.

A third reason lies in the change of government policy regarding joint state-private enterprises, so that for all practical purposes they became no different from state enterprise. Since the private "owners" were entitled solely to a fixed rate of dividends for a specified period, this policy change made the transformation of the joint sector into the state sector automatic. Thus the elimination of any immediate nationalization measures resulted in a fairly stable share of the state sector. This stable share, however, does not imply the absence of growth. On the contrary, as Column 1 of Table 11.2 shows, output value of the state sector increased at an average rate of 54.8 per cent per annum during 1949—1956.

The discussion in terms of output value of the entire industry tends to conceal certain facts. For example, over the period 1952—1956 the relative importance of the state sector increased in terms of pig iron output, but decreased in terms of the output of ingots and finished steel, although these changes were limited[3].

### Socialization of Private Industry

The general policy governing the socialization of private capitalist enterprises, as specified in Article 10 of the 1954 Constitution of the People's Republic of China, was one of utilization, restriction and transformation. The utilization aspect was prescribed by Mao Tse-tung in anticipation of an acute shortage of material and technical-managerial personnel in the early period of communist rule. In Mao's words, "owing to the backwardness of the economy, private capitalism ... must be allowed to remain for a long period after the nation-wide victory of the revolution; its development along those lines which are beneficial to the national economy is further needed in accordance with the division of labor ...; it still is an indispensable part of the national economy."[4] Thus it is

3 See Table 11 — A.2 in the Appendix.
4 *Mao Tse-tung hsüan-chi* (Selected works of Mao Tse-tung), Shanyang, 1948, p. 10.

not surprising to find in Table 11.2 a continual growth of output of the private capitalist sector from 1949 to 1953. Partly responsible for this increase was the entry of new firms. Of the 245 private capitalist iron and steel enterprises in operation in 1953, 146 were established after the communist takeover[5].

*Table 11.2 Annual Growth of Output Value of the Steel Industry by Institutional Sector, 1949—1956 (per cent)*

| Year | State | Private Capitalist | Joint State-Private | Handicraft | Cooperative |
|------|-------|--------------------|---------------------|------------|-------------|
| | (1) | (2) | (3) | (4) | (5) |
| 1950 | 228.6 | 148.1 | 250.1 | 234.5 | |
| 1951 | 45.1 | 68.6 | 101.6 | 40.7 | |
| 1952 | 53.4 | 15.2 | 90.1 | 55.5 | |
| 1953 | 32.2 | 57.5 | 66.9 | 64.1 | |
| 1954 | 24.9 | -26.2 | 96.9 | 40.5 | |
| 1955 | 24.3 | -24.8 | 53.9 | 60.6 | 34.5 |
| 1956 | 42.0 | -100.0 | 89.2 | -13.5 | 1.7 |
| 1949—1956 Average | 54.8 | -53.4 | 100.1 | 56.9 | — |

Sources: Tables 7.6 and 11-A.1; Industrial Statistics Section, State Bureau of Statistics, *Wo-kuo kang-t'ieh, tien-li, mei-t'an, chi-hsieh, fang-chih, tsao-chih kung-yeh ti chin-hsi* (The past and present of China's iron and steel, electric power, coal, machine-making, textile and paper industries), Peking: Statistics Publishing House, 1958, pp. 13 and 29.

The above quotation also made it clear that the growth of the private capitalist sector was to be circumscribed. Those lines of industrial pursuits not interpreted by the government as beneficial to the national welfare and the people's livelihood were to be restricted. The policy of allowing but limiting the development of the private capitalist sector contained an element of practical wisdom. Outright nationalization of private industrial enterprises at the beginning of the communist regime would not only have been administratively difficult and politically unwise, but also detrimental to the communist objective of increasing the national product. Furthermore, so long as the government was capable of controlling the development of the private capitalist sector, the latter could be made to fit into the overall development planning.

The transformation aspect of the general policy governing the socialization of private capitalist enterprises consisted in encouraging and guiding them to the path of joint state-private undertakings. As a result, the output value of the joint sector on the average doubled every year from 1949—1956, as shown in Column 3 of Table 11.2[6]. Concomitantly the number of joint enterprises increased from

5 Ching Hua, *et al, Ch'i-nien lai wo-kuo szu-ying kung-shang-yeh ti pien-hua, 1949 —1956* (Changes in China's private industry and commerce in the past seven years), Peking, 1957, p. 91.
6 The increase in its finished steel output was particularly outstanding. See Table 11 — A.2 in the Appendix.

4 in 1949 to 178 in 1956[7]. The number more than tripled from 1955 to 1956, as a result of stepping up the socialization program in the latter part of 1955 and early 1956. In the latter year, the private capitalist sector virtually disappeared from the steel industry[8]. In view of the automatic transformation from the joint state-private sector to the state sector, the socialization of the private capitalist sector of the steel industry was for all practical purposes completed by the end of 1956.

To complete the coverage of the socialization of private establishments in the steel industry, it remains to examine the changes in the handicraft and cooperative sectors. The transformation of the handicraft into the cooperative sector apparently did not take place until 1954. Prior to that year, there were no cooperatives in the steel industry, as can be seen from Column 5 of Tables 11.1 and 11.2. In fact, the output value of the handicraft sector continued to increase from 1949 to 1955. During this period, its growth almost kept pace with that of the steel industry as a whole. The comparable growth rates are reflected in the stable share of the handicraft sector in the overall output value of the industry (see Column 4 of Table 11.1).

Although the cooperative sector made a good start in 1954 (in which year its output value amounted to 38.2 per cent of that of the handicraft sector)[9], in the following year its growth lagged behind the latter sector. In 1956, while the output of the handicraftsmen declined, that of cooperatives continued to increase though at a drastically reduced rate, as shown in Columns 4 and 5 of Table 11.2. Such slow progress in transforming private to collective ownership signified the lack of sufficient initiative on the part of handicraftsmen coupled with the government's preoccupation with collectivizing agriculture.

The rise of people's communes together with the mass steel campaign in 1958 appears to have enhanced considerably the relative importance of collective ownership in the steel industry. However, the actual effect must have been limited inasmuch as the sub-standard products of the small native furnaces were excluded from the output data of the steel industry. While most of these furnaces disappeared, some were subsequently converted into small modern furnaces. With the waning influence of people's communes, the majority of these furnaces became state-owned under the jurisdiction of provincial governments. Thus the two campaigns of 1958, perhaps, somewhat hastened the socialization of the handicraft sector, the remnant of private ownership in the steel industry.

---

7 The number of joint state-private enterprises was as follows: 4(1949), 6(1950), 16(1951), 19(1952), 27(1953), 45(1954), 58(1955), 178(1956). *KTMCFT*, pp. 13 and 29.
8 Only a limited number of private capitalist enterprises remained in 1956 in the production of pig iron. Their aggregate output, however, amounted only to some 0.001 per cent. See Table 11 — A.2 in the Appendix.
9 Derived from data presented in Table 11—A.1 in the Appendix.

# APPENDIX 11 — A

## OUTPUT VALUE AND MAJOR PRODUCTS OF
## THE STEEL INDUSTRY BY INSTITUTIONAL SECTOR

Annual output value of the five sectors of the steel industry during 1949–1956 are presented in Table 11-A.1. Discussion of the institutional changes in the steel industry solely in terms of aggregate output value fails to show the relative output behavior of the sectors by product. Obtainable data on the major products in physical quantities for 1952–1956 are, therefore, presented in Table 11-A.2. Such a breakdown shows the percentage distribution of pig iron, ingot steel and finished steel in each of the sectors. In addition, it shows, among other things, that the role of the individual handicraftsmen and the cooperative sector in the steel industry was limited to pig iron production.

Table 11—A.1. *Output Value of the Steel Industry by Institutional Sector, 1949—1956 (in thousand yuan at 1952 prices)*

| Year | State-Owned | Joint State-Private | Private Capitalist | Handicraft | Cooperative |
|------|-------------|---------------------|--------------------|------------|-------------|
|      | (1) | (2) | (3) | (4) | (5) |
| 1949 | 158,231 | 5,742 | 27,323 | 502 | — |
| 1950 | 519,962 | 20,102 | 67,778 | 1,679 | — |
| 1951 | 754,633 | 40,520 | 114,269 | 2,362 | — |
| 1952 | 1,157,250 | 77,041 | 131,629 | 3,674 | — |
| 1953 | 1,529,368 | 128,608 | 207,327 | 6,030 | — |
| 1954 | 1,909,717 | 253,204 | 152,924 | 8,475 | 3,236 |
| 1955 | 2,373,899 | 389,707 | 115,046 | 13,607 | 4,352 |
| 1956 | 3,371,464 | 737,259 | a | 11,764 | 4,428 |

a. Negligible.

Source: Industrial Statistics Section, State Bureau of Statistics, *Wo-kuo kang-t'ieh, tien-li, mei-t'an, chi-hsieh, fang-chih, tsao-chih kung-yeh ti chin-hsi* (The past and present of China's iron and steel, electric power, coal, machine-making, textile and paper industries), Peking: Statistics Publishing House, 1958, pp. 10, 11, 30 and 31.

Table 11–A.2. Major Products of the Steel Industry by Institutional Sector, 1952–1956 (in tons)

| Sector | Product | 1952 Output | Percentage Share of Total | 1953 Output | Percentage Share of Total | 1954 Output | Percentage Share of Total | 1955 Output | Percentage Share of Total | 1956 Output | Percentage Share of Total |
|---|---|---|---|---|---|---|---|---|---|---|---|
| | | (1) | (2) | (3) | (4) | (5) | (6) | (7) | (8) | (9) | (10) |
| State-owned | Ingot steel | 1,811,813 | 93.9 | 2,098,310 | 93.9 | 2,939,789 | 94.4 | 3,687,975 | 95.2 | 4,674,469 | 96.9 |
| | Finished steel | 1,274,579 | 94.5 | 1,617,631 | 91.2 | 1,978,518 | 89.0 | 2,485,567 | 87.1 | 3,973,643 | 89.0 |
| | Pig iron | 1,089,924 | 83.1 | 1,401,027 | 79.9 | 1,535,793 | 78.1 | 1,891,091 | 75.5 | 2,979,685 | 76.0 |
| Joint state-private | Ingot steel | 12,701 | 0.7 | 10,867 | 0.5 | 42,162 | 1.4 | 61,156 | 1.6 | 90,718 | 1.9 |
| | Finished steel | 69,231 | 5.1 | 146,211 | 8.2 | 245,578 | 11.0 | 365,156 | 12.8 | 491,779 | 11.0 |
| | Pig iron | 93,406 | 7.1 | 135,254 | 7.7 | 285,434 | 14.5 | 458,014 | 18.3 | 941,290 | 24.0 |
| Private capitalist | Ingot steel | 53,941 | 2.8 | 65,410 | 2.9 | 46,852 | 1.5 | 27,873 | 0.7 | 662 | (0.001) |
| | Finished steel | 4,699 | 0.4 | 10,112 | 0.6 | 499 | (0.02) | 2,382 | 0.1 | — | — |
| | Pig iron | 128,567 | 9.8 | 217,880 | 12.4 | 144,140 | 7.4 | 155,712 | 6.2 | — | — |
| Handicraft | Pig iron | 50,130 | 2.6 | 59,511 | 2.7 | 79,056 | 2.5 | 77,793 | 2.0 | 48,852 | 1.0 |
| Cooperative | Pig iron | — | — | — | — | 5,844 | 0.2 | 17,624 | 0.5 | 11,548 | 0.2 |

Source: Industrial Statistics Section, State Bureau of Statistics, Wo-kuo kang-t'ieh, tien-li, mei-t'an, chi-hsieh, fang-chih, tsao-chih kung-yeh ti chin-hsi (The past and present of China's iron and steel, electric power, coal, machine-making, textile and paper industries), Peking: Statistics Publishing House, 1958, pp. 30 and 31.

## Chapter 12

# SCALE, COST AND TECHNOLOGY

This chapter analyzes changes in the scale of production in terms of cost structure and choice of technique. The development pattern of the steel industry is particularly significant in view of its designation as the leading industry in the national industrialization program. This role for steel has stemmed from the planners' determination to achieve self-sufficiency in this important metal within the shortest possible time.

### Emphasis on Large-Scale Operation[1]

The development policy of the communist regime is to convert China from a backward, agricultural country into an advanced, industrial state. To achieve this objective, economic planners were striving for the latest technology and the largest possible scale of operation. Accordingly, the 156 Soviet aid projects constituted the core of China's industrial construction plan. While the emphasis on large-scale operation and up-to-date technology facilitated a thorough transformation of the Chinese economy, it at the same time enabled China to take greater advantage of Soviet technical aid.

The way in which this emphasis was expressed in the steel industry can be seen from Table 12.1, which compares the largest blast furnace, open hearth and blooming mill planned in China, with those available in USSR and USA. As shown in the table, the maximum blast furnace capacity planned in China was greater than that existing in the Soviet Union in 1957[2], and the maximum roll diameter planned in China was greater than that existing in the United States. Construction of such equipment was largely completed in 1958.

The planners' emphasis on enlarging the scale of operation was reflected in increases in the average capacity of smelting equipment. The average useful capacity of blast furnaces under the jurisdiction of the Ministry of Metallurgical Industry was 224 m³ in 1952 and 309 m³ in 1956. Similarly the average floor space of open hearths under the jurisdiction of the Ministry was 28.5 m² in 1952 and 40.7 m² in 1956[3].

---

1 For this emphasis, the reader should refer to the cases of enlarging furnace capacity in rehabilitation and reconstruction, given in Chapters 4 and 5.
2 An identical furnace of 1,513 m³ was completed in the Soviet Union in September 1958, and six others were under construction.
3 *KTMCFT*, p. 16. The trend toward enlarging the production scale can also be illus-

*Table 12.1. Largest Metallurgical Equipment in China, USSR and USA, 1957*

| Type of Equipment | Unit | China (Planned) | USSR | USA |
|---|---|---|---|---|
| Blast furnace | Useful capacity in m³ | 1,513a | 1,386 | 1,810 |
| Open hearth | Rated capacity in tons | 500b | 500 | 500 |
| Bloomer | Roll diameter in mm | 1,150c | 1,150 | 1,000 |

a. Construction completed in November 1958.
b. Construction completed in October 1958.
c. Construction scheduled for completion in 1959.

Source: Industrial Statistics Section, State Bureau of Statistics, *Wo-kuo kang-t'ieh, tien-li, mei-t'an, chi-hsieh, fang-chih, tsao-chih kung-yeh ti chin-hsi* (The past and present of China's iron and steel, electric power, coal, machine-making, textile and paper industries), Peking: Statistics Publishing House, 1958, p. 14.

The emphasis on large-scale operation can also be seen from the relatively large amount of investment in the three key steel bases (Anshan, Wuhan and Paotow). They absorbed 62 per cent of the industry's aggregate capital investment in the first plan quinquennium. Their share was envisaged to be 40 per cent in the Second Five-Year Plan[4]. Thus, roughly one half of the industry's capital investment was to be used in bringing about the largest possible scale of operation embodying the latest technology.

## Rise of A Small-Scale Production Front

The trend toward enlarging the scale of operation discernible in the first plan quinquennium was overshadowed in 1958 by a frantic mass movement for opening up a second industrial front consisting of small-scale, labor-intensive production units using indigenous techniques. In iron and steel, this movement was vigorously carried out under the slogan of "the entire nation making steel." Some sixty million people from all walks of life reportedly participated, in varying degrees, in the mining of ore and coal and in the smelting of iron and steel, and the number of producing units multiplied. The number of native iron smelting

3 (cont'd)
trated by the rising incremental ratio of blast furnaces with an effective volume over 100 m³ to those with an effective volume of 100 m³ or below during 1954—1956:

| Year | Incremental Ratio |
|---|---|
| 1954 | 0.0769 |
| 1955 | 0.2000 |
| 1956 | 0.2857 |

Similarly all the open hearths added in 1955 and 1956 were each with a floor area over 30 m². Ronald Hsia, "The Development of Mainland China's Steel Industry Since 1958," *The China Quarterly*, July-September 1961, p. 115.

4 *Yeh-chin pao* (Metallurgy), weekly, Peking, No. 25, 1957, p. 22.

furnaces, for instance, increased from some 12,000 in June to half a million within three months; by the end of 1958, some two million such furnaces had been built or rebuilt[5].

The construction of such primitive, labor-intensive "backyard furnaces" was in apparent contradiction to the earlier emphasis on large-scale operation. This change needs an explanation. The communist authorities were deeply concerned over the drastically reduced rate of industrial growth in 1957[6]. Their concern was compounded by the approaching exhaustion of Soviet credit. Yet they refused to accept the view that with the broadening of the industrial base the tempo of industrial development was bound to decline, and insisted that industrialization could proceed more rapidly. To speed up the tempo of development, they discarded the concept of balanced growth, and envisaged development as a dialectic process from balance to imbalance and to a new balance, emphasizing the temporary and conditional nature of any state of balance[7].

This concept of balance led logically to a policy reorientation with greater emphasis on linkage effects (both forward and backward)[8]. Since the steel industry has the greatest total linkage[9], it is not surprising that the communist authorities chose steel as the leading link in the new development strategy. The small-scale production front was, therefore, created in the steel industry to ensure that it could perform its assigned task as the leading sector.

This second production front was also created to meet the shortage of iron and steel, which became acute in 1958 because of the sudden spurt in demand for agricultural implements required to fulfill the agricultural plan, the enlarged scale of water conservancy construction, and the popularization of new-type local means of transport[10]. In addition, the three million-odd rural factories established in the first half of 1958 and the 26,000 people's communes formed subsequently all tended to increase the demand for iron and steel. The people's communes, for instance, were expected to require some ten million tons of iron and steel in the course of 1959.

5 Wang Chen-chih, "Tui kang-t'ieh sheng-chan chung chi-ke ching-chi wen-ti ti ch'ien-chien" (Preliminary views on some economic problems in connection with iron and steel production), *Chi-hua ching-chi* (Planned economy), monthly, Peking, December 1958, p. 21; Wu Li-yung, "Hen-hen-ti chua wei wan-ch'eng i-ling-ch'i-ling wan tun kang erh fen-tou" (Strive forcefully to accomplish [the target of] 10.7 million tons of steel), *Ibid.*, October 1958, p. 1.
6 The rate of industrial growth decreased from 31.1 per cent in 1956 to 7.0 per cent in 1957. Ronald Hsia, "China's Industrial Growth, 1953—1957," *The Annals of the American Academy of Political and Social Science*, Vol. 321 (January 1959), p. 73.
7 Mao Tse-tung, "Kuan-yü cheng-ch'üeh ch'u-li jen-min nei-pu mao-tun ti wen-ti" (On the correct handling of contradictions among the people), *Jen-min jih-pao*, June 19, 1957.
8 Forward linkage effects have the tendency toward pushing ahead subsequent stages of production; backward linkage effects tend to pull up the activity level at the preceding stages of production. Albert L. Hirschman, *The Strategy of Economic Development*, New Haven, 1959, pp. 98—104.
9 *Ibid.*, p. 107. A glance at the steel row and column of the input-output matrix of an industrial economy will reveal the total linkage of the steel industry.
10 An example of the new-type local means of transport is a cart with ball-bearing axles.

In view of the materials, skill and equipment available for capital construction and the length of time required, it was impossible to expand modern smelting facilities in time to meet the growing demand for iron and steel. Furthermore, even if it had been possible to increase in time the smelting capacity of existing plants, the inadequate transport facilities coupled with the concentration of steel centers would have proved a serious bottleneck in the distribution not only of iron and steel but also of steel products and agricultural implements to consumption points scattered over the country. Thus the creation of a diffused production front appeared to be a sensible approach toward meeting the urgent needs. Such an approach also made sense in minimizing investment outlays by utilizing locally available human, material and financial resources.

## Scale and Construction Costs

This section examines cost differences in constructing three broad categories of steel firms in China, viz., large, medium-sized and small. The latter category, however, does not include small *native* iron and steel works whose construction costs are known to be extremely low[11]. The dubious quality of their products and the limited use of such products could hardly justify even the exceedingly low investment costs.

Obtainable cost estimates for constructing large, medium-sized and small iron and steel works are presented in Table 12.2, together with their respective gestation lags. These estimates referring to the "representative" scale for each of the three categories show the relative advantage of building small and medium-sized

*Table 12.2. Estimated 1958—1959 Construction Costs of Integrated Steel Works*

| Scale | Annual Steel Capacity (in thousand tons) | Capital Construction Costs (in million yuan at current prices) | Gestation Period (in years) |
|---|---|---|---|
|  | (1) | (2) | (3) |
| Large | 1,500 | 800 — 1,000 | 8 — 9 |
| Medium | 300 — 400 | 100 — 150 | 4 — 5 |
| Small | 160 | 50 — 100 | 2 — 3 |

Sources: *Jen-min jih-pao*, August 19, 1957; *Yeh-chin pao* (Metallurgy), Peking, No. 25, 1957, p. 22; and *Kuang-ming jih-pao*, Peking, November 19, 1957.

11 For example, the cost of constructing a small *native* iron and steel works in Kuhsien, Shansi, with an annual capacity of 1,200 tons of pig iron, 1,000 tons of ingot steel, 900 tons of rolled steel, 180 tons of refractory bricks and 2,000 tons of coke, amounted to 10,000 yuan. The capital cost on the basis of per-ton ingot steel capacity thus came to 10 yuan, as compared with a minimum of 500 yuan for large steel cobines. Even if allowance is made for any downward bias arising from the probable underreporting of labor cost in the construction of *native* works, the difference remains striking. *Hung-ch'i* (Red flag), monthly, Peking, No. 10, 1958, p. 12; *NCNA*, September 22, 1959.

integrated works. The amount of investment required for constructing a large combine with an annual ingot steel capacity of 1.5 million tons could be used for constructing 6–7 medium-sized integrated works each with an annual capacity of 300–400 thousand tons. On the assumption that the given amount of investment was used for building 6 steel works each with an annual capacity of 350 thousand tons, the aggregate annual capacity would come to 2.1 million tons. Similarly, the same amount of investment could be used for constructing 11–13 small steel works each with an annual capacity of 160 thousand tons or an aggregate capacity of some 2 million tons per annum.

The difference in construction costs attributable to scale can be seen more readily from the required amount of capital investment per ton of ingot steel capacity. The latter, during 1958–1959, came to 500–700 yuan for large combines and 300–500 yuan for medium-sized and small works[12]. For specialized plants, the difference in construction costs was more pronounced. For example, in the construction of ten small seamless steel tube plants in Peking, Tientsin, Canton, Sian, Taiyuan, Nanchang and other places in 1958, the amount of capital investment on a per-ton capacity basis was estimated to be 10 per cent of the amount invested in the Anshan Seamless Tube Plant[13]. In addition, the combined capacity of these plants exceeded that of the Anshan Seamless Tube Plant by 10 thousand tons[14]. One major factor responsible for the lower construction costs of smaller plants was in the use of equipment produced in China. The construction of a steel combine with an annual ingot steel capacity of 1.5 million tons, for instance, would require blowers capable of blowing 1,500 m³ of air per minute for its blast furnaces and bloomers with roll diameters of at least 1,000 mm. For such types of equipment, however, high import prices had to be paid, as they could not be manufactured in China[15].

The construction of smaller iron and steel works had the additional advantage of a shorter gestation period. As can be seen from Table 12.2, it would take 8–9 years to build a large combine. For such a combine to be in partial operation would require 5–6 years, the same length of time needed to complete a medium-sized one. The construction of small works, on the other hand, would take only 2–3 years. The multiplication of small producing units was thus expected to meet the rising demand for steel. The resource endowments of the country also favored the choice of a smaller production scale. A 1.5 million ton steel combine would require an iron ore deposit of some 150 million tons (based on 50% Fe content) and a 300–400 thousand ton works, an ore deposit of only 20–30 thousand tons. Geological surveys in the mid-1950's indicated that while iron ore

---

12 Capital construction costs for building steel works were 30–40 per cent lower in 1958–1959 than during the first plan period. *NCNA*, September 22, 1959.
13 *Ibid.*, May 2, 1958.
14 Each of these plants has an annual capacity of 7,000 tons. Capacity of the Anshan Steel Tube Plant was 60 thousand tons per annum after its completion in 1953. *Ibid.*; Table 5.3.
15 *Yeh-chin pao*, No. 25, 1957, p. 22.

deposits reaching the level of 150 million tons were scarce, deposits in the neighbourhood of 20—30 thousand tons were available in most provinces[16].

Cost differences attributable to scale can also be illustrated by the construction of blast furnaces. In the first plan period, construction costs per cubic meter of furnace volume came to 25,000 yuan for furnaces of approximately 1,000 m³, and 12,500 yuan for 80 m³ of a standard design[17]. With the lowering of construction costs in 1958—1959, the cost per cubic meter of furnace volume was estimated at 14,000—18,000 yuan for large furnaces and less than 10,000 yuan for small furnaces[18]. The actual cost of building small furnaces was considerably less in some cases. For instance, the construction of a 6.5 m³ furnace in Funing *hsien*, Hopeh, cost 40,000 yuan, or approximately 6,000 yuan per cubic meter of furnace volume[19].

From the viewpoint of minimizing capital investment and maximizing output in the short run, the relatively lower construction costs and shorter gestation period of medium-sized and small iron and steel works made their construction more desirable. But, to determine their overall economic advantage, it is necessary to look into the variable cost relative to scale.

## Scale and Production Costs[20]

The shift of relative emphasis to a smaller scale of operation affected the variable cost as well as the fixed cost. The comparative advantage enjoyed by smaller producing units in construction costs tended to be diminished by their higher production costs. On a per-ton output basis, the latter averaged in the third quarter of 1959 somewhat above 250 yuan as against 150 yuan for iron produced by large furnaces[21].

A breakdown of the variable cost according to scale reveals that small furnaces operated with a relatively high cost for raw materials and a relatively low cost for labor. Raw materials accounted for 65—75 per cent of the variable cost for small blast furnaces and labor for 5—10 per cent. The corresponding figures for large blast furnaces were 60 and 20 per cent[22]. It, therefore, appears that the high pig iron production costs of small furnaces were attributable primarily to the high

16 Notably, Shantung, Honan, Hopeh, Anhwei, Kiangsu, Chekiang, Hunan, Hupeh, Kwangtung, Fukien, Szechwan, and Yunnan. *Ibid.*
17 *Chi-hua ching-chi* (Planned economy), Peking, No. 4, 1957, p. 10; *Yeh-chin pao*, No. 25, 1957, p. 23.
18 *Ta-kung pao*, Hong Kong, October 7, 1959; *Kuang-ming jih-pao*, March 29, 1958; *Chi-hua ching-chi*, No. 4, 1958, p. 31.
19 *Ibid.*, No. 6, 1958, p. 47.
20 Following the Chinese practice, "production cost" is used in this study to refer solely to "variable cost." Hence the two terms are used interchangeably.
21 Here small blast furnaces refer to those ranging from 6.5—28 m³, and large furnaces those ranging from 500—1600 m³.
22 *Yeh-chin pao*, No. 40, 1959; *CTCHK*, p. 226.

costs of material inputs, as expressed in their high coke rates, low outgoing quality levels and low utilization coefficients.

The difference between large and small blast furnaces in these respects has already been considered in Chapter 8. The concern here is to show how changes in these factors affected production costs. Table 12.3 presents the cost and technical data of a small blast furnace (22 m³) in Tsinan during the first three quarters of 1959. It can be seen from the table that the reduction in production costs (notably in the second quarter) was accompanied by a decrease in coke rate and an increase in both the outgoing quality level and the furnace coefficient.

To lower the cost of iron production by small blast furnaces ranging from 6.5–28 m³, the plan of setting cost ceilings for different regions or plants was adopted at the National Conference of Small Blast Furnace Operators convened in Hantan, Hopeh, during September 16–23, 1959[23]. The cost ceilings are shown

*Table 12.3. Cost and Technical Data of a Small Blast Furnace in Tsinan, First Three Quarters of 1959*

| Quarter | Production Costs (yuan/ton of output) | Furnace Coefficient (tons/m³/24 hrs.) | Outgoing Quality Level (per cent) | Coke Rate (tons/ton of output) |
|---|---|---|---|---|
| | (1) | (2) | (3) | (4) |
| First | 531.66 | 0.882 | 24.40 | 2.651 |
| Second | 296.47 | 1.131 | 78.59 | 1.544 |
| Third | 288.55 | 1.433 | 90.40 | 1.269 |

Source: *Kang-t'ieh* (Iron and steel), Peking, No. 1, 1960, p. 12.

*Table 12.4. Planned Cost Ceiling of Iron Production by Small Furnace, September 1959 (in yuan per ton of pig iron output)*

| Province, Autonomous Region or Plant | Cost Ceiling |
|---|---|
| Anshan, Wuhan, and Lungyen Plants (small blast furnaces only) | 120 |
| Yunnan | 180 |
| Hunan and Kweichow | 200 |
| Shansi, Szechwan, Hopeh and Kiangsu | 220 |
| Anhwei, Shantung, Inner Mongolia and Honan | 250 |
| Chekiang, Hupeh, Kiangsi, Kwangtung, Liaoning, Kwangsi, Fukien and Ningsia | 280 |
| Kirin, Heilungkiang, Shensi, Tsinghai, Kansu and Sinkiang | 300 |

Source: *Yeh-chin pao* (Metallurgy), Peking, No. 40, 1959.

23 *Yeh-chin pao*, No. 40, 1959.

in Table 12.4. Substantially lower cost ceilings were set for the small furnaces at large steel centers, where they obviously enjoyed the advantage of external economies. Regional differences in variable cost as reflected in these ceilings were considerably smaller than those prevailing prior to the introduction of ceilings. In August 1959, production costs of small blast furnaces ranging from 6.5–28 m³ in nine provinces, as shown in Table 12.5, varied from 84.36–553.80 yuan per ton of iron output. This is compared with the range of 120–300 yuan for cost ceilings given in Table 12.4.

*Table 12.5. Cost of Pig Iron Production by Small Blast Furnace, August 1959*
*(in yuan per ton of pig iron output)*

| Plant and Location | Cost |
|---|---|
| Shuicheng Iron & Steel Plant, Kweichow | 84.36 |
| Wanfu Iron & Steel Plant, Szechwan | 96.54 |
| Anfu Iron & Steel Plant, Kiangsi | 159.37 |
| Jenho Iron Plant, Hunan | 172.42 |
| Changchih Iron & Steel Plant, Shansi | 195.84 |
| Shihchiachuang Iron & Steel Plant, Hopeh | 207.99 |
| Shuiye Iron Plant, Honan | 218.62 |
| Kaiyuan No. 1 Iron & Steel Plant, Liaoning | 451.10 |
| Chiamussu Iron & Steel Plant, Heilungkiang | 553.80 |

Source: *Yeh-chin pao* (Metallurgy), Peking, No. 40, 1959.

The effectiveness of setting cost ceilings for the production of pig iron in small blast furnaces depended primarily on the possibility of lowering their coke rates as well as raising their outgoing quality levels and furnace coefficients. By virtue of the extensive improvements in production techniques applicable to small blast furnaces, fifty small producing units in various parts of the country were able to lower their costs of producing pig iron at a level comparable to those for large blast furnaces early in 1960[24].

24 The per-ton cost of pig iron production by these units was 150 yuan or less in January 1960. Their distribution by province is as follows:

## Converter vs. Open Hearth

The rise of small blast furnaces in 1958 was accompanied by building of side-blown converters. The relatively small size of converters[25] coupled with simplicity in their operation made possible a more intensive use of labor. The difference between converters and open hearths, therefore, was not confined solely to scale, it also entailed a choice of technique. The rapid growth of converter steel relative to open-hearth steel thus meant a shift to a smaller scale of operation and a higher labor intensity. Such a shift was bound to affect the input and cost structure in the production of ingot steel.

*Inputs* — In theory, there should be no difference in steel refining whether by open hearth or converter. Differences in input requirements between the two types of furnace arose chiefly from the methods employed in their operation. Data on the input structure of the two types of furnace during 1953–1956 are presented in Table 12.6 with the following observations.

First, on a per-ton output basis, converter steel requires, on the average, 349 kilograms more pig iron than does open-hearth steel. Taking the inputs of metals as a whole, the margin is narrowed to 74 kilograms.

Second, the average proportion of pig iron in the overall amount of metal inputs during 1953–1956 comes to 95.7 per cent for converter steel as against 70.4 per cent for open-hearth steel. This wide discrepancy can be attributed to the large amount of steel scrap required in the production of open-hearth steel. In fact, the acute shortage of steel scrap in China provided a valid ground for the growing use of converters.

Third, a comparison of Columns 3 and 4 with Columns 8 and 9 in the table shows that converter steel requires almost as much fuel as open-hearth steel. This is contrary to the common belief that the utilization of internal heat in converters

24 (cont'd)

| Province or Autonomous Region | Number of units |
|---|---|
| Szechwan | 12 |
| Hunan | 8 |
| Shansi | 6 |
| Yunnan | 5 |
| Kwangsi | 4 |
| Kweichow | 4 |
| Kiangsi | 3 |
| Anhwei | 2 |
| Hopeh | 2 |
| Kwangtung | 2 |
| Fukien | 1 |
| Shantung | 1 |
| Total | 50 |

For the names and particulars of these producing units, see *Yeh-chin pao*, No. 12, 1960, p. 27.

25 The size of side-blown converters ranged from a capacity of 0.5 ton per blow to 5–6 tons per blow. For the development of such basic lined converters, see Chapter 9.

provides an effective means of lowering fuel consumption. The explanation lies in the inclusion of fuel consumption by cupolas in the data given in the table. As pointed out in Chapter 9, cupolas are indispensable in the operation of converters for providing liquid pig iron at a high temperature.

Finally, as can be seen from Column 5, each ton of open-hearth steel requires more than 200 kilograms of iron ore input (based on 55% Fe content). These represent high-quality ores, the shortage of which raises the relative advantage of steel-making by converters.

*Table 12.6. Input Structure of Open-Hearth and Converter Steels, 1953—1956 (in kilograms per ton of output)*

| Year | Open-Hearth Steel | | | | | Converter Steel | | | |
|---|---|---|---|---|---|---|---|---|---|
| | Pig Iron | Other Metals | Coke | Coal | Ores (55% Fe) | Pig Iron | Other Metals | Coke | Coal |
| | (1) | (2) | (3) | (4) | (5) | (6) | (7) | (8) | (9) |
| 1953 | 769 | 348 | 2.83 | 389 | 231 | 1,148 | 42 | 156 | 0.50 |
| 1954 | 784 | 328 | 3.73 | 379 | 225 | 1,124 | 61 | 150 | 0.50 |
| 1955 | 763 | 327 | 1.71 | 359 | 201 | 1,105 | 56 | 139 | 0.39 |
| 1956 | 783 | 298 | 1.81 | 308 | 206 | 1,117 | 43 | 140 | 1.64 |
| 1953—56 Average | 775 | 325 | 2.52 | 359 | 216 | 1,124 | 51 | 146 | 0.76 |

Sources: *Yeh-chin pao* (Metallurgy), Peking, No. 1, 1958, p. 34; *Tung-chi kung-tso* (Statistical work), Peking, No. 18, 1957, p. 33.

*Production costs* — The per-ton costs of converter steel have been estimated to be 80—90 per cent of that of open-hearth steel[26]. The higher production costs of the latter stem essentially from the high prices of steel scrap, which was in short supply. In 1957, for instance, the purchase price for scrap was raised from 300 yuan to as much as 700 yuan per ton[27].

In considering cost differences, one should not overlook output quality. For quality reasons, converter steel was used primarily in the manufacture of agricultural implements, light engineering components and light structural sections, although changes in production techniques had, in some cases, narrowed considerably the quality gap between the two types of steel[28].

*Construction costs* — At the First National Conference on Converter Production Techniques convened in Tangshan by the Iron and Steel Bureau of the Ministry of Metallurgical Industry during July 6—14, 1956, the costs for constructing a converter plant with an annual capacity of 200,000 tons were estimated to be roughly half the amount for constructing an open-hearth shop of similar capa-

26 *Kuang-ming jih-pao*, February 7, 1956; *Kung-jen jih-pao*, March 19, 1958.
27 *Yeh-chin pao*, No. 1, 1958, p. 34.
28 *Kuang-ming jih-pao*, February 7, 1956; *Jen-min jih-pao*, February 9, 1958.

city[29]. On a per-ton output basis, construction costs came to 20 yuan for converter steel as against 50 yuan for open-hearth steel. With allowance for the higher consumption of metals (particularly of pig iron) by converters, their construction costs amounted to 29 yuan per ton of output[30]. It was further pointed out at the Conference that the construction of such a converter plant would take about a year. The gestation period of an open-hearth shop of equal capacity, on the other hand, would be from eighteen months to two years[31].

The lower costs for building a converter plant can be attributed ultimately to the relatively simple method of steel refining by converters, which require a much shorter heat time and less ancillary installations, in comparison with the open hearth. For a given quantity of output, the shorter heat time is tantamount to reducing the furnace size. Thus, within a given period, a converter can produce 8—10 times as much as an open hearth of equal per-heat capacity[32]. The relatively small size of converters and their limited need for ancillary installations make their construction cost correspondingly less in terms of material and labor inputs per ton of output. In addition, the simple designs of converters allow the use of labor-intensive techniques as well as low-cost domestic materials and equipment.

Another important consideration in choosing converters for the new production front was the need for treating the low-quality iron produced by the small blast furnaces. Its exceptionally high phospherous and sulphur content practically ruled out the possibility of treating it in the open hearth. Such iron, however, could be treated more readily in the basic side-blown converter. Thus, with the improvements in converter production techniques, the relative importance of converter steel was elevated.

### The Dichotomous Pattern

With a small-scale production front added to the large enterprises envisaged in the First Five-Year Plan, a dichotomous development pattern emerged in 1958. Thus, small iron and steel works were developed simultaneously with giant combines like Wuhan Steel and Paotow Steel. While the latter with their advantage of the economies of scale and command over the latest technology were to become the backbone of China's steel industry, the small works were expected to develop gradually into modern works each with an annual capacity of 200,000—800,000 tons and possibly into integrated works of 800,000—1,000,000 ton capacity, so that they could better complement the huge combines.

This dichotomous pattern of developing the steel industry should be appraised from the viewpoint of the size of the country relative to available transport facilities, the distribution of iron and coal deposits, the dispersion of consumption points, and the possibility of input substitution. Inadequate transport facilities do

29 *Kung-jen jih-pao*, July 21, 1956.
30 *Yeh-chin pao*, No. 1, 1958, p. 34.
31 *Chung-kuo ching-nien pao*, April 10, 1958.
32 *Ibid.*

not permit a concentrated development of giant steel centers[33]. Such a development, even if feasible, would be uneconomic in view of the size of the country and its scattered consumption points. The wide dispersion of iron and coal deposits (which are found almost in every province) and the possibility of using anthracite and charcoal as a partial substitute for coke in small blast furnaces similarly tend to favor the dichotomous development pattern.

Ironically, however, these objective considerations were only incidental to the policy decision on bringing about a small-scale production front. The major consideration in this decision, as pointed out previously, was that the short gestation period, the low construction cost, and the use of domestic material and surplus labor in building small iron and steel works tended to speed up the growth of the steel industry. Consequently the small-scale production front was marked by a sudden increase in labor-intensity and a terrible waste of economic resources.

In the last quarter of 1958, it generally took 50—60 man-days to produce one ton of pig iron from a native furnace. The corresponding labor input in Anshan Steel was only one man-day[34]. This is not all. The 4.16 million tons of iron and 3.08 million tons of steel produced by the small native furnaces in 1958 were declared officially as sub-standard products of limited use. Worse yet, the wholesale deterioration of output quality proved disturbing to the production line of the steel industry. The low-quality iron produced from native furnaces was unfit for steel-making without further treatment. Similarly, steel produced by native methods was, as a rule, too brittle to be handled by modern rolling mills.

Hence before 1958 ended, small native furnaces were gradually replaced in most parts of the country by modern furnaces of somewhat larger size. This was accompanied by an improvement in input quality and a reduction in labor-intensity. The conversion of native into modern small blast furnaces resulted in a rise of outgoing quality level from below 50 per cent in the first quarter of 1959 to above 80 per cent in November of the same year[35]. This transformation resulted also in a decrease of labor input per ton of pig iron output from 60 to 10 man-days, as in the case of Tsaohsien, Anhwei province[36]. With the transformation of this production front in terms of mechanization, integration and size, and with the cessation of Soviet aid, the dichotomous development pattern of China's steel industry was further cemented.

33 Anshan Steel, for instance, had to ship two million tons of iron ores from China Proper to meet its 1957 requirements. *Chi-hua ching-chi*, No. 4, 1958, p. 23.
34 *A Decade of Mao's China*, Bombay, 1960, pp. 72—73; *CTCHK*, p. 697.
35 The outgoing quality level is based on reports from fourteen provinces. *Yeh-chin pao*, No. 4, 1960, p. 6.
36 *Jen-min jih-pao*, December 8, 1958.

*Chapter 13*

# LOCATIONAL CHANGES

A high degree of concentration characterized the locational pattern of the steel industry in pre-communist China. About two thirds of the country's pig iron and ingot steel capacities were found in the Northeast while there was hardly any iron or steel produced either in the South or in the Northwest. Central and Southwest China were insignificant as iron and steel producers.

Communist economic planners considered this locational pattern unsatisfactory from the standpoint of China's economic development and national defense. They emphasized the importance of widening the dispersion of industrial location. In their planning of new capital construction, accordingly, regional development constituted a key note. Each of the economic regions was to have an integrated industrial system with its own steel centers.

Aside from the consideration of national defense, this locational policy made sense in terms of raw material supply and transportation. In China, iron ore and coal deposits are found in nearly every province or autonomous region. The extremely inadequate transport facilities, on the other hand, made it difficult to ship steel to different points of consumption. At the time of the communist takeover, there were less than 22,000 kilometers of railway in a country of 9.6 million square kilometers. On a per capita basis, it came to a trivial figure of 0.04 meter.

Given the wide distribution of iron ore and coal deposits and given the vast size of the country and its dense population, it appeared reasonable to set up steel centers in each of the economic regions. In addition to economy in transportation, a wide geographical distribution of the steel industry had the advantage of facilitating mechanization of agriculture. As a result of adherence to this policy, a new locational pattern emerged for the steel industry by 1961.

In this chapter, locational changes are traced in terms of capacity distribution (in the case of blast furnaces) or output distribution (in the case of ingot steel) among seven economic regions. These regions, as defined by the 5th Session of the Communist Party Central Committee held in March 1958, are shown in Table 13.1.

*Wartime Changes*

With the outbreak of the Sino-Japanese hostilities, smelting equipment was dismantled and removed to the interior in anticipation of Japanese occupation. The removal was followed by wartime construction and expansion of iron and steel works, particularly in the Japanese occupied areas. Locational changes during the period of Sino-Japanese hostilities were in favor of the Northeast at the expense of Central China. The share of the latter region in the country's aggregate blast furnace capacity, for instance, declined from the prewar 8.4 per cent to 0.3 per cent at the time of Japanese surrender in August 1945. The share of the

Table 13.1. *Economic Regions as defined by CCP Central Committee, March 1958*

| Economic Region | Components (Province or Autonomous Region) |
|---|---|
| Northeast | Heilungkiang, Kirin, Liaoning |
| North | Inner Mongolia, Hopeh, Shansi |
| East | Shantung, Kiangsu, Anhwei, Chekiang, Kiangsi, Fukien |
| Central | Honan, Hupeh, Hunan |
| South | Kwangtung, Kwangsi |
| Northwest | Sinkiang, Kansu, Shensi, Tsinghai |
| Southwest | Szechwan, Kweichow, Yunnan |

Sources: *Ho-p'ing ho she-hui chu-i wen-t'i* (Peace and socialism), No. 5, 1959, p. 22; *Jen-min jih-pao*, November 10, 1959; *Chi-hua ching-chi* (Planned economy), Peking, No. 7, 1958, pp. 7—10.

Northeast region, on the other hand, rose from 60.6 to 67.8 per cent during the same period. For the remaining regions in which iron-smelting capacity existed[1], changes in their shares in the overall capacity distribution were negligible during the war.

### Locational Changes under Communist Planning

The communist policy of widening the dispersion of industrial location was to be implemented through capital construction planning. In rehabilitation planning, however, this dispersion policy was inhibited by the objective of minimizing the incremental capital-output ratio. Thus the apparently wider dispersion of blast furnace capacity between August 1945 and 1953, as can be seen from Table 13.2, could not be attributed to locational policy. It was, in fact, brought about primarily by Soviet removals of equipment and installations from iron and steel bases in the Northeast, which resulted in a substantial decrease in the country's overall blast furnace capacity. Accordingly the doubling of the Southwest share in the aggregate blast furnace capacity represented no increase in its absolute capacity. Without Soviet removals, the share of the Northeast would not have declined as much and the dispersion of blast furnace capacity would not have widened as much.

In contrast to the illusory widening of dispersion in the reconstruction phase, the implementation of the First Five-Year Plan brought about a greater concen-

1 These include the North, the East and the Southwest, as no smelting facilities were installed in the South or the Northwest.

tration (see Table 13.2). The reconstruction and expansion of Anshan Steel was
envisaged in the First Five-Year Plan as the most urgent task, and the building
of two new key steel bases (Wuhan and Paotow) did not get started until the
latter part of the quinquennium. While this priority scheme accentuated the
concentration of the steel industry in the Northeast, it did not conflict with the
long-run policy of widening locational dispersion. On the contrary, the extension
of existing steel bases was a *sine-qua-non* for the establishment of new bases in
terms of technical support and material supply. Anshan Steel was the largest
single supplier of iron and steel for the construction of new steel bases in the first
plan period. Thus the share of the Northeast in the country's overall blast furnace
capacity rose from 59.1 per cent in 1953 to 79.6 per cent in 1957. This increased
share of the all-important Northeast reduced the shares of the other regions. The
exceptionally large decrease in the percentage share of the Southwest represented a
negligible change in its blast furnace capacity.

Changes in regional distribution of the steel industry in terms of ingot steel
output are shown in Table 13.3, which presents a somewhat different picture from
that of blast furnace capacity distribution. Changes in output distribution among
regions, of course, can be attributed to variations in furnace productivity as well
as capital construction. In examining the data given in Table 13.3, it is therefore
necessary to bear in mind the discrepancy between capacity and output.

Regional distribution in terms of ingot steel output shows a slightly wider
dispersion in 1953 than in 1945[2]. Here again, percentage redistribution during the
rehabilitation phase had little to do with the communist policy on industrial
location. Speedy output restoration in Shanghai and Tayeh accounted for the
increased shares of East and Central China. The virtually unchanged share of the

*Table 13.2. Regional Distribution of Blast Furnace Capacity, 1945ᵃ, 1953 and 1957
(per cent)*

| Economic Region | 1945a | 1953 | 1957 |
|---|---|---|---|
|  | (1) | (2) | (3) |
| Northeast | 67.8 | 59.1 | 79.6 |
| North | 19.7 | 25.1 | 14.4 |
| East | 7.6 | 5.7 | 4.0 |
| Central | 0.3 | 0.8 | 0.5 |
| Southwest | 4.6 | 9.3 | 1.5 |
| Total | 100.0 | 100.0 | 100.0 |

a. Before Soviet dismantling and removal of equipment and installations.

Sources: Computed from data given in *Chukyo tekkogyo chosa hokokusho — kigyohen*
(Survey report of the steel industry of Communist China — enterprise edition), prepared
by the Cabinet Research Chamber of the Japanese Government, Tokyo, 1955, *passim*;
F. Okazaki, *Chugoku no tekkogyo to kikaikogyo no gijutsu suijun* (Technical level of the
steel and machinery industry in China), Tokyo, 1962, *passim*; and other sources.

2 Before Soviet dismantling and removal of equipment and installations.

*Table 13.3. Regional Distribution of Ingot Steel Output, 1945ᵃ, 1953 and 1957 (per cent)*

| Economic Region | 1945a | 1953 | 1957 |
|---|---|---|---|
| | (1) | (2) | (3) |
| Northeast | 65.3 | 65.9 | 67.8 |
| North | 30.5 | 25.4 | 10.7 |
| East | 1.7 | 5.5 | 14.7 |
| Central | 0.6 | 2.1 | 4.1 |
| Southwest | 1.9 | 1.1 | 2.7 |
| Total | 100.0 | 100.0 | 100.0 |

a. Before Soviet dismantling and removal of equipment and installations.

Sources: Computed from data given in *Chukyo tekkogyo chosa hokokusho — kigyohen* (Survey report of the steel industry of Communist China — enterprise edition), prepared by the Cabinet Research Chamber of the Japanese Government, Tokyo, 1955, Supplementary Volume, *passim*; F. Okazaki, *Chugoku no tekkogyo to kikaikogyo no gijutsu suijun* (Technical level of of the steel and machinery industry in China), Tokyo, 1962, *passim*; and other sources.

Northeast can be attributed chiefly to difficulties encountered in restoring Anshan's No. 2 steel plant which, as pointed out in Chapter 4, was completely stripped during Soviet removals[3].

Table 13.3 reveals that the locational spread of ingot steel output increased during the first plan quinquennium. The shares of the East and the Central region continued to increase owing mainly to capacity expansion and improved performance of the steel mills in Shanghai and Tayeh. Ingot steel output in Shanghai increased from 75,000 tons in 1952 to 480,000 tons in 1957, as a result partly of new facilities added, partly of the reconstruction and renovation of the existing facilities (notably in No. 3 Iron and Steel Plant) and partly of improvements in furnace productivity. The construction of two new converter shops in Shanghai's No. 1 Iron and Steel Plant in 1956, for instance, gave the Eastern region an additional rated capacity of 250,000 tons per annum; the installation of six more converters in Shanghai's No. 6 Iron and Steel Plant in 1957 added another 50,000 tons of annual rated capacity. Improvements in furnace productivity can be illustrated by Shanghai's No. 3 Iron and Steel Plant. The utilization coefficients of its open hearths showed an annual average increase rate of 34 per cent during the first plan quinquennium[4]. Tayeh's ingot steel output was boosted chiefly by the four large open hearths and four electric furnaces moved there from Dairen in 1955, in addition to the new open hearth built in 1954.

The share of the Northeast in the country's overall ingot steel output in 1957 also showed a slight increase. Chiefly responsible for this increase were the rehabilitation of open hearths Nos. 10—15 in Anshan's No. 2 steel plant and the

3 No. 2 steel plant was rehabilitated between November 1954 and December 1956. See Chapter 5.
4 *Kang-t'ieh*, No. 18, 1959, p. 806.

construction of open hearths Nos. 16—19, both completed by the end of 1956[5]. In addition, the average open-hearth coefficient of Anshan Steel rose from 5.17 in 1953 to 6.76 in 1957[6]. The more than doubling of the relative importance of the Southwest in ingot steel production can be credited mainly to the rapid reconstruction of Nos. 101, 102 and 105 Plants in the region. The fact that these were included among the Soviet-aid projects of the First Five-Year Plan pointed to their importance. Consequently, the 1957 share of the Southwest in the nation's total was more than restored to its 1945 level after its decrease in 1953. The 1957 shares of the four regions were increased apparently at the expense of North China, where the development of steel-refining facilities during the plan quinquennium was practically confined to the relatively small steel plants at Tangshan and Tientsin.

### The Emerging Pattern

The locational pattern of China's steel industry in 1961 can be seen from the map placed at the beginning of the book and from Table 13.4. Whereas the former shows the geographical distribution of the larger iron and steel producers[7], the table gives the percentage distribution of blast furnace capacity and ingot steel output by economic region. Despite the different bases used, a decidedly wider dispersion was attained in 1961 through the rise of iron and steel bases in regions in which they were hitherto absent, and through a higher rate of capacity or output increase in regions other than the all-important Northeast. Undoubtedly all this would not have been feasible in a matter of years without the 1958 all-out steel campaign and the subsequent rise of the small-scale production front.

South China and the Northwest, neither of which produced in 1957 any noticeable amount of either steel or iron, have since become iron and steel producing regions. Whereas the contribution of South China to the country's overall iron-smelting capacity or steel output amounted to not much more than 2 per cent, the relative importance of the Northwest surpassed that of the Southwest by a sizable margin particularly in iron-smelting. Behind the rising importance of the Northwest was the construction, beginning in 1958, of two sizable new iron and steel works in Sinkiang (Payi and Hami). In view of the discovery in 1958 of extensive iron ore deposits in Chingtiehshan, Kansu, and the subsequent organization of the Chiuchuan Iron and Steel Corporation comparable in scale to Paotow Steel, the importance of the Northwest is yet to unfold.

The share of Central China in the overall blast furnace capacity increased 30-fold between 1957 and 1961. For this spectacular gain (while the contribution particularly of two new iron and steel combines, Lienyuan in Hunan and Anyang in Honan, should not be overlooked), major credit was due to Wuhan Steel,

---

5 See Chapter 5.
6 *Chi-hua ching-chi*, No. 4, 1958, p. 22.
7 For the main characteristics of these producers, see *List of Iron and Steel Plants in China*, appended to this study.

whose iron-smelting capacity, nil in 1957, constituted more than 8 per cent of the national total in 1961[8].

Prior to 1958, pig iron production in East China was more or less confined to Maanshan, Anhwei. The blast furnace capacity of the region was under 600 m³ in

Table 13.4. Regional Distribution of Iron and Steel, 1961 (per cent)

| Economic Region | Blast Furnace Capacity | Ingot Steel Output |
|---|---|---|
| | (1) | (2) |
| Northeast | 31.8 | 20.7 |
| North | 17.5 | 17.9 |
| East | 15.8 | 29.5 |
| Central | 15.6 | 13.3 |
| South | 2.2 | 2.1 |
| Northwest | 13.5 | 9.5 |
| Southwest | 3.6 | 7.0 |
| Total | 100.0 | 100.0 |

Sources: Derived from data given in F. Okazaki, Chugoku no tekkogyo to kikaikogyo no gijutsun suijun (Technical level of the steel and machinery industry in China), Tokyo, 1962, passim; and other sources.

1957. By 1961, it grew to above 8,000 m³. Consequently, the regions's share in the national total nearly quadrupled (see Column 3 of Table 13.2 and Column 1 of Table 13.4). Although in 1961, Anhwei remained the province with the largest blast furnace capacity in the region, its prominence was reduced by the rise in importance of Kiangsu and Shantung as iron-producing provinces. In Kiangsu, for instance, Shanghai's No. 1 Iron and Steel Plant built two 255 m³ furnaces in 1959. In the same year, two blast furnaces of equal size were erected in the Nanking Iron and Steel Works. Similarly in Shantung, four blast furnaces with an aggregate capacity of 710 m³ were installed in the Tsinan Iron and Steel Works in 1959. In addition, other provinces in the region such as Kiangsi and Fukien which had no iron-smelting facilities to speak of during the first plan quinquennium, subsequently became iron producers. For example, the Sanming Iron and Steel Works in Fukien built in 1959 two blast furnaces with an aggregate capacity of 510 m³, and the Pingsiang Iron and Steel Works in Kiangsi built in 1960 seven furnaces with a total capacity of 982 m³.

The doubling of Southwest China's share in the overall blast furnace capacity between 1957 and 1961 was not sufficient to elevate the region to prominence. Although it surpassed the South in terms of iron-smelting capacity available, it still lagged far behind the other regions. Within the Southwest region, the rising importance of Yunnan is worth noting. Between 1958 and 1961, the Kunming Iron and Steel Corporation built four sizable blast furnaces (Nos. 1–4). By 1961,

8 See Tables 5.6 and 5.8.

Yunnan threatened Szechwan as the leading iron-producing province of the region, despite the capacity expansion at the Chungking Iron and Steel Corporation.

The share of North China in the overall blast furnace capacity of the country rose from 14.4 per cent in 1957 to 17.9 per cent in 1961 (see Column 3 of Table 13.2 and Column 1 of Table 13.4). This comparatively small increase was attributable notably to the relatively late start of Paotow Steel[9] coupled with the cut-back in industrial capital construction in 1961. On the other hand, the rising importance of other producers in the region should not be overlooked, particularly the Lungyen Iron and Steel Corporation in Hopeh and the Taiyuan Iron and Steel Corporation in Shansi, where seventeen blast furnaces with a combined capacity of 2,550 m³ were built between 1958 and 1961.

The substantial decline in the relative importance of the Northeast as revealed in Table 13.4 should not conceal the absolute increase in its blast furnace capacity between 1957 and 1961. In Anshan, as noted in Chapter 5, the 1,513 m³ No. 10 blast furnace was completed late in 1958 in addition to 140 small furnaces with an aggregate capacity of 4,440 m³. Also, tho medium-sized blast furnaces were built in Tunghua, Kirin, in 1959.

The 1961 locational distribution of steel output is shown in Column 2 of Table 13.4. A comparison with Column 1 reveals a considerable concordance, with however the notable exception of the Northeast and East China. Whereas the Northeast remained the leading iron-smelting region, its lead in ingot steel production passed on to East China. The explanation lies chiefly in the speedy rise in the share of converter steel in the overall ingot steel output, together with the concentration of the Northeast in open-hearth steel. The share of converter steel, as pointed out in Chapter 6, rose from 14.7 per cent in 1957 to 51.9 per cent in 1960, while as late as 1961, Anshan alone accounted for more than half of the nation's open-hearth steel output. The speedy rise in the importance of converter steel, as pointed out in the preceding chapter, originated from the campaign for small-scale production, which more than the introduction of overall planning has hastened the locational dispersion of China's steel industry.

### Determinants of Industrial Location

A closer examination of the locational pattern of the steel industry existing in 1961 shows that within each region there were one or two major steel centers, such as Anshan and Penki in the Northeast, Shanghai and Maanshan in the East, Chungking in the Southwest, Wuhan and Tayeh in Central China, Taiyuan and Paotow in the North, Canton in the South, and Hami in the Northwest. These major centers were supplemented by secondary iron and steel centers, most of

9 The blast furnace capacity of Paotow Steel constituted less than 4 per cent of the 1961 national total.

which had developed from small and semi-modern plants built during the steel campaign.

As far as the major steel centers are concerned, their locations are more or less in accordance with the policy set out in the First Five-Year Plan of establishing industrial enterprises in the vicinity of available raw material supply and consumer markets. The presence of large iron ore deposits has had a preponderant influence in determining the location of major centers, as evidenced in the case of Anshan Steel which has easy access to the iron ore deposits at Takushan, Yingtaoyuan and Kungchangling. Similarly, Wuhan Steel was established to take advantage of the iron ores from Tayeh and Sinyu. In the case of Paotow Steel, the rich iron ore deposits at Peiyunopo were a deciding factor in the choice of its location.

The pull of consumer markets on the location of major steel centers, on the other hand, is less apparent. Some steel centers such as Shanghai and Chungking are also machine-building centers. Some new steel mills and new machine-building plants were established in the same area to serve each other, as in Kunming, Kweiyang and Urumchi. The influence of consumer markets is, nevertheless, discernible in the location of certain new steel mills set up to take advantage of established machine-building centers, as their primary markets. Thus, steel works were developed in Peking, Nanking and Canton to meet the demand of the machine-building industry already established in these areas. On the whole, however, input availability coupled with considerations of national defense and transport costs appears to have been more influential than the pull of demand in determining the location of major iron and steel centers in China.

# PART VI
# RECENT DEVELOPMENTS

## Chapter 14

# POST-1960 DEVELOPMENTS

As a result of the Leap Forward debacle, the withdrawal of Soviet aid and the severe agricultural crisis, the communist economic planners had to cut back drastically industrial construction and consolidate the industrial sector from the beginning of 1961[1]. The Leap mentality of quantitative gains was replaced by an overwhelming emphasis on qualitative improvement. The effect of this policy reorientation on the steel industry was an immediate sharp decline in output quantity and a gradual increase in the variety of its output[2]. This chapter examines the significant changes in output variety and quality, and in steel technology during the 1960's.

## Output Behavior

The exact extent of output decline in 1961 is not known owing to the blackout of official statistics. However, some estimates have been made which can serve as a rough guide to the probable post-1960 output behavior of the major sectors of the steel industry. Among others, K. P. Wang of the US Bureau of Mines has estimated the output quantities of major products. His estimates are presented in Table 14.1. These estimates are higher than some others. R. F. Emery, for instance, estimated China's ingot steel production at 7 million tons in 1963 and 10 million

---

1 During the period of industrial adjustment, capital construction in the steel industry did not cease completely. At Anshan, for example, more than 30 new factories and workshops were built during 1961—1963. In 1963, a limestone mine and an iron mine were under construction at Penki, and so was a large concentration plant at Maanshan. *NCNA*, Peking, March 27, 1963; *Jen-min jih-pao*, September 14, 1963.

2 In connection with policy reorientation, it is of interest to note two documents relating to the steel industry, viz., the "Constitution of Anshan Steel" and the "Constitution of Maanshan Steel." The former document was prepared by Mao Tse-tung in March 1960 to perpetuate the spirit of the Great Leap. It contained the following principles: (1) "politics takes command" to be maintained, (2) Party leadership to be strengthened, (3) mass movement to be promoted, (4) the policy of "two-participations (cadres taking part in productive labor and workers in management), one-change (removing unreasonable regulations and systems) and union-of-three (uniting workers, cadres and technical personnel)" to be implemented, and (5) technical revolution to be initiated.

The "Constitution of Maanshan Steel" was based on the "Seventy Regulations governing the Work of Industrial and Mining Enterprises" disclosed in July 1961 under the sponsorship of Liu Shao-chi and Po I-po. This document, in contrast to the "Constitution of Anshan Steel," stressed the importance of capital equipment, output quality as well as quantity, material incentive, and management by experts. It served as the policy guideline for the development of the Chinese steel industry in the 1960's up to the Cultural Revolution. *Jen-min jih-pao*, October 18, 1968.

tons in 1965[3], as against Wang's estimates of 12 and 15 million tons respectively. On the other hand, Wang's estimates show an increase in ingot output of 17 per cent in 1964, in comparison with Chou En-lai's claim of 20 per cent[4].

A comparison of Wang's estimates with the data given in Tables 6.1, 6.3, 6.4, 6.6 and 6.9 shows that the decrease of production in 1961 was very drastic indeed. It amounted to roughly one half in the case of metallurgical coke, ingot steel and pig iron, 30 per cent in the case of finished steel, and 10 per cent in the case of iron ore. The relatively smaller output decrease in iron ore and finished steel appears to make sense as these constituted bottlenecks in the development of the steel industry. Following this line of reasoning, the output behavior of metallurgical coke should resemble that of iron ore rather than ingot steel or pig iron. Here the explanation lies, perhaps, in the comparatively low quality of coke produced prior to 1961[5]. From 1962–1966, the output of major products increased

Table 14.1. Estimated Output of Major Sectors of the Steel Industry, 1961–1966 (in million tons)

| Year | Iron Ore[a] | Pig Iron | Ingot Steel | Finished Steel | Coke |
|------|-------------|----------|-------------|----------------|------|
| 1961 | 50 | 15 | 9.5 | 8 | 15 |
| 1962 | 43 | 15 | 10 | 9 | 15 |
| 1963 | 50 | 17 | 12 | 10 | 15 |
| 1964 | 53 | 18 | 14 | 11 | 15 |
| 1965 | 56 | 19 | 15 | 12 | 16 |
| 1966 | 57 | 20 | 18 | n. a. | 17 |

a. Converted to equivalent 30 — 40 per cent Fe ore.

Sources: K. P. Wang, "The Mineral Resource Base of Communist China," *An Economic Profile of Mainland China*, New York, 1968, p. 174; US Bureau of Mines, *Minerals Yearbook* 1966, Washington, 1967, Vol. I — II, p. 990; *China Trade and Economic Newsletter*, No. 137, September, 1966.

steadily. By 1965, iron ore and finished steel surpassed their 1960 output levels, and in the following year the 1960 level of ingot steel output was also restored.

No sooner had the previous peak levels of the major products of the steel industry been restored than the Great Proletarian Cultural Revolution was under way. At the start of the Revolution, the steel industry as well as the economy at large were little affected. Subsequently with the transport tie-ups, some steel-smelting centers felt a pinch in the supply of inputs, particularly coal. While the steel industry could not escape the effect of economic dislocations and chaos

3 "Recent Economic Development in Communist China," *Asian Survey*, June 1966, p. 307.
4 *China Trade and Economic Newsletter*, No. 137, September 1966.
5 As pointed out previously, three quarters of the nation's coke output in 1959 came from small producing units.

caused by the Revolution, many steel centers were plagued by internal struggles between different factions. Thus early in 1967, Wuhan Steel had to stop its operation for a time. In August of the same year, a fierce battle broke out at Anshan Steel between workers and red guards, which damaged several blast furnaces. Things got so much out of hand there that a military affairs control committee had to be set up to take charge of the complex. Steel production in Shanghai in the early months of 1968 amounted only to about two thirds of the corresponding period in 1966. Even Paotow Steel suffered some interruptions in October 1968. On the whole, the mining sector appeared to have suffered more damage than smelting, refining or rolling.

With the decline of the Cultural Revolution, the steel industry resumed its normal operation. Again there were reports from various steel centers of output increases. The 1969 iron ore output of Anshan Steel, for instance, increased 65 per cent. Similarly in 1969, the gross output of the Penki Iron and Steel Works rose by 45 per cent and the finished steel output of Maanshan showed a 30 per cent increase[6]. All indications appear to point to the probability that in 1969 production of the major sectors of the steel industry was restored to the 1966 level.

## Quality and Variety

The attention of the industry in the early 1960's, as indicated previously, was focused on output variety and quality. As a measure for ensuring output quality standards, most iron and steel enterprises tightened up their quality inspection system. The Chungking Iron and Steel Corporation and the Tayeh Steel Plant, for example, subjected their output to more rigorous quality tests than required by the Ministry of Metallurgical Industry. The Shihchingshan Iron and Steel Corporation, on the other hand, instituted a rigid inspection system for its inputs such as coke, iron ore and refractory materials, that were shipped there from other enterprises[7]. This dual inspection was to make doubly sure that the specified quality standards were maintained.

The policy of consolidation and adjustment with its keynote on quality and variety brought about a nation-wide rise in the outgoing quality level of converter steel from 88.2 per cent in 1960 to 94.6 per cent by the end of 1961[8]. As converter steel constituted more than half of China's ingot steel output, this increase was indeed significant. Quality improvement can also be seen from the rising proportion of finished steel reaching the top grade at Anshan. It increased from 89 per cent in 1961 to 94 per cent in 1962[9].

The increase in output variety was more impressive. In 1961, for instance, some

---

6 *NCNA*, Shengyang, December 24 and 29, 1969; *NCNA*, Peking, December 24, 1969.
7 *Jen-min jih-pao*, July 4, 1963.
8 *CNS*, Peking, December 27, 1961.
9 *Kung-jen jih-pao* (Daily worker), Peking, August 18, 1962.

400 new products were trial-produced. The number of new products was raised to about 700 in 1966[10]. Among the notable new products which appeared in the 1960's were cold rolled plates and strips, silicon steel rails and plates, tinplates, ball bearing steel, boiler steel, heat-resisting steel, low-carbon stainless steel, high tensile stainless steel tubes, and low-alloy steel tubes, sections and rails[11].

The successful production of low-alloy steels by existing equipment was particularly noteworthy in view of its effect on the output structure of the Chinese steel industry in the 1960's. These steels compare favorably to carbon steels in tensile strength and corrosion resistance. They are reportedly $30-100$ per cent more durable than carbon steels. Low-alloy steel rails, for example, are claimed to be twice as durable as carbon steel rails. For certain usage, they are substitutable for chrome-nickel steel. In addition, their use tends to reduce the size and weight of the final product, thus lowering metal input. The use of low-alloy steel for making high-pressure containers with an annual capacity of 50,000 tons of synthetic ammonia is reported to result in lowering the weight of the container by almost 40 per cent.

By 1966, fourteen low-alloy steels were successfully produced for use in building ships, automobiles, tractors, high-pressure containers, electricity-transmission equipment, bridge girders, locomotives, rolling stock and rails. Subsequently the variety as well as output quantity increased rapidly. Some 150 low-alloy steels were produced or trial-produced by mid-1969, and their aggregate output had risen 30-fold since 1965. In 1969, practically every steel mill in China was producing low-alloy steels. At Shanghai No. 3 Iron and Steel Plant, low-alloy steels in 1968 already constituted more than 20 per cent of its total output[12].

There is little doubt that economic planners in China attached considerable importance to the development of low-alloy steels. At the meeting convened by the Ministry of Metallurgical Industry in Wuhan during the second quarter of 1969, for instance, advanced experience in developing low-alloy steels was summed up and popularized, and plans for further developing low-alloy steels were mapped out. This development should have far-reaching significance in view of China's rich deposits of non-ferrous metals.

By mid-1960's, China became 95 per cent self-sufficient in finished steel in terms of variety. Her steel industry was able to produce alloy steels for automobile shafts and bodies, high manganese steel plates and low-alloy steels for tractors, and steel plates for ships and icebreakers — steels for which China previously had to rely on imports[13].

---

10 *Kung-jen jih-pao*, December 30, 1961, and December 27, 1966.
11 *Ibid.*, August 18, 1962; Iron and Steel Overseas Market Study Committee, Japan, *op. cit.*, pp. 26 — 29.
12 *Jen-min jih-pao*, February 10, 1966 and August 25, 1968; *NCNA*, Peking, May 1, 1968 and June 17, 1969.
13 *Kung-jen jih-pao*, August 18, 1962; Iron and Steel Overseas Market Study Committee, Japan, *op. cit.*, pp. 26 — 29; *Jen-min jih-pao*, July 24, 1965; *Ta Kung Pao*, Peking, December 4, 1965.

*Imports and Technology*

A greater self-sufficiency in the variety of steel output is undoubtedly a significant indication of the capability of the Chinese steel industry. It, however, does not tell us whether the output of each variety is sufficient to meet the demand. Therefore, it should not be construed as an index of the country's need for steel imports. The latter is related to variations in the scale of capital construction and the tempo of industrialization *vis-à-vis* the level and structure of domestic steel output. Thus it is not surprising that the rapid increase in output variety during the 1960's was accompanied by a continual rise in steel imports since 1962.

China's imports of finished and semi-finished steel, as pointed out previously, declined in 1961–1962 as a result of the downturn in general economic activity[14]. The trend in steel imports was reversed in 1963. Available data on China's trade with non-communist countries show that steel imports from these countries rose 33.1 per cent in 1963, 118.0 per cent in 1964, 65.5 per cent in 1965, 108.3 per cent in 1966 and 37.4 per cent in 1967[15]. Although steel imports from non-communist countries showed nearly a 13-fold increase from 1962–1967, the 1967 level surpassed the previous peak (registered in 1958) by less than 35 per cent[16].

A breakdown of the 1967 total by country reveals that Japan was by far the largest supplier responsible for 39 per cent of China's steel imports from non-communist countries. Next to Japan was West Germany which contributed 19 per cent of the same total[17]. If imports from communist countries are included, their percentage shares become 32.6 and 15.8 respectively. As a source of steel supply to China, West Germany was in 1967 virtually as important as all the communist countries put together[18].

From the viewpoint of the development of the Chinese steel industry, the importance of Japan and West Germany was not confined to their quantitative superiority. Of more far-reaching importance was their supply of steel plants complete with installation and training services, which represented a propitious importation of up-to-date technology. In June 1965, the Kobe Steel Works of Japan signed a contract with the China National Technical Import Corporation for supplying a wire-drawing mill. This was followed by another contract signed in September 1966, under which the Hitachi Shipbuilding and Engineering Plant

---

14 See Appendix 6-B.
15 The percentage increases are computed from data given in *Summary of Country-by-Commodity Series: Free World Countries-Exports*, 1962–1967, prepared by International Trade Analysis Division, Bureau of International Commerce, US Department of Commerce, Washington, D.C., 1963–1968.
16 China's steel imports from non-communist countries amounted to US$195,696,000 in 1958, $19,182,000 in 1962 and $263,429,000 in 1967.
17 In 1967, steel imports from Japan and West Germany came to US$102,663,000 and $49,701,000 respectively.
18 China's steel imports from communist sources in 1967 have been estimated at US$51.6 million or 16.4 per cent of the overall steel imports.

of Japan was to supply China with a pelletizing plant. This plant costing US$3.3 million embodied the latest technology and was intended for Wuhan Steel whose low-grade ores were particularly in need of concentration. Similarly, West Germany was under contract to supply a cold-rolling mill (specializing in alloyed high-quality steels), and a pipe-rolling mill. The US$17 million contract for the former mill was signed in December 1965, and the $13 million contract for the latter mill, in mid-1967[19].

Of greater significance to the development of the Chinese steel industry was the import from Austria of an L-D (Linz-Donawitz) steel plant embodying up-to-date technology in steel making. The L-D oxygen conversion process was first developed by VOEST (Vereinigte Österreichische Eisen- und Stahlwerke) in 1949[20]. After three years of testing involving larger melting units and further development work, VOEST built its first L-D steel plant in November 1952. Subsequently this new process was adopted by steel makers in various parts of the world. By 1965, nineteen countries were producing L-D steel[21]. Consequently its share in world steel output was rising from 1 per cent in 1957 to 6 per cent in 1961 and 11 per cent in 1965[22].

This speedy development clearly shows the superiority of the L-D process. It is capable of turning out all steel grades formerly produced in the open hearth, and most grades formerly produced in the electric-arc furnace. Furthermore, high-quality L-D steels can be made by using any kind of iron with practically any carbon, sulphur, manganese and phosphorus contents. In addition, the cost of building an L-D plant with an annual capacity of one million tons is about 30 per cent lower than that of constructing an open-hearth plant of equivalent capacity. The saving in production (variable) cost is even greater. It amounts to less than 60 per cent of the production cost of open-hearth steel.

Realizing the advantages of the L-D process[23], China invited an Austrian steel delegation to visit Peking in May 1963 with a view to purchasing a complete L-D steel plant. It was not until December 1965 that a contract was signed between the China National Technical Import Corporation and VOEST for the delivery of a steel plant to the Taiyuan Iron and Steel Corporation. This plant contained,

19 In addition, the China National Technical Import Corporation signed in October 1965 a contract with the Italian Innocenti Society for the import of a seamless tube plant.
20 In June 1949, VOEST succeeded in blowing in a 2-ton crucible the first heat of steel by applying the process for refining steel with pure oxygen by top-blowing.
21 Austria, Canada, France, West Germany, Japan, Brazil, the United States, the Netherlands, Belgium, Luxemburg, India, Portugal, Spain, Italy, the United Kingdom, Norway, Sweden, Argentina, and Australia. In 1965, there were in these countries seventy-seven L-D steel plants with a total capacity of about 56 million tons.
22 *Pei-ching wan-pao* (Peking evening post), Peking, April 13, 1965.
23 A reference was made in *Yeh-chin pao* (October 1, 1956) of the "pure oxygen top-blown converter" in connection with Penki's experimentation with the duplex process — a process of steel refining used by the Bochumer Verein Steel Works in Bochum, West Germany.

among other things, two 30-ton L-D crucibles with an aggregate annual capacity of 600,000 tons[24].

It is worth noting that about a year before the signing of this contract, a pilot L-D plant containing small crucibles was built at the Shihchingshan Iron and Steel Corporation[25]. A question arises immediately in one's mind: why should China choose to spend her precious foreign exchange (£5 million) for buying a complete plant while she was already capable of building one herself? The answer is not difficult to determine. The plant China was importing incorporated all the latest developments in the L-D process and its variations. Also, the crucibles were considerably larger than China was capable of producing. Since the efficiency of the crucible is determined by the tap-to-tap time of a heat, larger crucibles enjoy a distinct advantage in that the blowing time is independent of the size of the crucible.

The development of this pilot project at Shihchingshan together with the import of a VÖEST plant led to the successful installation in September 1966 of an L-D plant at the Shanghai No. 1 Iron and Steel Works. This plant, like the imported one, had two 30-ton crucibles with an aggregate annual capacity of 600,000 tons. In connection with this significant achievement, two related developments are noteworthy. First, China's successful production of seamless oxygen cylinders overcame the problem of high cost in importing such cylinders. Second, the installation of an imported oxygen tonnage plant in Shanghai assured oxygen supply for steel refining. With these external economies, a second L-D plant was built in Shanghai in September 1969. This plant has a higher degree of automation. The entire process from charging to tapping is controlled automatically. Of greater significance, all the equipment installed in this plant was manufactured in China, including the lance (whose manufacture requires much experience and precision work), the electric drive for tilting the crucible, instruments for recording the pressure of cooling water and of oxygen conduits, and the gas-cooling and gas-cleaning equipment.

The L-D process suits the development of the Chinese steel industry particularly well. While consistent with the policy of developing converter steel for lower construction costs, shorter gestation lags and higher output, it fits in nicely with the post-1960 trend towards qualitative improvement. L-D steels, as pointed out previously, are at least equivalent in quality to open-hearth steels. For the production of all standardized structural steels, they even rival electric steels. The greater part of the steel program normally reserved for the electric-arc furnace can be produced by the L-D process. Alloyed L-D steels are found to be equal to the corresponding electric-arc steels in purity and susceptibility to cementation and hardening. The low hydrogen content of L-D steel constitutes an additional advantage in the production of alloyed steels.

24 Its installation was completed probably late in 1967, after some delay caused by the Cultural Revolution.
25 The size of the crucibles was less than ten tons each. *Hsin wan pao* (New evening post), Hong Kong, November 19, 1969.

In the case of the first L-D plant in Shanghai, the construction of the two crucibles took about six months. It took even less time in the case of the second plant[26]. The total cost of constructing an L-D plant complete with oxygen plant and gas-cleaning plant comes to almost one third less than that of an open-hearth plant of the same output capacity. The argument that since open-hearth plants use mostly scrap as input they do not require much additional blast furnace capacity, does not apply to China where scrap is extremely scarce and the cost of building small modern blast furnaces exceedingly low[27]. Here the relatively low-quality pig iron produced by small blast furnaces matters little, inasmuch as the L-D process treats pig iron with high phosphorus content efficiently and brings about excellent desulphurization. In addition, the scarcity of scrap in China makes the L-D process attractive because iron ore can be used for cooling in lieu of scrap.

The tap-to-tap time for the 30-ton L-D crucibles in the Shanghai No. 1 Iron and Steel Works comes to 30 minutes. Thus each of them produces 60 tons of steel per hour, or about one-third more than a 400-ton open-hearth furnace. Although the tap-to-tap time of an L-D heat is comparable to that of a side-blown converter, the degree of utilization of the latter is lower primarily because of the higher frequency of its repairs. The L-D crucibles can reach a maximum life of 600 heats in comparison with the maximum life of 120 heats for side-blown converters.

Another advantage of the L-D process to China is that since most of her iron ores are phosphatic in character, oxidation of the phosphorus content produces a slag which can be used as phosphatic fertilizer. In addition, purification of the exhaustion gas makes possible the recovery of gas which can yield synthetic ammonia. Thus the exhaustion gas and the slag are turned into chemical fertilizers to meet the urgent needs of Chinese agriculture[28].

In view of the superiority of the L-D process and its particular suitability to the Chinese economy, it is not surprising that by 1970 L-D steel plants were installed at the Canton Iron and Steel Works in Kwangtung, the Lienyuan Iron and Steel Works in Hunan, and the Hanyang Iron and Steel Works in Hupeh, in addition to Shihchingshan, Taiyuan and Shanghai. As China has acquired the know-how in building steel plants applying the latest L-D process and the capability of producing all the necessary equipment for such plants, a new course is charted for the future development of her steel industry.

26 *Shang-hai chi-hsieh* (Shanghai machinery), Monthly, Shanghai, No. 9, 1966, pp. 28—30; *NCNA*, Shanghai, September 28, 1969.
27 For the cost of building small blast furnaces, see Chapter 12.
28 *Shang-hai chi-hsieh, op. cit.*

*Chapter 15*

# SUMMARY AND CONCLUSIONS

In its early development, China's *modern* iron and steel industry was character-ized by a pyramiding capacity structure in which iron output was large relative to ingot steel, and ingot steel output large relative to finished steel. Such a struc-ture reflected mainly the tendency of an underdeveloped economy to concentrate on production requiring relatively simple techniques. While technological back-wardness and other attributes of under-development made difficult a coordinated growth of the various sectors of the steel industry, these factors were complicated by the predominance of foreign interests which geared the development of the industry according to the needs of their own steel industries. Consequently, China remained in 1936 an exporter of iron ore and pig iron and an importer of iron and steel products.

Another early distinctive feature of China's steel industry was its concentration in the Northeast, which in 1937 accounted for 98 per cent of the pig iron and 93 per cent of ingot steel output in the country. The prominence of the Northeast continued during the war period through capacity expansion under Japanese entrepreneurship and an increased rate of equipment utilization. Its output of iron and steel more than doubled during this period. In China Proper, on the other hand, despite new construction the industry was handicapped by the dismantling and removal of equipment to the interior prior to the Japanese occupation. While this confronted the Japanese occupation authorities with an arduous task of rehabilitation, some of the smelting equipment moved to the interior was never put into operation.

After World War II, China's steel industry was crippled by Soviet removals of metallurgical equipment and other installations from iron and steel bases in the Northeast, and by civil conflicts between nationalist and communist troops. The extent of damage to the productive capacity caused by Soviet removals varied with different sectors of the industry. Iron ore concentration facilities in the Northeast, for instance, were completely stripped, whereas loss in smelting and rolling facilities amounted to 50–70 per cent. The civil conflicts inflicted serious damage to Anshan, Penki, Lungyen, Tangshan and Tayeh.

The extensive damage made rehabilitation a difficult task confronting the communist regime. The period of rehabilitation formally began with the commu-nist takeover of the mainland in 1949 and ended with the launching of the First Five-Year Plan in 1953. Since the communist regime defined rehabilitation in terms of output rather than capacity, the completion of economic rehabilitation in 1952 merely meant that the actual output was restored to the pre-communist peak level. With the exception of rolling, the pre-1945 operating capacity was not restored. Capacity restoration, for instance, came to 45 per cent for blast furnace and 77 per cent for open hearth.

Development of the steel industry under communist planning was focused on the construction and reconstruction of three key bases which constituted the backbone of the industry. The First Five-Yean Plan assigned top priorities to the construction and reconstruction of Anshan Steel, which was envisaged as the core of the Northeast industrial base and as a major source of material and technical support for building other industrial bases. The Plan also specified the construction of two new steel centers in Wuhan and Paotow to form the nuclei of two industrial bases in the hinterland. Thus the importance of their construction extended beyond the growth of the steel industry; it reflected the economy's potential industrial development.

The importance of the three bases to the steel industry by 1961 can be gauged by their aggregate share in the nation's overall furnace capacity. It came to 38 per cent for blast furnace and 91 for open hearth. The relative standing of Anshan Steel was particularly noteworthy in 1957. It alone contributed 59 per cent of the total blast furnace capacity and 81 per cent of the total open-hearth capacity. By 1961, its respective shares dropped to 26 per cent and 56 per cent, attributable largely to the rising importance of Wuhan and Paotow.

Judging by the nature of capital construction carried out at the three key steel bases, the communist planners were aiming at the latest technology and the largest possible scale of operation. Such a policy could take full advantage of available Soviet aid, particularly in the construction of the two new steel bases where it extended from prospecting, site selection, designing, supply of equipment down to the actual construction and installation. Because of this heavy dependence, the subsequent abrupt withdrawal of Soviet aid extensively interrupted the capital construction program of the steel industry.

The importance economic planners attached to the steel industry can be judged by the sizable investment poured into it. For the period 1950—1958, 16 per cent of the overall industrial capital investment went to the steel industry. Investment in steel showed continuous, though irregular, increases throughout this period except 1951. The decline in 1951 was due to the threat of the Korean War and the exposure of Anshan and other steel centers to land and air attack. This considera-tion delayed the restoration of equipment and installations removed by Soviet troops, and accordingly reduced the investment requirements of the steel industry.

Increasing investment in the steel industry brought about a growing output. The latter increased from 610 million yuan in 1950 to 12,340 million yuan in 1960 (both at 1952 prices), or at an annual average rate of 35 per cent. Excluding the rehabilitation years (1950—1952), the gross output increased 8-fold. As a result of its rapid growth, the steel industry became increasingly important in the overall industrial structure and in the economy. Its percentage share in the gross industrial output rose consistently and more than doubled between 1950 and 1957. Its increasing importance to the economy can be gauged by the rising ratio of its gross output to national income. This ratio stood at 1.4 per cent in 1950, 7.9 per cent in 1960 and 10.2 per cent in 1965. The upward trend was interrupted in 1958 and 1961. Confusion and dislocations created by the all-out steel campaign in 1958 caused the growth of the steel industry to lag behind the overall economic growth. The decline in the ratio in 1961 was attributable to the policy shift from quantitative gains to qualitative improvement.

Growth of the steel industry in terms of gross output tends to conceal the divergent growth rates of its major products. During 1952–1960, their annual average growth rates (based on output quantities) ranged from 31 per cent for finished steel to 39 per cent for pig iron. The divergence resulted chiefly from the communist policy of developing the steel industry at a maximum tempo, for at maximum rates of capacity expansion mining could not keep pace with smelting and refining. The inability of rolling, casting and forging capacities to increase as rapidly was further complicated by the deterioration in the quality of steel input resulting from the mass steel campaign. Consequently the output ratio of finished products to ingot steel fell continuously from 90 per cent in 1957 to 62 per cent in 1960.

Partly responsible for the rapid growth of China's steel industry were increases in the productivity of labor and capital equipment. Output per production worker in the steel industry nearly doubled from 1952–1956. This impressive increase in labor productivity was attributable to a host of factors including improved production technique, greater intensity and better organization of work. The lack of close correlation between fixed assets per worker and labor productivity can be explained, to some extent, by (1) the usual time lag of labor force expansion behind the installation of fixed assets, (2) effects of technological changes on the productivity of capital equipment, and (3) the complication of intangible factors such as morale and competitive spirit, the effect of which can be considerable in view of the ingenious human engineering techniques used in a communist country.

Of greater importance, at least in the short run, was the increase in the productivity of capital equipment. The average annual rate of increase came to 10 per cent for blast furnaces (1949–1959), 13 per cent for open hearths (1949 –1959), 33 per cent for converters (1952–1956) and 20 per cent for electric furnaces (1952–1958). Largely responsible for such increases were changes in production techniques, which led to a reduced input consumption, improved output quality and higher rate of furnace operation. Notable improvements included (1) raising the smelting intensity of blast furnaces beyond 1.2 without causing "lumping of slag" which at one time plagued a number of furnaces in the country, and (2) developing a three-ladle steel-tapping method to allow further increases in the charging capacity of open hearth.

During the rehabilitation years, rapid increases in the productivity of capital equipment were instrumental in effecting output restoration with only partial capacity rehabilitated. Furnace productivity, in fact, served as an effective lever between capacity and output. The 1952 national average blast furnace utilization coefficient, for instance, was raised to 1.024 from the pre-communist figure of

0.890. This signified that technological advancement, the force behind rising furnace productivity, tends to render elastic the economic limits set by a given level of technology.

The 1958 steel campaign has brought to the foreground the importance of furnace size to its productivity. The findings on blast furnace productivity confirm the economies of scale. The productivity of large and medium-sized furnaces was substantially higher than that of small ones. The average coefficient for the first half of 1959, for instance, came to 0.700 for the latter furnace group and 1.562 for the former group. Given the objective of maximizing the immediate output, the policy implication of this substantial difference naturally was to raise the productivity of small furnaces. Such a policy was favored by the greater possibility of improving the working methods and equipment designs of small furnaces.

The poor performance of small furnaces in terms of productivity was accompanied by their relatively high variable cost. On a per-ton output basis, the average variable cost of small blast furnaces was two-thirds higher than that of large furnaces. A breakdown of the variable cost according to scale reveals that small furnaces operated with a relatively high cost for raw materials and a relatively low cost for labor. The inference appears to be that the higher operating expenses of small furnaces stemmed primarily from the high costs of material inputs, as reflected in their high coke rates, low outgoing quality levels and low utilization coefficients. In view of the wide discrepancy in these parameters between small producing units of different localities, substantial differences in their production costs are expected. During August 1959, for instance, cost variation in nine provinces came to more than 500 per cent. By March 1960, however, improvements in production techniques made it possible for 50 small producing units to lower their costs to a comparable level with large blast furnaces.

In steel refining, increasing emphasis was placed on the construction of converters. The choice of converters was based on lower capital and operating costs as well as the need for treating the exceptionally high phosphorus and sulphur content of iron produced by small furnaces. The cost of building a converter plant amounted to about half of that for an open-hearth shop of similar capacity, and the variable cost of converter steel, on a per-ton basis, came to 80—90 per cent of that of open-hearth steel. In addition, the acute shortage of scrap and high-quality iron ores both of which are indispensable in the operation of open hearths constituted another ground for the growing use of converters.

The shift of relative emphasis to a smaller scale of production was prompted chiefly by the anxiety on the part of the communist regime to maximize immediate output at minimum capital investment, so as to meet the enhanced demand for steel in 1958. Accordingly, the relatively lower construction costs and shorter gestation period of smaller iron and steel works became particularly desirable. The amount of investment required for constructing a large combine with an annual ingot steel capacity of 1.5 million tons could be used for constructing 6—7 medium-sized or 11—13 small integrated works with an aggregate annual capacity of 2 million tons. In addition, a large combine required a gestation period of at least 8–9 years, whereas only 2–3 years were needed for constructing a small works. For a large combine to be in partial operation, it required 5–6 years, or the same length of time for building a medium-sized integrated works.

With a diffused small-scale production front added to the large enterprises envisaged in the First Five-Year Plan, a dichotomous development pattern emerged. Small iron and steel works developed simultaneously with giant combines like Wuhan Steel and Paotow Steel. While the latter with their advantage of the economies of scale and command over the latest technology were to become the backbone of China's steel industry, the small works were expected to develop gradually into modern works of somewhat larger size and possibly into integrated medium-sized works, so that they could better complement the huge combines.

By virtue of this dichotomous pattern of development, China's steel industry achieved by 1961 a decidedly wider locational dispersion than envisaged by the communist economic planners. Particularly noteworthy was the rise of the Northwest as an iron and steel producing region, in view of the extensive iron ore deposits discovered in Chingtiehshan, Kansu. In 1957, this region produced no steel or iron to speak of, but in 1961 it had about 14 per cent and 10 per cent respectively of the nation's blast furnace and ingot steel capacities. Its Chiuchuan Iron and Steel Corporation will one day rank among China's steel giants. The rise of Wuhan and Paotow Steels has reduced Anshan's pre-eminence, which will most probably continue to dwindle with the rising importance of Chiuchuan Steel.

This trend became more apparent in the 1960's. The increasing importance of Shanghai as a steel center and the sizable expansion of Maanshan Iron and Steel Works were sufficient to raise the standing of the East China region as a steel producer. The finished steel output of the Shanghai No. 3 Steel Works, for example, was substantially increased in the 1960's. Similarly, three up-to-date open hearths, a heavy rolling mill and an ore concentration plant (with an annual capacity of 5.4 million tons) were added in the Maanshan Iron and Steel Works between 1961 and 1966. The future of Central China and the Southwest as steel-producing regions is also promising in view of the discovery of immense rich iron ore deposits at Changyang, Patung and Chienshih in western Hupeh, and at Panchihhwa in Szechwan.

The policy on steel development in the 1960's shifted its focus from quantity to quality and variety. In the early 1960's, most iron and steel enterprises tightened up their quality inspection system. Dual inspection was instituted to ensure that the standards specified by the Ministry of Metallurgical Industry were rigorously maintained. Consequently the outgoing quality level (especially of converter steel) showed a considerable rise.

Concomitantly the number of new products trial-produced each year almost doubled between 1961 and 1966. Among the new products, low-alloy steels produced by existing facilities have had a profound effect on the output structure of the steel industry in the 1960's. As they are lighter, more durable and more corrosion-resistant than carbon steels, their production increased rapidly. By 1969, almost all steel plants in the country were producing low-alloy steels. This development is particularly relevant to China in view of her rich deposits of non-ferrous metals.

With increases in variety and improvements in quality achieved in the mid-1960's, the attention of the steel industry was partially redirected to quantity. Accordingly a policy of equal emphasis on quality and quantity began to be implemented. As a result, the production of ingot steel increased 20 per cent in 1966. During 1967–1968, however, the steel industry like other industries was affected by the Cultural Revolution. Reports from China indicate that construction as well as production were interrupted in many steel centers including An-shan, Wuhan, Paotow and Shanghai. At Anshan Steel, things got very much out of hand and it had to be placed under the control of a military affairs control committee.

Before 1968 ended, the steel industry was back to its normal operation. Under the movement of "grasping revolution and promoting production" and with the assistance of People's Liberation Army personnel, output increases in 1969 were reported from various steel centers, notably Anshan, Penki, Maanshan, Shanghai and Peking. There is little doubt that the 1966 output levels of major steel products were restored in 1969. In addition, capital construction was stepped up. For example, a modern large open-hearth shop was completed at Wuhan Steel and a blooming mill was ready to go into production at the Capital Iron and Steel Corporation by the end of the year. The increase in output variety in 1959 can be gauged by the 370-odd new products successfully trial-produced at Anshan Steel.

The increase in the variety of steels in the early 1960's made China less dependent on external sources for certain types of steels. However, with the rising sophistication and the increasing scale of industrialization, a higher degree of self-sufficiency in variety does not necessarily imply declining imports. In fact, China's overall steel imports almost quadrupled from 1964–1967. As a source of steel supply, Japan was by far the most important. In 1967, for instance, nearly one third of China's steel imports came from Japan in comparison with one sixth supplied by West Germany, the second most important source. Japan's steel exports to China more than doubled from 1967–1969. In the latter year, Japan shipped as much as 1.26 million tons of ordinary and special steels to China.

Of greater importance has been the import of plants complete with installation and training services, as it represents a propitious importation of up-to-date technology. From 1965 to 1967, China signed with Japan, West Germany, Italy and Austria six contracts for the import of pelletizing, refining and rolling plants. Of these, the import of an L-D steel plant from VÖEST is particularly significant, since the L-D process is capable of turning out alloyed open-hearth steels and electric-arc steels at a higher speed and a much lower cost. It suits the development of the Chinese steel industry particularly well. While consistent with the adopted policy of developing converter steels, the L-D process fits in admirably with the post-1960 trend towards qualitative improvements. Besides, not only can this process treat efficiently low-quality iron produced by small blast furnaces, it lessens the problem created by the scarcity of scrap. In addition, the byproducts of the L-D process (phosphatic fertilizer and synthetic ammonia) are beneficial to Chinese agriculture.

China is now capable of building L-D steel plants complete with the latest equipment and techniques. This opens a new page of steel making in China. Thus L-D plants are found not merely in Peking, Shanghai and Taiyuan, but also in Canton, Lienyuan (Hunan) and Wuhan. Their geographical distribution confirms the communist policy of widening the dispersion of industrial locations. Behind this policy is the conviction that in a vast underdeveloped country like China where natural resources are yet little known, even less tapped, there is a strong probability of discovering extensive rich iron and coal deposits. In this light, the potentiality of China's steel industry is yet to unfold. In the unfolding process, however, it will undoubtedly encounter similar problems and bottlenecks as this study has borne out. In their proper solution lies the long-term prospects of steel in China.

# APPENDIX

## LIST OF IRON AND STEEL PLANTS IN CHINA

This list is arranged alphabetically and contains all known iron and steel works with annual ingot capacity of 100,000 tons or more, showing their general location and main characteristics such as their important products, furnace type and capacity, rolling facilities and major sources of raw material supply. Blast furnace capacity is given in cubic meters (m³) and steel furnace capacity in rated tonnage per heat unless otherwise indicated. While the known capacity or output of each major product of the individual enterprise is also presented, it may differ in time reference and coverage from data given on furnaces and equipment. Sources are too numerous to mention.

*Anshan Iron & Steel Corporation* in Liaoning. Principal products: rail, structural shapes, sheet, plate, welded and seamless tubes, parts for agricultural implements, and other finished products. Ten blast furnaces: No. 1, 585 m³; No. 2, 596 m³; No. 3, 917 m³; No. 4, 1,102 m³; No. 5, 917 m³; No. 6, 916 m³; No. 7, 916 m³; No. 8, 975 m³; No. 9, 944 m³; No. 10, 1,513 m³. Consume iron ore from Yingtaoyuan, Tunganshan, Tahushan and coal from Kailuan, Peipiao, Penki, Tunghua, Chisi. No. 1 steel plant has nine open hearths: Nos. 1–4, 100 tons each; Nos. 5–6, 150 tons each; Nos. 7–9, 180 tons each; a mixer of 600 tons. No. 2 steel plant has ten open hearths: Nos. 10–19, average of 340 tons (actual); a mixer of 600 tons. No. 3 steel plant has five open hearths: Nos. 20–22, 440 tons (actual) each; Nos. 23–24, 500 tons each. Electric furnace shop. Two blooming mills, large bar mill (800 mm), medium bar mill, two small bar mills, two plate mills, seamless tube shop, pipe-welding shop, other rolling mills and foundry. 1959 output: pig iron, 5,270,000 tons; ingot steel, 5,050,000 tons; rolled steel, 4,000,000 tons.

*Anyang Iron & Steel Corporation* in Honan. Eight blast furnaces: No. 1, 255 m³; No. 2, 100 m³; 6 with 28 m³ each. Consume iron ore from Tengfeng-chingwan, Neihuang, Fenghuangling and coal from Tsiaotso, Pingtingshan, Hopi. Converter shop with four furnaces of 3–6 tons each. Rolling mills. Construction started in August 1958. Began production in the 2nd quarter of 1959. Construction completed by the end of 1959. 1959 capacity: pig iron, 700,000 tons; ingot steel, 600,000 tons; rolled steel, 500,000 tons.

*Canton Iron & Steel Plant* in Kwangtung. Five blast furnaces: No. 1, capacity unknown; No. 2, 255 m³; No. 3, 255 m³; 2 small blast furnaces of 54 m³ each. Converter shop. Medium bar mill (250–400 mm); small bar mill (250 mm), wire mill (150 mm), and other rolling mills. Planned 1962 output: pig iron, 1,200,000 tons; ingot steel, 2,000,000 tons; rolled steel, unknown (1958 output: 250,000 tons). An L-D plant was installed in 1969.

*Capital Iron & Steel Corporation.* See Shihchingshan.

*Changchih Iron & Steel Plant* in Shansi. Prior to 1959, known as Kuhsien Iron & Steel Plant. Four blast furnaces: Nos. 1–2, 100 m³ each; Nos. 3–4, 255 m³ each. Consume iron ore from Pingshun and coal from Luan. Seamless tube mill (started operation early in 1961), and other rolling mills. 1959 output: pig iron, 195,000 tons (planned); ingot steel, 155,000 tons; rolled steel, 138,000 tons.

*Chefoo Iron & Steel Plant* in Shantung. Construction started in the 3rd quarter of 1958; scheduled completion by the end of 1961. In partial operation in 1960. Planned 1961 output: pig iron, 100,000 tons; ingot steel, 100,000 tons; rolled steel, unknown.

*Chekiang Panshan Iron & Steel Plant.* Four blast furnaces: No. 1, 82 m³; No. 2, 27.5 m³; No. 3, 255 m³; No. 4, 255 m³. Consume iron ore from Lichu and coal from Hwainan, Kukiang, Hushan. Converter shop. Rolling mills with an annual aggregate capacity of 120,000 tons. Construction started in August 1958; scheduled completion in 1962. Partial operation in 1960. Planned 1962 output: pig iron, 300,000 tons; ingot steel, 240,000 tons; rolled steel, 200,000 tons.

*Chengteh Iron & Steel Plant* in Hopeh. Consume iron ore from Pengchiapo, Yentushan and coal from Kailuan. 1962 output: pig iron, 600,000 tons (planned); ingot steel, 500,000 tons; rolled steel, unknown.

*Chengtu Steel Tube Plant* in Szechwan. Principal product: seamless tubes. Built in 1958.

*Chiuchuan Iron & Steel Corporation* in Kansu. Construction started in September 1958. Consume iron ore from Chingtiehshan and coal from Shihtsuishan. Planned on a scale comparable to Paotow Steel.

*Chungking Iron & Steel Corporation* in Szechwan. Principal products: alloy steels, large rail, light rail, structural shapes, and other rolled products. Three blast furnaces: No. 1, 134 m³; No. 2, 55 m³; No. 3, 620 m³. Consume iron ore from Chikiang, Panchihhwa and coal from Chungliangshan. Three open-hearth shops: No. 1 with 2 small furnaces; No. 2 with 2 medium-sized furnaces; No. 3 with small open hearths plus small electric furnaces. Converter shop with 6 furnaces of 6 tons each and 5 cupolas of 20 tons each. Large bar mill, medium bar mill, small bar mill, large rail mill, light rail mill, and other rolling mills. 1961 output: pig iron, 1,500,000 tons; ingot steel, 1,200,000 tons; rolled steel, 1,00,000 tons.

*Dairen Steel Plant* in Liaoning. Principal products: alloy steels, metallurgical equipment, motor vehicles, machinery, rolled products for generators. No blast furnaces. Electric furnace shop. Converter shop. Blooming mill (650 mm), medium bar mill (600 mm), small bar mill, sheet mill, wire mill and foundry.

*Fushun Steel Plant* in Liaoning. No blast furnaces. Electric furnace shop. Rolling mills. 1960 ingot steel capacity: 700,000 tons.

*Hainantao Iron & Steel Corporation* in Kwangtung. Two blast furnaces of 100 m³ each. 1959 output: pig iron, 700,000 tons; ingot steel, 350,000 tons; rolled steel, 240,000 tons.

*Hami Iron & Steel Plant* in Sinkiang. Principal products: rail, seamless tubes and other rolled products. Five blast furnaces with capacities ranging from 255 – 620 m³. Converter shop. 1958 output: pig iron, 800,000 tons (planned); ingot steel, 600,000 tons; rolled steel, unknown.

*Hantan Iron & Steel Corporation* in Hopeh. Eight blast furnaces: Nos. 1–2, 255 m³ each; 6 with 55 m³ each. Also 70 small blast furnaces of 6.5 m³ each. Consume iron ore from Tsushan, Wuan and coal from Fengfeng. Converter shop. 1958 capacity: pig iron, 900,000 tons; ingot steel, 600,000 tons; rolled steel, 500,000 tons.

*Hupeh Iron & Steel Plant.* Construction started in March 1958. Consume iron ore from Yuehcheng, Tayeh and coal from Pingsiang. 1960 capacity: pig iron, 200,000 tons; ingot steel, 100,000 tons; rolled steel, 80,000 tons.

*Kunming Iron & Steel Corporation* in Yunnan. Four blast furnaces: No. 1, 71 m³; No. 2, 210 m³; No. 3, 210 m³; No. 4, 255 m³. Small converters and small electric furnaces. Medium bar mill, small bar mill. 1959 ingot steel output: 500,000 tons.

*Kweiyang Iron & Steel Plant* in Kweichow. Four blast furnaces: Nos. 1–2, 100 m³ each; 2 small blast furnaces of 55 m³ each. Consume iron ore from Tuyun, Tsungyi and coal from Kiensi. Two converters and one electric furnace. 1961 output: pig iron, 900,000 tons; ingot steel, 500,000 tons; rolled steel, 40,000 tons.

*Lienyuan Iron & Steel Plant* in Hunan. Five blast furnaces: 2 with 835 m³ each; 2 with 100 m³ each; and 1 of 255 m³. Consume iron ore from Chahwamiao and coal from Pingsiang. Construction started in 1957. 1961 ingot steel capacity: 100,000 tons. An L-D plant was added in 1969.

*Linfen Iron & Steel Plant* in Shansi. Principal products: plate, sheet, seamless tube and other rolled products. One blast furnace of 100 m³. Consume local iron ore and coal from Lingshih, Fensi. Planned 1962 output: pig iron, 1,000,000 tons; ingot steel, 500,000 tons; rolled steel, unknown.

*Liuchow Iron & Steel Plant* in Kwangsi. Construction started in July 1958. 1st stage construction calls for two blast furnaces of 255 m³ each, with an annual capacity of 250,000 tons. No. 1 furnace started production in February 1960.

*Lungyen Iron & Steel Corporation* in Hopeh. Ten blast furnaces: No. 1, 210 m³; No. 2, 218 m³; No. 3, 250 m³; No. 4, 255 m³; 6 small blast furnaces of 54 m³ each. Consume iron ore from Pengchiapo, Yentushan, Hsuanhwa and coal from Kailuan, Tatung.

*Maanshan Iron & Steel Corporation* in Anhwei. Seventeen blast furnaces: 2 of 255 m³ each; 5 each with a capacity of 210–250 m³; one of 82 m³; 6 each with a capacity of 34 – 71 m³; 3 of 8 m³ each. Consume local iron ore and coal from Hwainan. Converter shop with 21 furnaces of 3 tons each. Electric furnace shop with two furnaces: one 3-ton, and one 5-ton. Rolling mills: one of 250 mm; two of 500 mm; five of 300 mm. Planned 1958 ingot steel output: 1,500,000 tons.

*Nanking Iron & Steel Plant* in Kiangsu. Two blast furnaces of 255 m³ each. 1960 output: pig iron, 270,000 tons; ingot steel, 100,000 tons; rolled steel, 80,000 tons. Construction started in 1958.

*Nanning Iron & Steel Plant* in Kwangsi. Construction completed in 1960. 1960 output: pig iron, 270,000 tons (planned); ingot steel, 100,000 tons; rolled steel, 80,000 tons.

*Paotow Iron & Steel Corporation* in Inner Mongolia. Principal products: rail, sheet, plate, seamless tube (with very small diameter), structural shapes. No. 1 blast furnace of 1,513 m³ completed September 1959. Consume iron ore from Peiyunopo and coal from Shihtuaitze. Open-hearth shop: No. 1, 660 tons (actual) and a mixer of 1,300 tons. Plate mill and other rolling mills. Planned 1961 output: pig iron 1,467,000 tons; ingot steel, 1,470,000 tons; rolled steel, 1,100,000 tons.

*Penki Iron & Steel Corporation* in Liaoning. Principal products: low phospherous pig iron, special high-quality alloy steels. Four blast furnaces: Nos. 1—2, 400 m³ each; Nos. 3—4, 920 m³ each. Consume iron ore from Nanfen and local coal. Electric furnace shop with 10 furnaces. Converter shop with 12 furnaces. Blooming mill (650 mm); small bar mill (300—500 mm) and other rolling mills. 1958 output: pig iron 1,500,000 tons; ingot steel, 145,000 tons.

*Pingsiang Iron & Steel Plant* in Kiangsi. Seven blast furnaces: 2 of 250 m³ each; 4 of 100 m³ each; 1 of 82 m³. Converter shop with 3 furnaces. Rolling mills. 1962 capacity: pig iron, 500,000 tons; ingot steel, 300,000 tons; rolled steel, unknown.

*Sankiang Iron & Steel Plant* in Szechwan. Planned 1962 ingot steel output: 200,000 tons.

*Sanming Iron & Steel Plant* in Fukien. Two blast furnaces of 255 m³ each. Consume iron ore from Lungyeh. Converter shop with four furnaces. Medium bar mill (250—350 mm), and tube mill. Construction started in June 1958; 1st stage ended in 1959; 2nd stage in 1960. 1959 output: pig iron, 280,000 tons (planned): ingot steel, 200,000 tons; rolled steel, 150,000 tons.

*Shanghai Alloy Steel Plant.* Constructed in 1959. Annual capacity of 200,000 tons. No blast furnaces.

*Shanghai No. 1 Iron & Steel Plant.* Principal products: seamless tube, sheet, plate, cast pipes (water pipes). Two blast furnaces of 255 m³ each. Two more of similar capacity under construction. Open-hearth shop with 2 small furnaces. Three converter shops: No. 1 with an annual capacity of 150,000 tons; No. 2 with an annual capacity of 100,000 tons; No. 3 with an annual capacity of 600,000 tons. Blooming mill, seamless tube mill, plate mill, other rolling mills and foundry. 1960 output: pig iron, 250,000 tons; ingot steel, 900,000 tons; finished steel, 300,000 tons. An L-D plant was added in 1966. (An additional L-D converter was built in Shanghai in 1969. Its exact location has not been revealed.)

*Shanghai No. 2 Iron & Steel Plant.* No blast furnaces. 1958 rolled steel output: 410,000 tons; 1959, 880,000 tons (planned).

*Shanghai No. 3 Iron & Steel Plant.* Principal products: plate, sheet, seamless tube. No blast furnaces. Open-hearth shop with 2 small furnaces. Converter shop with 2 furnaces. Blooming mill, plate mill, sheet mill, seamless tube mill. Planned 1958 ingot steel output: 1,000,000 tons.

*Shanghai No. 5 Iron & Steel Plant.* Principal products: special steels. No blast furnaces. Converter shop: 1958 capacity 600,000 tons. Electric furnace shop. Rolling mills.

*Shanghai No. 6 Iron & Steel Plant.* No blast furnaces. Converter shop with 6 furnaces of 3 tons each and 4 cupolas. 1959 ingot steel output: 102,000 tons.

*Shanghai Steel Tube Plant.* Principal products: seamless and welded tubes. Annual capacity of 10,000 tons.

*Shaohsing Iron & Steel Plant* in Chekiang. Four small blast furnaces of 27.5 m³ each. Consume iron ore from Lichu and coal from Hwainan, Hushan. 1957 output: pig iron, 40,000 tons (planned); ingot steel, 100,000 tons; rolled steel, unknown. Smelting and rolling capacity expanded in 1958.

*Shenyang Steel Plant* in Liaoning. No blast furnaces. Steel furnaces: electric, open hearth and converter. Rolling mills and foundry. 1960 ingot steel capacity: 300,000 tons.

*Shihchingshan Iron & Steel Corporation* outside Peking (now known as Capital Iron & Steel Corporation). Principal products: seamless tube, cast pipes and other rolled products. Three blast furnaces: No. 1, 413 m³; No. 2, 512 m³; No. 3, 963 m³. Also various small blast furnaces with a daily aggregate output of 38.5 tons (March 1958). Consume iron ore from Yentushan, Pengchiapo and coal from Kailuan, Chingching, Chengfeng. Converter shop with 7 furnaces: 4 of 30 tons each and 3 of 3 tons each, plus 3 cupolas of 15 tons each. Blooming mill, medium bar mill, small bar mill, electric pipe-welding shop, cold strip mill and other rolling mills. Casting installation (cont.) for turning out all types of cast pipes. 1961 capacity: pig iron, 1,900,000 tons; ingot steel, 1,000,000–1,200,000 tons; finished steel, 1,000,000–1,200,000 tons. An L-D plant was added early in 1965.

*Sian Iron & Steel Plant* in Shensi. Principal products: high carbon steel, alloy steels, seamless tube. Converter shop with an annual capacity of 300,000 tons. Electric furnace shop. Construction started in July 1958. 1960 output: pig iron, 800,000 tons; ingot steel, 300,000 tons.

*Siangtan Iron & Steel Plant* in Hunan. Principal product: wire. One blast furnace of 750 m³. Consume iron ore from Chahwamiao, Chaling and coal from Pingsiang. Wire mill (250 mm) and other rolling mills. 1961 ingot steel capacity: 1,200,000 tons.

*Sining Iron & Steel Plant* in Tsinghai. Small blast furnaces. Converter shop with an annual capacity of 130,000 tons. Rolling mills. 1959 ingot steel capacity: 130,000 tons.

*Sinkiang Payi Iron & Steel Plant.* Principal products: sheet, plate, tube. Five blast furnaces of 255 m³ each. Two converters and one electric furnace. Rolling mills. Construction started in the autumn of 1958; scheduled completion in 1960. Partial production in 1958: pig iron, 800,000 tons (planned); ingot steel, 600,000 tons; rolled steel, unknown.

*Sinyang Iron & Steel Plant* in Honan. Consume iron ore from Tengfeng-chingwan, Neihuang, Fenghuangling and coal from Tsiaotso, Pingtingshan, Hopi. Converter shop with three furnaces. 1960 capacity: pig iron, 350,000 tons; ingot steel, 250,000 tons; rolled steel, unknown.

*Sinyu Iron & Steel Plant* in Kiangsi. Construction started in November 1958. 1962 capacity: pig iron, 2,000,000 tons; ingot steel, 1,500,000 tons; rolled steel, unknown.

*Soochow Iron & Steel Plant* in Kiangsu. One blast furnace of 82 m³. Converter shop. Rolling mills. 1958 output: pig iron, 150,000 tons; ingot steel, 100,000 tons; rolled steel, unknown.

*Taiyuan Iron & Steel Corporation* in Shansi. Principal products: sheet, plate, seamless tube, alloy steels, and other products. Nine blast furnaces: No. 1, 146 m³; No. 2, 291 m³; No. 3, 963 m³; 6 small blast furnaces of 55 m³ each. Consume iron ore from Lungyen, Tingsiang, Ningwu and coal from Tatung, Luan, Ningwu. Three steel plants: No. 1 with 3 open hearths each with a capacity of 30—50 tons and electric furnaces; No. 2 with 2 electric furnaces of 8 tons each (moved from Tangshan Steel Plant), and converters; No. 3 with converters only. Blooming mill, medium (300—530 mm) and small bar mill, sheet mill, seamless tube mill, other rolling mills and foundry. Planned 1963 ingot steel output: 2,000,000 tons. An L-D plant with an annual capacity of 600,000 tons was added in 1967.

*Tangshan Steel Plant* in Hopeh. Principal products: rail, I-beams, and other structural shapes. Electric furnace shop. Converter shop. Three rolling mills and foundry.

*Tayeh Steel Plant* in Hupeh. Principal products: a large range of high-quality and special steels. Five small blast furnaces. Consume local iron ore and coal from Pingsiang, Hwainan. Steel furnaces: 1 small open hearth, 2 converters and 7 electric furnaces. (Four large open hearths and 3 electric furnaces had been moved to Dairen Steel Plant in 1955). Blooming mill, medium bar mill (continuous), small bar mill (continuous). Planned 1959 output: ingot steel, 900,000 tons; rolled steel, 400,000 tons.

*Tientsin No. 1 Steel Plant* in Hopeh. Principal products: wire, rod and other structural shapes. No blast furnaces. Open-hearth shop. Converter shop. Blooming mill, wire mill and other rolling mills. 1960 capacity: ingot steel, 1,400,000 tons; rolled steel, 350,000 tons.

*Tsiaotso Iron & Steel Plant* in Honan. Nineteen blast furnaces: 1 of 54 m³; 12 of 22 m³ each; 4 of 13 m³ each; 2 of 8 m³ each. Consume iron ore from Tengfengchingwan, Neihuang, Fenghuangling and coal from local sources and Pintingshan and Hopi. Converter shop. Rolling mills.

*Tsinan Iron & Steel Plant* in Shantung. Principal products: plate, seamless tube. Four blast furnaces: Nos. 1—2, 255 m³ each; Nos. 3—4, 100 m³ each. Consume iron ore from Kinling, Kotien and coal from Tzechwan, Poshan. Converter shop. One electric furnace. Blooming mill, plate mill, seamless tube mill. 1960 capacity: pig iron, 900,000 tons; ingot steel 600,000 tons; rolled steel, 500,000 tons. Construction started in July 1958 and completed in 1960.

*Tsingtao Iron & Steel Plant* in Shantung. Principal products: high-quality steels, alloy steels and other rolled products. Nineteen blast furnaces, each with a capacity of 13—55 m³. Consume iron ore from Kinling, Kotien and coal from Tzechwan, Poshan. Converter shop with 43 furnaces each with a capacity of

0.5—0.6 ton. Electric furnace shop with 4 furnaces each with a capacity of 1.5—8 tons. Rolling mills. 1959 capacity: pig iron, 400,000 tons; ingot steel, 250,000 tons; rolled steel, 200,000 tons. Construction started in the 3rd quarter of 1958 and completed by the end of 1959.

*Tunghua Iron & Steel Corporation* in Kirin. Principal products: sheet, seamless tube. Two blast furnaces of 255 m³ each. Also a large number of small blast furnaces with an aggregate annual capacity of 1,200,000 tons. Consume iron ore from Talitze, Lannitang, Laoling and local coal. Steel plant with an annual capacity of 600,000 tons. Sheet mill, seamless tube shop. 1959 capacity: ingot steel, 600,000 tons; rolled steel, 500,000 tons.

*Tzepo Iron & Steel Plant* in Shantung. Consume iron ore from Kinling, Kotien and coal from Tzechwan, Changchiu, Poshan. Construction started in the 3rd quarter of 1958; scheduled completion by the end of 1961. In partial operation in 1959. 1961 capacity: pig iron, 200,000 tons; ingot steel, 100,000 tons; rolled steel, unknown.

*Wuhan Iron & Steel Corporation* in Hupeh. Principal products: rail and other structural shapes, seamless tube (with very small diameter). Three blast furnaces: No. 1, 1,385 m³; No. 2, 1,436 m³; No. 3, 1,513 m³. No. 4, 1,513 m³ under construction. Consume iron ore from Tayeh and coal from Pingtingshan (Honan), Hwainan (Anhwei), Pingsiang (Kiangsi). Open-hearth shop with 5 furnaces: No. 1, 250 tons; Nos. 2—5, 500 tons each. Converter shop with 3 furnaces of 1.5 tons each. Rolling mills. Planned 1960 output: pig iron, 1,500,000 tons; ingot steel, 1,500,000 tons; rolled steel, 1,100,000 tons.

*Yangchuan Iron & Steel Plant* in Shensi. Six blast furnaces: 2 of 255 m³ each; 2 of 100 m³ each; 1 of 8 m³; 1 of 6 m³. Consume iron ore from local sources and Shouyang, Sishan and coal from Shouyang, Chingching. Converter shop. Rolling mills.

*Yungsin Iron & Steel Plant* in Kiangsi. Planned 1962 ingot output: 1,000,000 tons.

# MAP, GRAPH AND TABLES

## Map

Geographical Distribution of Iron and Steel Centers in China

## Graph

## Tables

# INDEX

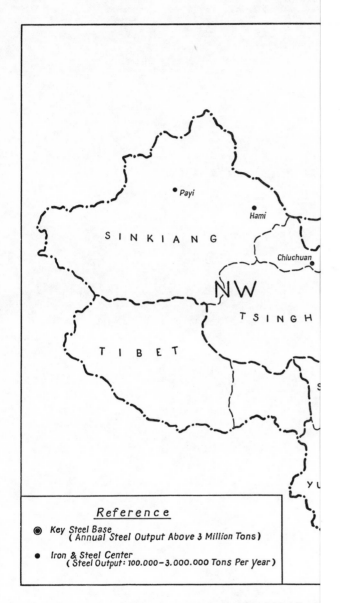

SINKIANG

• Payi

Hami

Chiuchuan •

NW

TSINGH

TIBET

S

Y U

*Geographical Distributi*